Computational Methods for Process Engineers

J.P. Mmbaga, K. Nandakumar, R.E. Hayes
Department of Chemical & Materials Engineering
University of Alberta,

COMPUTATIONAL METHODS FOR PROCESS ENGINEERS
Copyright © 2014, J.P. Mmbaga, K. Nandakumar, R.E. Hayes

MATLAB is a registered product of: The MathWorks, Inc. 3 Apple Hill Drive Natick, Massachusetts 01760 USA.

Published by:

ALPHA Education Press
A division of
ALPHA Fluidics Associates Inc.

#307, 10621 - 100 Ave NW
Edmonton, AB
T5J 0B3 Edmonton, AB

ISBN 978-0-9938764-00

Digitally printed in Canada by

PageMaster
PUBLICATION SERVICES INC.
www.pagemaster.ca

CONTENTS

LIST OF TABLES

Revolutionary advances in hardware and software technology have made computer aided design and analysis a standard tool in engineering practice. While this puts a lot of power at the hands of the end user, in order to use them wisely and interpret the results correctly, the users are expected to have a sound knowledge of the relationship between the physical world and the mathematical model and that between the mathematical model and the numerical approximation.

The text is intended for both senior level undergraduate and first year graduate students without comprehensive numerical background. Motivation for the text has grown from the authors need to provide a text which covers both advanced features of numerical methods and specific applications in the process engineering field.

ACKNOWLEDGEMENTS

No major work can be developed in vacuum. It is neccesary to acknowledge previous published works which have influenced the development of this text. A number of authors have influenced our learning in this field, including Amundson (1966), Finlayson (1980), Hoffmann (1992), Rao (2002) and Chapra (2005).

Previous course instructors who have taught the subject in the department, specifically Dr. Carolina Diaz-Goano and Dr. Jos Derksen are acknowledged. Special thanks to Dr. Petr Nikrityuk for giving useful and insightful comments on the manuscript. We would also like to thank Dr. Rajab Litto for re-doing some of the graphs and all assistants and TA's who have worked on various numerical problems during KN's tenure at the department of chemical and materials engineering, University of Alberta.

The original manuscript for this book was developed from lecture notes by KN over the last 25 years, with the aim of introducing the computing facilities at the department of chemical and materials engineering. The notes were later expanded and elaborated by JPM and REH.

Notwithstanding any efforts made by others, all errors and omissions in this text remain the sole responsibility of the authors.

JPM   KN   REH

To see a World in a Grain of Sand, And a Heaven in a
Wild Flower, Hold Infinity in the palm of your hand,
And Eternity in an hour

— WILLIAM BLAKE

CHAPTER 1

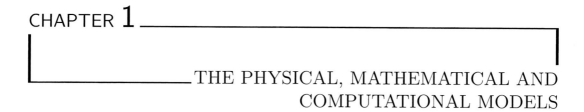

THE PHYSICAL, MATHEMATICAL AND COMPUTATIONAL MODELS

1.1   Introduction

In the Trekkie language, the *prime directive* of a process engineer should be explore and understand physical and chemical processes involved in converting a raw material into a useful product. Use this knowledge in designing, constructing and operating chemical process plants. This definition is as arbitrary as anything else that one might propose. In fact if one substitutes the word process in the above definition with any other (such a mechanical or electrical) it would remain equally valid. This is because the basic principles and the scientific methodology we use to uncover such principles remain the same in any field of engineering or science. A broader, although highly personal, view of the our attempt to understand the physical world, describe it in the language of mathematics, and finally investigate its consequence by means of

1

analytical, graphics or numerical methods is shown in Figure 1.1.

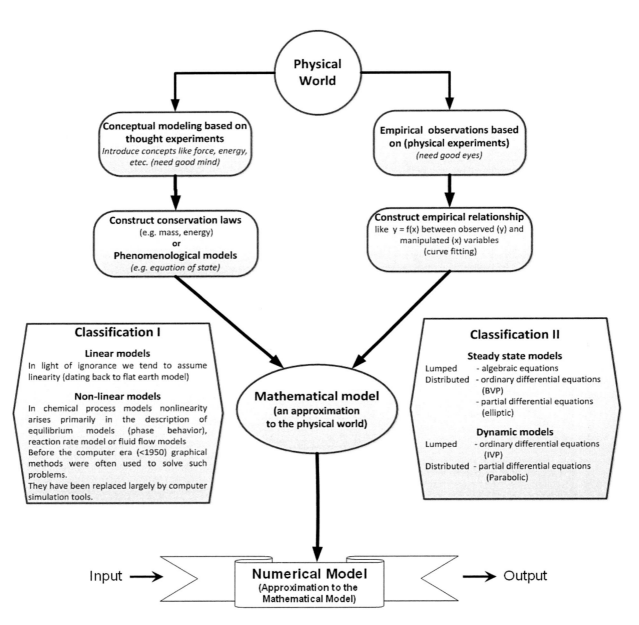

Figure 1.1: Scheme of things - a personal perspective

A mathematical model is at best an approximation to the physical world. Such models are constructed based on certain conservation principles and/or empirical observations. Those curious about the nature of the physical laws should read a delightful little book by Feynman (1967) on the character of physical laws. As a matter of convenience mathematical models can be classified as *linear or non-linear, steady-state or dynamic, lumped or distributed.* Examples to illustrate each type of model are provided later in this chapter. In general, non-linearity is found to occur quite naturally and frequently in nature; it is also very dificult to analyse non-linear models without the aid of a computer.

A numerical model (or a computer simulation tool) is an approximation to the mathematical model. Although the importance of mathematical modelling in chemical engineering was recognized since the early 1920s, it was the text by Bird et al. (1960) on *Transport Phenomena* that has proved to be the major inspiration in exploring the link between the physical world and the mathematical one for *transport processes* involving momentum, heat and mass transfer. Since then, a number of outstanding texts have appeared that explore this relationship for reaction and equilibrium processes as well. While such studies form the core of chemical engineering curriculum, the importance of sharpening our mathematical abilities, and the need to incorporate these as part of the curriculum was recognized and aided by the appearance of early text books by Amundson (1966) and Jenson & Jeffreys (1963). These dealt specifically with mathematical applications of chemical engineering. The texts by Lapidus (1962) and Rosenbrock (1966) served a similar purpose in introducing digital computational methods in the analysis of chemical processes.

We are now at a new threshold; computers have become quite pervasive. Significant advances have been made in our ability to analyse non-linear systems. The advances in both the hardware

and software technology have been revolutionary. As a result of
these advances, computer aided design and analysis has become
a standard tool as evidenced by the success of several commercial
packages such as ASPEN PLUS, PROCESS, HYSIM, VMGSim
(steady state process simulators), FLOW3D, ANSYS FLOW DY-
NAMICS, STAR CCM+, COMSOL MULTIPHYSICS (fluid dynamics simulators), HCOMP, IMPULSE, OLGA, STONER SPS
(multiphase and transient pipeline flow simulators) etc. In addition to such simulators that are specific for certain classes of
problems, general purpose mathematical tools such as MATLAB
(for matrix linear algebra functions), Mathematika and MAPLE
(for symbolic computation) provide easy access to a vast array
of mathematical functions and the ability to process them both
symbolically and numerically. Such packaged tools tend to accomplish the following:

(i) codify the most advanced algorithms,

(ii) assemble a vast database (in the case of physical properties)
    and knowledge base in the case of mathematical functions (in
    MAPLE and Mathematika) and

(iii) make these accessible to the end user through an intuitive
    interface.

While this puts a lot of power at the hands of the end user,
in order to use them wisely and interpret the results correctly,
the users are expected to have a sound knowledge of the relationship between the physical world and the mathematical model and
that between the mathematical model and the numerical approximation. One is well served to remember the cliche *garbage in,
garbage out!*

   In this text we examine the link between the mathematical
and the numerical model. There are a lot of computational tools
available to engineers. A basic introduction to MATLAB can be

found in Appendix A. MATLAB is used throughout in illustrating various algorithms.

1.2 Classification of chemical process models

In modelling chemical processes, one is interested in tracking material and energy of process streams from the raw material stage to the finished product state. The *state of a stream* is characterized by the concentration of the various species that it carries and its temperature, pressure and flow rates. Applying the laws of conservation of mass, energy and momentum allows us to track changes in the state of the system. Typically we subject the raw material streams to either physical treatment to add or remove chemical species exploiting such property differences as density, solubility, volatility, diffusivity etc. (transport and equilibrium processes) or, chemical treatment to alter the chemical structure (reaction processes).

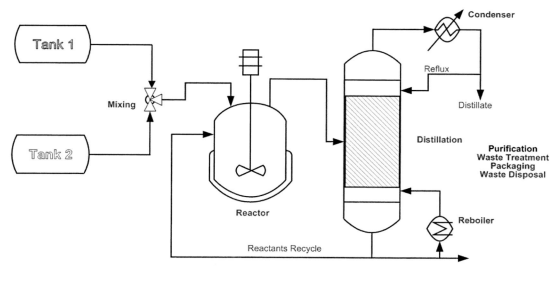

Figure 1.2: A typical chemical process

Figure 1.2 shows a typical sequence for processing raw material from feed to product.

If the state variables are assumed to be independent of time and spatial position, then we often have a lumped parameter, steady state model resulting in a set of coupled algebraic equations. If they are assumed to have no spatial variation, but are time dependent, then we have lumped parameter, dynamic models which result in ordinary differential equations of the initial value type. If there is no time dependence, but there is a spatial variation and that too restricted to one dimension (for reasons of symmetry or scale), then we have ordinary differential equations of the boundary value type. If both spatial and time dependence are important, then we end up with partial differential equations, which are further classified into parabolic, elliptic and hyperbolic equations. The classiffcation outlined in this paragraph are illustrated with specific examples in the next sections. The examples are drawn from *transport, equilibrium and reaction processes*. The objective is to sensitize you to the model building process in the hope that you would begin to appreciate the relationship between the physical world and the mathematical model that represents it.

1.3 Lumped parameter, steady state models

1.3.1 Example of a stagewise separation process

Consider a stagewise separation process shown in Figure 1.3. Suppose we wish to process a gas stream at a rate of V kmole/s containing a pollutant at a mole fraction of y_4. We wish to remove the pollutant by scrubbing it with a solvent in a counter-current 3-stage separation device. The liquid rate is, say, L kmole/s and it contains a pollutant concentration of x_0 (which may be zero for a pure solvent stream). Only the pollutant transfers from the

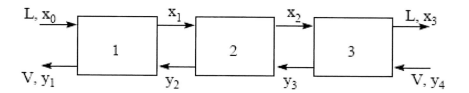

Figure 1.3: Three stage separation process

gas phase to the liquid phase and we make use of the solubility differences between the inert carrier gas and the pollutant. So far we have made an attempt to describe a physical world. Is the description adequate to formulate a mathematical model? How do we know that such a model should result in a steady state, lumped parameter model? The answer is no, we dont! We need to further define and refine the problem statement. For a process engineer this is the most important step viz. understand the objective of the task and the nature of the process (the physical world) to formulate a mathematical model. Let us continue with the description of the problem.

The state variables in this problem are $(L, V, x_0, x_1, x_2, x_3, y_1, y_2, y_3, y_4)$. By focusing only the steady state operation, we remove the dependence of state variables on time. Such a model cannot clearly answer any questions concerning start up or shutdown of this process. Next, we assume that in each stage the gas and liquid are mixed thoroughly so that there is no spatial variation of concentration within the equipment. This is the so-called lumped parameter approximation.

We further assume that the streams leaving a stage are in thermodynamic equilibrium. This implies that for a given inlet streams, no matter what we do inside the process equipment, the exit concentrations cannot be changed as they have reached an invariant state. To state it another way, there is a unique relationship, $y = f(x)$, between the exit concentrations of each stage and this relationship could be determined in a laboratory and entered into a database. Often this relation is expressed as, $y = Kx$ where K is called the equilibrium ratio; at extremely low concentration range K may be assumed to be a constant (results in a linear model), while at higher concentrations the equilibrium ratio may itself be a function of concentration, $K(x)$ (results in a non-linear model). While experience and experimentation suggest that such relationships do exist, study of equilibrium thermodynamics takes this one step further in attempting to construct predictive models for the function, $y = f(x)$ by examining the equilibrium process at a molecular level. Let us continue with the assumption that the equilibrium model is given by

$$y_i = Kx_i \qquad i = 1, 2, 3 \tag{1.1}$$

where we have introduced the subscript i to indicate the equilibrium relationship is valid for each stage of the separation process. This yields us three equations, but recall that the state of this 3-stage separation train is described by 10 variables: $(L, V, x_0, x_1, x_2, x_3, y_1, y_2, y_3, y_4)$. At this stage we ask ourselves if there are other laws or principles that this system should obey. Conservation laws such as mass, momentum and energy conservation should come to mind. In the present case our objective has been narrowly focused on tracking the concentration of the pollutant in each of the three stages. In particular we have not concerned ourselves with flow and heat effects. Let us speculate briefly what these effects might be! Heat transfer effects might include heat of absorption, while flow effects will include imperfect mixing in a stage. The later in fact has serious consequence in negating two of our earlier assumptions: viz. lumped parameter system implying concentration is spatially uniform in each stage and the exit streams are in thermodynamic equilibrium. Nevertheless, we still proceed with the assumption of perfect mixing; a model description that takes into accounts such realities often becomes intractable. Neglecting heat and flow effects, we have only mass conservation principle. Applying this for the pollutant species around each of the three stages, we obtain,

$$
\begin{array}{lll}
\text{Stage 1:} & V(y_2 - y_1) = L(x_1 - x_0) & \\
\text{Stage 2:} & V(y_3 - y_2) = L(x_2 - x_1) & (1.2) \\
\text{Stage 3:} & V(y_4 - y_3) = L(x_3 - x_2) &
\end{array}
$$

Note that in each of these equations, the left hand side represents the amount of pollutant that has been removed from the gas phase and the right hand side represents the same amount of material absorbed into the liquid phase. Now we have a total of six equations, but still ten variables. Hence we conclude that we have four degrees of freedom. This implies that we can choose four of the variables and the remaining six variables must be determined by satisfying the six equations.

One can also write an overall balance, taking all three stages as one group:

$$
\text{Overall:} \quad V(y_4 - y_1) = L(x_3 - x_0) \quad (1.3)
$$

This, however, is not an independent equation since summing equations (1.2) produces equation (1.3). This will be used later in introducing concepts of linear independence and rank of matrices.

Specifications: a 3-stage linear system

Let us assume that we pick the four variables associated with the inlet streams to be specified, viz. (L, V, x_0, y_4). Defining $S = L/KV$ (a known value) and eliminating variables (y_1, y_2, y_3) from equations (1.2) we get the following system of three equations

$$
\begin{bmatrix}
(1+S) & -1 & 0 \\
-S & (1+S) & -1 \\
0 & -S & (1+S)
\end{bmatrix}
\begin{bmatrix}
x_1 \\ x_2 \\ x_3
\end{bmatrix}
=
\begin{bmatrix}
Sx_0 \\ 0 \\ y_4/K
\end{bmatrix}
\tag{1.4}
$$

in the unknowns (x_1, x_2, x_3). This can be represented in compact matrix form as:

$$
\boldsymbol{T}x = b \tag{1.5}
$$

where $\boldsymbol{T}$ represents the tridiagonal matrix

$$
\begin{bmatrix}
d_1 & c_1 & 0 \\
a_1 & d_2 & c_2 \\
0 & a_2 & d_3
\end{bmatrix}
=
\begin{bmatrix}
(1+S) & -1 & 0 \\
-S & (1+S) & -1 \\
0 & -S & (1+S)
\end{bmatrix}
$$

and

$$
\boldsymbol{x} =
\begin{bmatrix}
x_1 \\ x_2 \\ x_3
\end{bmatrix}
\qquad
\boldsymbol{b} =
\begin{bmatrix}
b_1 \\ b_2 \\ b_3
\end{bmatrix}
=
\begin{bmatrix}
Sx_0 \\ 0 \\ y_4/K
\end{bmatrix}
$$

First variation: n-stage separation sequence

Once we have expressed the mathematical model in a symbolic, matrix form as in equation (1.5), we can generalize the model to any number of stages. Suppose there are n stages, then we merely have,

$$
\boldsymbol{T} =
\begin{bmatrix}
d_1 & c_1 & 0 & \cdots & 0 \\
a_1 & d_2 & c_2 & \cdots & 0 \\
 & & \ddots & & \\
0 & 0 & a_{n-2} & d_{n-1} & c_{n-1} \\
0 & \cdots & 0 & a_{n-1} & d_n
\end{bmatrix}
\qquad
\boldsymbol{x} =
\begin{bmatrix}
x_1 \\ x_2 \\ \vdots \\ x_{n-1} \\ x_n
\end{bmatrix}
\qquad
\boldsymbol{b} =
\begin{bmatrix}
b_1 \\ b_2 \\ \vdots \\ b_{n-1} \\ b_n
\end{bmatrix}
$$

where $a_i = -S, d_i = (1+S), c_i = -1$. Efficient algorithms for solving such system will be developed in Chapter 3.

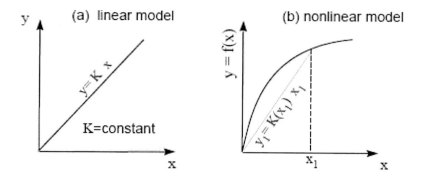

Figure 1.4: Linear and nonlinear equilibrium model stages.

Second variation: nonlinear equilibrium model

Instead of assuming the equilibrium ratios, K in equation (1.1) to be constant as in figure 1.3a, if they are found to be dependent on concentrations x, then we have a nonlinear system of equations. One can then interpret the $K(x)$ values to be the slopes of the chord as shown in figure 1.3b, which is no longer a constant, but depends on x. This implies that, $S(x) = L/K(x)V$ and hence T becomes a function of x. Thus the elements in T cannot be determined without knowing the solution x. An intuitive approach to resolving this dilemma in solving such systems, $T(x)x = b$ might be to make an initial guess for x^{old} and use this guess to evaluate, $K(x^{old})$, $S(x^{old})$ and hence $T(x^{old})$ and obtain a new solution for x^{new} by solving the linearized system, $T(x^{old})x^{new} = b$. One can repeat this procedure until the difference between the new and the old values of x becomes vanishingly small. Although there are numerous variations on this scheme, a large class of nonlinear problems are solved within the conceptual frame work (i) estimating an initial guess (ii) devising an algorithm to improve the estimate and (iii) checking for convergence of the result.

Third variation: alternate specification

In all of the previous cases we considered the inlet streams to be specified viz. (L, V, x_0, y_4). This would be typical for performance analysis problems where the output of an existing process is desired, given its inlet conditions. A design engineer, who gets into this game at an earlier stage, might face an alternate problem. For example, environmental regulations might dictate that the exit concentration of the pollutant y_1 be below a certain acceptable level. Thus the four degrees of freedom might be used up in specifying (V, x_0, y_4, y_1). Assuming once again a linear equilibrium model (K constant), the system of equations (1.2) in the unknown set (L, x_2, x_3) can be written as:

$$f_1(L, x_2; V, y_1, x_0) := V(Kx_2 - y_1) - L(y_1/K - x_0) \quad = 0$$
$$f_2(L, x_2, x_3; V, y_1, x_0) := KV(x_3 - x_2) - L(x_2 - y_1/K) \quad = 0$$
$$\tag{1.6}$$
$$f_3(L, x_2, x_3; V, y_4) := V(y_4 - Kx_3) - L(x_3 - x_2) \quad = 0$$

In spite of assuming a linear equilibrium model, the above set of equations are non-linear! Why? Although the mathematical model has remained the same for various specifications, we have nice tridiagonal matrix structure for some specifications while no such structure exists for others.

1.3.2   Process flow sheet simulation

Consider the flow sheet shown in figure 1.5. It is an extremely simple unit consisting of a reactor and a separator. We are given the mole fractions of components in the recycle stream and the exit stream from the reactor. We are asked to determine the molar rates of CO and H_2 in the inlet stream, the recyle rate R and the product rate, P. In analysing this problem we setup

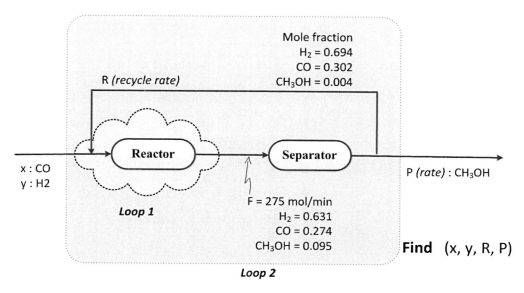

Figure 1.5: Example of material balance equations in a process flow sheet.

a series of material balance equations. Focusing on the reactor loop (loop 1) shown in dashed line in figure 1.5, we can write the following three component material balance equations:

C-balance: $\qquad x + R(0.302 + 0.004) = (0.274 + 0.095) \times 275$

or

$$\boxed{x + 0.306R = 101.475}$$

H_2-balance: $\qquad y + R(0.694 + 0.008) = (0.631 + 20.095) \times 275$

or

$$\boxed{y + 0.702R = 225.775}$$

O-balance: $\qquad x + R(0.302 + 0.004) = (0.274 + 0.095) \times 275$

or

$$\boxed{x + 0.306R = 101.475}$$

Note that the O balance equation is redundant and in the language of linear algebra, these three equations do not form a *linearly independent* set of equations. So we proceed to construct additional equations by examining material balance around the full flow sheet (loop 2). These give rise to:

$$\text{C-balance:} \qquad x = P$$

$$H_2\text{-balance:} \qquad y = 2P$$

These five equations can be arranged in a matrix form as,

$$\begin{bmatrix} 1 & 0 & 0.306 & 0 \\ 0 & 1 & 0.702 & 0 \\ 1 & 0 & 0.306 & 0 \\ 1 & 0 & 0 & -1 \\ 0 & 1 & 0 & -2 \end{bmatrix} \begin{bmatrix} x \\ y \\ R \\ P \\ P \end{bmatrix} = \begin{bmatrix} 101.475 \\ 225.775 \\ 101.475 \\ 0 \\ 0 \end{bmatrix} \qquad (1.7)$$

Recognizing the redundancy between the first and third equations and also combining equations four and five to eliminate P, we can write the above set in an alternate form as

$$\begin{bmatrix} 1 & 0 & 0.306 \\ 0 & 1 & 0.702 \\ -2 & 1 & 0 \end{bmatrix} \begin{bmatrix} x \\ y \\ R \end{bmatrix} = \begin{bmatrix} 101.475 \\ 225.775 \\ 0 \end{bmatrix} \qquad (1.8)$$

1.3.3   Example of a multicomponent flash

Next, we examine a model for a multicomponent, isothermal flash process. This also results in a lumped, steady state model description. It is also an example of how a potentially large system system of algebraic equations can be reduced to a single equation in one unknown through clever manipulations. Thus root finding

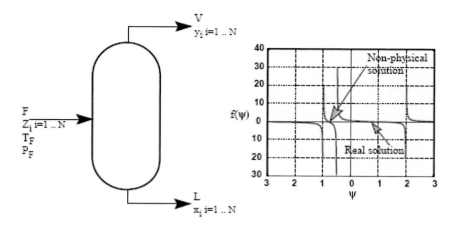

Figure 1.6: Multicomponent, isothermal flash process.

algorithms could be used effciently to solve this system. A sketch of the process is shown in figure 1.6. A feed stream of known flow rate, F, composition (mole fractions), $\{z_i | i = 1 \cdots N\}$, temperature, T_F and pressure, P_F is flashed into a drum maintained at a temperature and pressure of (T, P), respectively. Under right conditions, the feed will split into a vapor phase and a liquid phase. The objective is to predict the flow rate and compositions of the vapor, (V, y_i) and the liquid (L, x_i) phases. Each exit stream contains (N +1) unknowns. The assumptions are that the process is operating under steady conditions, perfect mixing takes place inside the drum (lumped approximation) and the exit streams are in thermodynamic equilibrium. The model equations are as follows:

Thermodynamic : Vapur Liquid Equilibrium (VLE) -(empirical model)

$$y_i = K_i(T, P)x_i \qquad i = 1 \cdots N \qquad (1.9)$$

Component material balance -(mass conservation) *

$$Fz_i = Vy_i + Lx_i \qquad i = 1 \cdots N \qquad (1.10)$$

Overall material balance

$$F = V + L \qquad (1.11)$$

Mole fraction constraints

$$\sum_i^N y_i = \sum_i^N x_i = 1 \qquad (1.12)$$

A simple count indicates that we have written down (2N + 3) equations for the (2N + 2) unknowns; but it is easy to verify that summing equations (1.10) over all components and using the mole fraction constraint, results in equation (1.11). Thus, equation (1.11) is not an independent one. Although these equations could be solved as a system of nonlinear algebraic equations, a much more efficient scheme is to eliminate all, except one variable and reduce the system into a single equation. First eliminate y_i from equation (1.10) using (1.9) to obtain

$$Fz_i = (K_iV + L)x_i \qquad or \qquad x_i = Fz_i/(K_iV + L)$$

Rearrange equation (1.12) as,

$$\sum_i^N (x_i - y_i) = 0 \qquad or \qquad \sum_i^N (1 - K_i)x_i = 0$$

Combine the last two equations as,

$$\sum_i^N \frac{(1 - K_i)Fz_i}{K_iV + L} = 0$$

---

*Observe the nonlinear terms in this equation: viz. product of unknowns $V \& y_i$ and $L \& x_i$

Eliminate L from above equation using (1.11) and define $\psi = V/F$ to get the final form of the flash equation as:

$$\boxed{\sum_i^N \frac{(1 - K_i)Fz_i}{(K_i - 1)\psi + 1} = 0} \qquad (1.13)$$

This is the so-called **Rachfold-Rice** flash equation. It is a single equation in one unknown, viz. ψ. In general the number of roots that a nonlinear equation posses cannot be known a priori. A possible sketch of the function is shown in figure 1.5b. Since ψ is defined as the fraction of feed that appears as vapor, (V/F), the physical world dictates that it must lie between (0, 1) and it is suficient if the search for the root is limited to this range. The flash equation (1.13) may posses other roots outside the range of interest (0, 1). Such roots are valid mathematical solutions of the problem, they are not physically relevant.

1.3.4 Example of a phenomenalogical model

In the previous two examples, models were built based on conservation laws. Models based on empirical observations are also quite common. The Pressure-Volume-Temperature (PVT) behavior of gases, for example, could be modeled by the ideal gas law viz. $PV = nRT$. A more refined model, called the Peng-Robinson equation of state is used widely in chemical engineering literature. It is given by the following equations:

$$P = \frac{RT}{(V - b)} - \frac{a(T)}{V(V + b) + b(V - b)} \qquad (1.14)$$

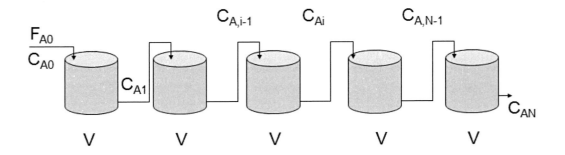

Figure 1.7: Reactors in series

where

$$a(T) = 0.45724 \frac{R^2 T_c^2}{Pc} \alpha(T_r, \omega)$$

$$b = 0.0778 \frac{RT_c}{P_c}$$

$$\alpha^{1/2} = 1 + m \left(1 - \sqrt{T_r}\right)$$

$$m = 0.37464 + 1.54226\omega - 0.26992.2\omega^2$$

Here T_c, P_c are the critical temperature and pressure of the component and ω is the accentric factor. These are properties of a component.

We define $T_r = T/T_c$ as the reduced temperature, and $Z = PV/RT$ as the compressibility factor. Equation (1.14) can be rearranged as a cubic equation in Z as follows:

$$\boxed{Z^3 - (1 - B)Z^2 + (A - 3B^2 - 2B)Z - (AB - B^2 - B^3) = 0}$$

(1.15)

where $A = aP/R^2T^2$ and $B = bP/RT$. For the class of problems where the pressure and temperature (P,T) are given and the material is identified (i.e., T_c, P_c, ω are known), the coeficients (A, B) in equation (1.15) can be calculated and hence the cubic equation can be solved to find the roots, Z. This allows the determination of the volume (or density) from $Z = PV/RT$.

1.3.5 Example of reactors in series

An example from chemical reaction engineering process that gives rise to a system of nonlinear equations is that of a continuously stirred tank reactor in series. A sketch is shown in figure 1.7. Consider an isothermal, irreversible second order reaction. The composition in each reactor is assumed to be spatially homogeneous due to thorough mixing. The reaction rate expression is given by,

$$r = kVC_i^2$$

where C_i is the exit concentration of component A from the i-th reactor, k is the reaction rate constant and V is the volume of the reactor. A material balance under steady state conditions on the i-th reactor results in,

$$kVC_i^2 = F(C_{i-1} - C_i) \tag{1.16}$$

Letting $\beta = kV/F$, we have the following n-simultaneous nonlinear equations.

$$f_i := \beta C_i^2 + C_i - C_{i-1} = 0 \qquad i = 1 \cdots N \tag{1.17}$$

While we have constructed N equations, there are (N +2) variables in total. They are $[C_0 \cdots C_N \beta]$. Hence we have two degrees of freedom. In analysing an existing reactor train, for example, one might regard (β, C_0) to be known and solve for the remaining N variables including the exit concentration C_N (and hence the conversion). In a design situation one might wish to achieve a specific conversion and hence regards (C_0, C_N) as knowns and solve for remaining N variables including β (and hence the volume V).

1.4   Lumped parameter, dynamic models

Lumped parameter, dynamic models arise typically when the spatial variation of the state variables can be ignored for some reason, but time variation cannot be ignored. Let us consider an example from heat transfer.

1.4.1   Example of cooling a molten metal

A sample of molten metal at an inital temperature of T_i is placed in a crucible (at an initial temperature of T_∞) and allowed to cool by convection. A sketch is shown in figure 1.8. Let $T_1(t)$ be the temperature of the molten metal at any time t and $T_2(t)$ be the temperature of the crucible. The argument used to justify neglecting spatial variation is that the thermal conductivity of the two materials are sufficiently large to keep the temperature of each material uniform within its boundaries. The conservation law statement is:

{rate of accumulation}= {rate in}-{rate out}+ {rate of generation}

Applying this first to the molten metal,

$$\frac{d}{dt}(m_1 C_{p1} T_1) = \underbrace{-h_1 A_1 (T_1 - T_2)}_{\text{heat loss from 1 to 2}} \tag{1.18}$$

Energy balance on the crucible results in,

$$\frac{d}{dt}(m_2 C_{p2} T_2) = \underbrace{-h_1 A_1 (T_1 - T_2)}_{\text{heat gain by 2 from 1}} - \underbrace{h_2 A_2 (T_2 - T_\infty)}_{\text{heat loss from 2 to } \infty} \tag{1.19}$$

These two equations can be presented using matrix notation as follows:

$$\frac{d\underline{\theta}}{dt} = A\underline{\theta} + \boldsymbol{b}$$

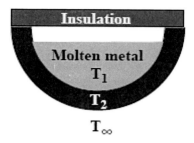

Figure 1.8: Heat transfer from a molten metal.

where

$$\underline{\theta} = \begin{bmatrix} T_1 \\ T_2 \end{bmatrix} \qquad \boldsymbol{A} = \begin{bmatrix} -\dfrac{h_1 A_1}{m_1 C_{P1}} & \dfrac{h_1 A_1}{m_1 C_{P1}} \\ +\dfrac{h_1 A_1}{m_2 C_{P2}} & -\dfrac{h_1 A_1 + h_2 A_2}{m_2 C_{P2}} \end{bmatrix} \qquad \boldsymbol{b} = \begin{bmatrix} 0 \\ \dfrac{h_2 A_2 T_\infty}{m_2 C_{P2}} \end{bmatrix}$$

The initial condition is

$$\underline{\theta}(t = 0) = \begin{bmatrix} T_1 \\ T_2 \end{bmatrix}$$

This problem depends on several parameters which are assumed to be known. A_1 is the heat trasfer area at the metal-crucible interface, A_2 is the area at the crucible-air interface. (h_1, h_2) are the corresponding heat transfer coeficients, (m_1, m_2) are the corresponding mass of the materials, (C_{p1}, C_{p2}) are the specific heats of the two materials. Since all of these are assumed to be known constants, the problem is linear.

1.4.2 Ozone decomposition

A number of mechanisms (some involving 40 steps and 40 equations) have been proposed to model the decomposition of ozone in the atmosphere. Let us consider a simple two-step model.

$$O_3 + O_2 \rightleftharpoons O + 2O_2$$
$$O_3 + O \rightarrow 2O_2$$

In the early stages of research, we were mainly concerned with identifying the mechanisms of ozone depletion in the atmosphere. For lack of better data, the compositions were assumed to be spatially homogeneous in the atmosphere, although we know now that there can be spatial variations. For the present purpose we will assume the compositions to be spatially uniform. Let y_1 be the composition of O_3 and y_2 be that of O.

The model equations are,

$$\frac{dy_1}{dt} = f_1(y_1, y_2) = -y_1 - y_1 y_2 + \beta \kappa y_2 \qquad (1.20)$$

$$\beta \frac{dy_2}{dt} = f_2(y_1, y_2) = y_1 - y_1 y_2 - \beta \kappa y_2 \qquad (1.21)$$

The initial compositions are $\underline{y}(t = 0) = [1.0, 0.0]$. The parameters are $\beta = 1/98$ and $\kappa = 3.0$. This is a system of two non-linear ordinary differential equations. It is an interesting problem in the limit of $\beta \rightarrow 0$. In the reaction analysis literature, the consequence of this limit is known as the quasi-steady-state-approximation. The physical interpretation is that the second reaction is much faster than the first one so that it can be assumed to have reached the equilibirum state at every instant of time. The second equation becomes an algebraic one. In the applied mathematics literature it is called the singular perturbation problem. From the computational point of view this limit gives rise to a phenomena called stiff systems. We will explore these features further in later chapters.

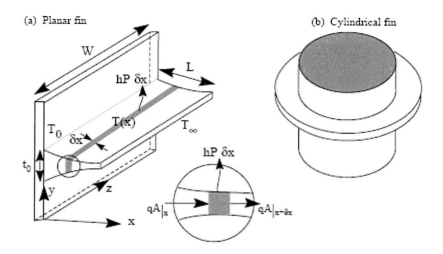

Figure 1.9: Heat transfer through a fin

1.5 Distributed parameter, steady state models

1.5.1 Heat transfer through a tappered fin

Let us examine an example from *transport processes*. Consider the use of a fin to enhance the rate of heat transfer. Basically, a fin provides a large heat transfer surface in a compact design. In the design and performance analysis of fins one might be interested in a variety of questions such as what is the effciency of the fin? (as a corollary what is a useful definition of fin effciency?), How many fins are required to dissipate a certain heat load?, What is the optimal shape of the fin that maximizes the heat dissipation for minimum weight of fin material? How long does it take for the fin to reach a steady state? etc. You will learn to develop answers to these questions in a heat transfer course. Our interest at this stage is to develop a feel for the model building process. A sketch of a fin is shown in figure 1.9. Let us first examine the steady state behavior of a planar fin shown in figure 1.9a.

The base of the fin is maintained at a uniform temperature of T_0 and the ambient temperature is T_∞. The state variable that

we are interested in predicting is the temperature of the fin, T.
In general it might be a function of all three spatial positions i.e.,
$T(x, y, z)$. (Note time, t is eliminated by assuming steady state).
If we know something about the length scales of the fin and the
material property of the fin, we make further assumptions that
will reduce the complexity of the problem. Let us also assume
that the fin is made of a homogeneous material* i.e., its thermal
conductivity, k is independent of position. If the length, L, of
the fin is much larger than the thickness, t_0, then we might argue
that the temperature variation in the y direction will be smaller
than that in the x direction. Thus we can assume T to be uniform in the y direction. Next, we examine what happens in the
z direction? This argument is somewhat subtle as it is based on
symmetries in the system. The basic premise here is that symmetric causes produce symmetric effects. An excellent and easily
accessible exposition on this topic can be found in Golubiksky
and Stewart (1993). First we assume that the ends of the fin in
the z direction are at infinity (or $W >> L$) so that the end effects
can be neglected. Since the temperature gradient within the fin is
caused by the driving force T_0 and T_∞ which are independent of z
direction, we can expect the fin to respond in a similar way - viz.
T to be independent of z. Note that the end effect, however small
it may be, is always present in a planar fin. By making W large
compared to L we reduce the error caused by the two-dimensional
effect near the ends. On the other hand the azimuthal symmetry
in the circular fin (figure 1.9b) make the problem truly one dimensional with temperature varying only in the radial direction.
Now that we have a better feel for what kinds of arguments or
assumptions make this problem one-dimensional, let us proceed
with constructing the model equation.

Since the temperature variation is present only in the x di-

---

*What types of materials might violate this assumption?

rection, we take an elemental control volume of thickness δx and identify the input and output sources of energy into this control volume. See figure 1.9. Energy enters by conduction mechanism at a rate of $(qA_C)|_x$ through the left boundary at x and leaves at a rate of $(qA_C)|_{x+\delta x}$ through the right boundary at $x + \delta x$. Heat is also lost by convection through the upper and lower boundaries, which is represented by $hP\delta x(T - T_\infty)$. Here q is the heat flux (W/m^2) by conduction. This is given by another phenomenological model called the Fourier law: $q = -k\frac{dT}{dx}$. k in the Fourier law denotes a material property called thermal conductivity (W/mK). A_C is the cross-sectional area which is allowed to be a function of x (tapered fin), h is the heat transfer coefficient (W/m^2K). P $=2w$ is the perimeter (m). The conservation law statement is:

{rate of accumulation}= {rate in}-{rate out}+ {rate of generation}

In symbolic terms, it is given by,

$$0 = (qA_C)|_x - (qA_C)|_{x+\delta x} - hP\delta x(T - T_\infty)$$

Dividing by δx and taking the limit of $\delta x \to 0$, we obtain,

$$0 = -\frac{d(qA_C)}{dx} - hP(T - T_\infty)$$

Using the Fourier law to replace q in terms of T ,

$$\boxed{\frac{d}{dx}\left[kA_C\frac{dT}{dx}\right] - hP(T - T_\infty) = 0} \qquad (1.22)$$

Equation (1.22) is a second order ordinary differential equation. The physical description dictates that two conditions be specified at the two ends of the fin, viz.

$$T(x = 0) = T_0$$
$$T(x = L) = T_\infty \qquad (1.23)$$
$$\left.\frac{dT}{dx}\right|_{x=L} = 0$$

This problem can be solved to obtain $T(x)$ provided the geometrical parameters $\{A_C(x), P\}$, the material property, k and the heat transfer environment $\{h, T_\infty, T_o\}$ are known. The problem is nonlinear if the thermal conductivity is a function of temperature, $k(T)$. In order to determine the effectiveness of the fin, one is interested in the total rate of heat transfer, Q through the fin. This is can be computed in one of two ways as given by,

$$Q = \int_0^L hP[T(x) - T_\infty]dx = -kA_C\left.\frac{dT}{dx}\right|_{x=0}.$$

1.5.2   Axial dispersion model

Another example from *transport processes* is the axial dispersion model for chemical reactors. This model is used in the design of tubular reactors (both packed beds and empty tubes). A sketch of a section of a tubular reactor is shown in figure 1.10. Let us examine the steady state behavior in this type of system.

According to Fick's law, the rate of diffusion of a substance is proportional to negative gradient of its concentration. For turbulent flow tubular reactor, reactant consumption and localized velocity fluctuations gives rise to concentration gradients and hence diffusion in both radial and axial direction. This representation of a flow reactor is termed as dispersed plug flow reactor, or simply the *dispersion model*. It can be used to simulate the behaviour of chemical reactors where complex radial and axial flow and transport takes place.

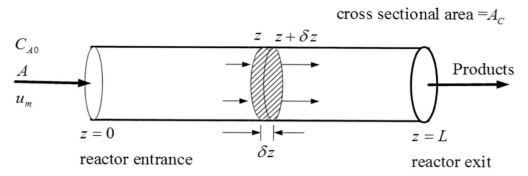

Figure 1.10: Tubular reactor with axial dispersion

We derive the dispersion model by considering the section of dispersed flow reactor shown in figure 1.10. Let the mean velocity of the fluid accross the tube be u_m (m/s) and the constant of proportionality between the dispersive flux of the reactant A and the negative gradient of A in the axial direction $(-dC_A/dz)$ be D_L (m^2/s). Since the concentration variation is present only in the *axial* direction, we take an elemental control volume of thickness δz and and cross-sectional area A_C (m^2). The rate $(mols/s)$ at which species A enter through the left boundary by convection (bulk flow) is $u_m A_c C_A|_z$ and the rate A entering by dispersion is $-D_L A_c dC_A/dz|_z$. The rate at which A leaves through the right boundary at $z + \delta z$ by bulk motion is $u_m A_c C_A|_{z+\delta z}$ and the rate dispersion, $-D_L A_c dC_A/dz|_{z+\delta z}$. There rate at which A is consumed by chemical reaction is obtained by multiplying the reaction rate r_A $(mol/m^3 s)$ with the volume of the control volume, $A_C \delta z$. The conservation law statement for this balance is:

{rate of accumulation}= {rate in}-{rate out}+ {rate of generation}

In symbolic terms, it is given by,

$$0 = \underbrace{(C_A u_m A_c)|_z}_{\text{bulk flow in}} - \underbrace{D_L A_c \frac{dC_A}{dz}\Big|_z}_{\text{dispersion in}} - \underbrace{(C_A u_m A_c)|_{z+\delta z}}_{\text{bulk flow out}} + \underbrace{D_L A_c \frac{dC_A}{dz}\Big|_{z+\delta z}}_{\text{dispersion out}}$$

$$+ \underbrace{r_A A_c \delta z}_{\text{reaction}}$$

Dividing by $A_c \delta z$ and rearranging

$$0 = -u_m \frac{(C_A)|_{z+\delta z} - (C_A)|_z}{\delta z} + D_L \frac{\frac{dC_A}{dz}|_{z+\delta z} + \frac{dC_A}{dz}|_z}{\delta z} - r_A$$

and taking the limit as $\delta z \to 0$, we obtain,

$$u_m \frac{dC_A}{dz} = D_L \frac{d^2 C_A}{dz^2} + r_A \qquad (1.24)$$

This is the *axial dispersion model*. We need boundary conditions as well as an expression for the reaction rate. Once these are obtained, the equation can be solved for $C_A(z)$ which can then be used to determine the reactor length, hence the mean residence time necesary to obtain a desired conversion of the reactant A. For a packed bed, the mean residence time is given by $\epsilon L/u_m$ where ϵ is the fraction of the bed occupied by the flowing fluid. Common boundary conditions for equation (1.24) are the so called "Danckwertz boundary conditions":

$$\text{At z} = 0: \qquad u_m C_A|_{z=0} - D_L \frac{dC_A}{dz}\Big|_{z=0} = C_{A0} \qquad (1.25)$$

$$\text{At z} = \text{L}: \qquad \frac{dC_A}{dz}\Big|_{z=L} = 0 \qquad (1.26)$$

The first boundary condition 1.25 recognizes for the fact that axial mixing can extend some distance upstream from the entrance of the reactor. To account for this we require that the flow far upstream of the reactor entrance (C_{A0}) be equal to the net flow of A at the reactor inlet. The second boundary condition 1.26 simply states that the concentration at the point where the flow leaves the reactor does not change.

The axial dispersion model with the Danckwertz boundary conditions represent a mixed boundary value problem. One way to solve such problem is to divide the reactor in small sections along the axial direction and approximate the derivatives using finite differences. These methods will be shown in this text.

1.6 Distributed parameter, dynamic models

1.6.1 Heat transfer through a tappered

As an example of a distributed, dynamic model let us re-examine the fin problem, but during the early transient phase. Let the fin be initially at the uniform ambient temperature of T_∞ At time $t = 0$ suppose the base of the fin at $x = 0$ is brought to a temperature of T_o. One migth ask questions like, how long will it take for the fin to reach a steady state? what will be the temperature at the tip of the fin at a given time? etc. Now we have the temperature as a function of both position and time, *i.e.*, $T(x, t)$. We can represent the rate of accumulation within a control volume symbolically as, $\frac{d(\rho A_C \delta x C_p T)}{dt}$ where the term in paranthesis is the energy (J) at any time within the control volume, C_p is the specific heat of the fin material (J/kg^oC) and ρ is the density of the material (kg/m^3). Thus the transient energy balance becomes,

$$\frac{\partial(\rho A_C \delta x C_p T)}{\partial t} = (q A_C)|_x - (q A_C)|_{x+\delta x} - h P \delta x (T - T_\infty)$$

Dividing by δx and taking the limit of $\delta x \to 0$, we obtain,

$$\frac{\partial(\rho A_C C_p T)}{\partial t} = -\frac{\partial(q A_C)}{\partial x} - h P (T - T_\infty)$$

Finally using the Fouriers law to replace q in terms of T,

$$\boxed{\frac{\partial(\rho A_C C_p T)}{\partial t} = \frac{\partial}{\partial x}\left[kA_C\frac{\partial T}{\partial x}\right] - hP(T - T_\infty)} \qquad (1.27)$$

Note that we have switched to partial derivatives as T is a function of both (x, t) and equation (1.24) is a partial differential equation. In addition to the boundary conditions specified in equation (1.23), we need an initial condition at $t = 0$ to complete the problem specification. The initial and boundary conditions are:

$$
\begin{aligned}
IC: \quad & T(x, t = 0) = T_\infty \\
BC1: \quad & T(x = 0, t) = T_0 \qquad\qquad\qquad\qquad (1.28)\\
BC2: \quad & T(x = L, t) = T_\infty \qquad\qquad\qquad \text{infinite fin}\\
& T(x = L, t) = T_S \qquad\quad \text{specified tip temperature, } T_S\\
& \left.\frac{dT}{dx}\right|_{(x=L,t)} = \frac{h}{k}(T_\infty - T) \qquad\qquad\quad \text{convective tip}
\end{aligned}
$$

1.7 Putting it all together - Overview

1.7.1 Mathematical models and Physical laws

In this section, we give an overall description of model types, formulation and solution. We choose the cooling of a spherical body under different conditions and assumptions to demonstrate different mathematical models and how their characterization evolves depending of the simplifying assumptions.

Let us consider a spherical object with mass m, density ρ, and a temperature T_i while suspended in a medium (environment) which has a different temperature T_∞.

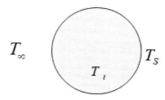

Figure 1.11: A sphere suspended in an environment at T_∞

Linear algebraic equation

Suppose the conditions are such that the temperature inside the sphere is same as the temperature at the surface (independent of position - uniform). If the surface temperature is T_S, the heat loss by convection from the surface of the sphere to the environment is governed by the Newtons law of cooling

$$q = h(T_S - T_\infty)$$

q heat loss per unit area (W/m^2)
T_S the surface temperature (K)
h heat transfer coefficient (W/m^2K)
T_∞ temperature of the surrounding medium
Hence we have a direct linear relationship between heat loss and the surface temperature. For any given surface temperature, we can compute the heat loss q.

Non-linear equation

Suppose we allow for other mechanism of heat loss to come into the picture, namely heat loss by radiation. In this case, the heat loss is determined by another physical relationship namely the Stefan-Boltzman law. When applied to a body which is in the presence of large surroundings, the law takes the form

$$q_{rad} = \epsilon\sigma(T_S^4 - T_{surr}^4)$$

where q_{rad} is the heat loss per unit area due to radiation, ϵ is the emissivity of the surface and σ a constant for radiation. This is a non-linear relationship because the temperature is raised to the power of 4. The total heat loss from the sphere becomes:

$$q = h(T_S - T_\infty) + \epsilon\sigma(T_S^4 - T_{surr}^4)$$

In the above two cases, the heat loss will continue untill the surface temperature is equal to the temperature of the environment. If this is to be prevented, some mechanism for generating energy inside the sphere must be accomodated to compensate for the heat loss.

Lumped parameter, dynamic model

Suppose we wish to monitor how the temperature of the sphere is changing with time. We are still not concerned about the temperature gradients within the sphere but would like to know how the temperature is changing with time. In this case, energy balance involves a rate component, namely the rate of change of the internal energy of the sphere, given by

$$\frac{d}{dt}(\rho C_P T)$$

The energy balance equation becomes

{rate of accumulation}= {rate in}-{rate out}+ {rate of generation}

$$\frac{d}{dt}(\rho C_P T) = -h(T - T_\infty)$$

We now have an equation involving derivatives, hence our model is differential equation. This is a transient system because the temperature changes with time. The information needed to solve such an equation is the value of the temperature at the beginning of the process. This is therefore an initial value problem.

Distributed model, partial differential equation

Suppose the conditions in our model sphere are such that we cannot ignore the temperature variations inside the sphere (in heat transfer jargon $Bi > 0.1$). Our model has to be formulated to include the changing flux inside the sphere. Assuming that the other properties are independent of temperature, and using Fourier's law for heat conduction inside the sphere, we can rewrite our energy balance equations in spherical coordinates as

$$\rho C_P \frac{\partial T}{\partial t} = \frac{1}{r^2} \frac{\partial}{\partial r} \left(r^2 k \frac{\partial T}{\partial r} \right)$$

or using chain rule and setting $\alpha = k/\rho C_P$, we can write

$$\frac{\partial^2 T}{\partial r^2} + 2r \frac{\partial T}{\partial r} = \frac{1}{\alpha} \frac{\partial T}{\partial t}$$

We no longer have an ordinary differential equation because there is more than one independent variable, namely r and t. We have a partial differential equation, which contains both first and second order partial derivatives. In order to solve this problem, it is no longer sufficient to know only the initial value, we also need the boundary conditions. This is because the equation given now does not say anything about the boundaries, *i.e.*, the surface of the sphere and the center of the sphere (for symmetry). We therefore need:

Initial conditions:

$$T(r, 0) = T_i$$

and boundary conditions

$$-k\frac{\partial T}{\partial r}\bigg|_{r=r_0} = h(T - T_\infty) \qquad (1.29)$$

$$\frac{\partial T}{\partial r}\bigg|_{r=0} = 0$$

The above examples shows how we can end up with very different models just because of the different conditions/assumptions posed as well as the desired results !!

1.7.2   Mathematical models, numerical approximations and errors.

A mathematical model is an equation which expresses the essential features of a physical system in mathematical terms. Symbolically, we can write the functional relationship as:

$$Y = f(X; p; F) \qquad (1.30)$$

where Y is dependent variable which describes the state or behaviour of the system. X represents the independent variables in the system (space dimensions or time) and p represents parameters that describe the properties of the system. The extra term, F, represents all other external influences which may act on the system.

Throghout history, mathematical models have been developed to describe physical phenomena. For instance, Newton's laws accurately describe many everyday phenomena. In order to demonstrate the concept of numerical modelling, lets use a common physical law which we all experience in everyday life, namely, Newton's second law of motion.

Based on observations (thought experiments), Sir Isaac Newton formulated the second law of motion which states that "*The time rate of change of the momentum of a body is equal to the resultant force acting on it*".

The mathematical expression of the second law is

$$ma = F \tag{1.31}$$

where F is the net force acting on the body (N), m is the mass of the body and a is the acceleration of the body (m^2/s). We can write this law in the form of equation (1.30) by dividing by the mass to give

$$a = \frac{F}{m} \tag{1.32}$$

where a is the dependent variable, m is a parameter representing property of the system and F is the forcing function.

Equation 1.32 is a mathematical model because:

- it describes a natural process in mathematical terms.

- it represents an idealization and simplification of reality.

- it can be used for predictive purposes.

The majority of problems in engineering involve differential equations. Differential equations are expressions which involve the derivative of the dependent variable. From physics, we know that acceleration is nothing but the rate of change of velocity, v, with respect to time, t, *i.e.*,

$$a = \frac{dv}{dt}$$

Therefore, if we wish to use v as the dependent variable, equation 1.32 can be written in a differential form as

$$\frac{dv}{dt} = \frac{F}{m} \tag{1.33}$$

If we wish to solve this equation for a particular situation, more information needs to be provided. Suppose we wish to determine the terminal falling velocity of a spherical ball of given diameter and mass is falling in a large medium of fluid as shown in figure 1.12. Ths situation could arise in the measurement of viscosity or simply free fall of droplets in a large medium. A simple force balance requires that the net force action on the body is a resultant of the force of gravity acting downwards, mg, and a resistance force acting upwards. This resistance force will also depend on the velocity as well as properties of the body, so a further relationship is needed.

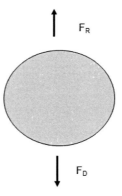

Figure 1.12: Force balance on a suspended object

Suppose we assume that the resistance force is directly proportional to the velocity, *i.e.*, $F_R = -kv$, where k is an additional parameter which is related to surface properties of the body as well as the surrounding fluid. The negative sign implies that the force is acting in the opposite direction of motion. Performing a force balance on the body we obtain

$$F = F_D - F_R = mg - kv \qquad (1.34)$$

Equation (1.33) can now be written in terms of the given parameters

$$\frac{dv}{dt} = \frac{mg - kv}{m} \qquad (1.35)$$

where g is the gravitational acceleration, m/s^2 and k is a constant with units of kg/s to make the equations consistent.

We use models to understand and predict physical phenomena. We must therefore find the solution to the model in order to be resolve the dependent parameter. If one can solve the mathematical equation without need of further simplifications and obtain an exact description of the depedent variable, the model is said to have an *analytical* solution. Mathematical concepts may be used to obtain the dependent variable as a function of the indepedent variables. For instance, in order to solve equation 1.35, calculus may be used to obtain velocity as a function of time,

$$v(t) = \frac{mg}{k}\left(1 - e^{(-k/m)t}\right) \qquad (1.36)$$

The solution is called an analytical or exact because it satisfies the original differential equation exactly. Many mathematical models of interest in engineering do not have analytical solutions. The alternative is to develop a numerical solution that approximates the exact solution !!!

In this respect, we seek to reformulate the problem so that it can be solved by arithmetic operations using digital computers. For the model example, we need to replace the first derivative with its approximate representation. Let us re-examine the model again, viz.

$$\frac{dv}{dt} = \frac{mg - kv}{m}$$

We note that the true derivative, which is a point slope, can be approximated by the two point slope as shown in figure 1.13 below.

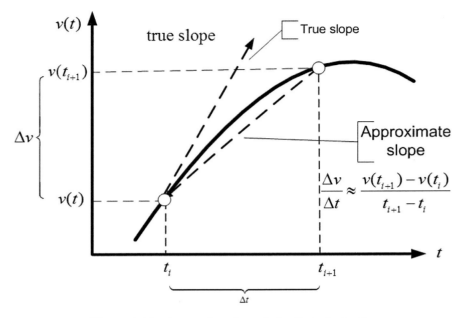

Figure 1.13: Approximation of the first derivative

Using the above approximation, we can replace the continuous derivative at point i, with the derivative based on two the points, i and $i + 1$.

$$\frac{v(t_{i+1}) - v(t_i)}{t_{i+1} - t_i} = \frac{mg - kv}{m} \approx \text{Slope} \qquad (1.37)$$

The equation can now be rearranged to yield the value of velocity at time t_{i+1} when the velocity is known at t_i.

$$v(t_{i+1}) = v(t_i) + \left[g - \frac{k}{m} v(t_i) \right] (t_{i+1} - t_i) \qquad (1.38)$$

The differential equation has been transformed into an algebraic equation which may be applied at different times using the slope and previous values of v and t. We can use this updating formula to compute the velocity at different times, starting from the initial known values. The outcome of carrying out this procedure with a sphere of $20mg$ falling in a fluid with flow resistance coefficient

$k = 0.015kg/s$ is shown in figure 1.14 below, together with the analytical solution.

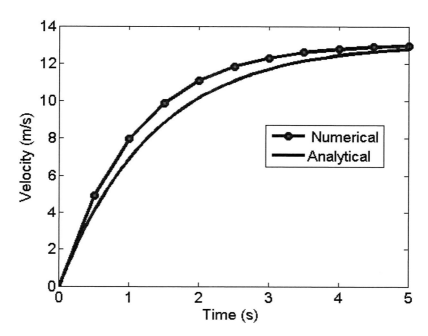

Figure 1.14: Comparison of numerical and analytical

The main difference between equation (1.38) and equation (1.36) is that the analytical solution is continuous, thus one can plug any value of t to obtain velocity at that time. On the other hand, equation (1.38) is merely an updating formula in discrete form. It has to be applied at the discrete points repeatedly in order to arrive at a final (desired) solution. This repeated application of the formula is called *iteration*. The application of equation 1.38, if carried using a computer, requires a specific set of instructions to be communicated in order to accomplish the tast as desired. These instructions constitute what we call *algorithms*.

1.7.3 Algorithms

The concept of algorithms is central to numerical analysis. An algorithm is a precisely defined sequence of steps for performing a specified task. For instance, in order to compute the velocity at different times, we will implement the following code:

```
Pseudo code
Set t=t_0 and v=v_0
Set tf
Set h
Set parameters k, g, m
Repeat while t < tf
{
Evaluate Slope=f(t,v,k,g,m),
Evaluate  v = v + h * Slope
Store t and v
Increment t = t + h
}
Print out t and v
```

The above set of instructions need to be put in a specific form in order for the computer to understand and implement the steps. We also need to determine the conditions under which an algorithm is expected to work and how accurately the solution produced by an algorithm approximates the exact solution.

1.7.4 Errors in numerical computation

Numerical methods yield approximate results. With such approximations, more questions come to the picture. How good is the approximation ?

How confident we are in our approximate result ? or "how much error can we tolerate in our calculation ?" We need to know how errors arise when we implement an approximation which involves a number of assumptions and simplifications. We can the devise measures to determine how each point estimate deviates from the exact solution.

Sources and types of errors

1. Model errors

    errors resulting from approximations and assumptions in representing the physical system. In our model problem, we have assumed a linear relationship between flow resistance force and velocity.

2. Machine errors

    errors resulting from machine round-off errors and/ or chopping of numbers due to limited representation of real numbers on the computer.

3. Truncation errors

    errors caused by use of truncated solution from an infinite series solution.

4. User and programming errors

    errors caused by human imperfection or coding implementation errors.

5. Data uncertainty

    errors resulting from the inaccuracy of measurement data. *e.g.*, for our model parameters, the constant k is obtained experimentally, so our final result will have large errors if the data is not accurate.

Error definitions

We shall use the following error definitions

True error

$$e = \text{exact value - approximate value}$$

Absolute error

$$|e| = |\text{exact value - approximate value}|$$

Relative error

$$e_r = \left| \frac{\text{exact value - approximate value}}{\text{exact value}} \right|$$

Percent error

$$\text{percent error } (\%) = \left| \frac{\text{exact value - approximate value}}{\text{exact value}} \right| \times 100$$

Approximate error

$$e_a = \left| \frac{\text{current approximation - previous approximate}}{\text{current approximation}} \right|$$

Stopping criterion

In computations, we are mostly concerned whether the absolute value of the approximate error is less than some specified number, we call tolerance, ϵ_S.

$$|e_a| = \epsilon_S$$

Scarborough (1966) has shown that we can be certain of a numerical approximation to at least n significant figures where n is the largest positive number for which

$$\epsilon_S < (0.5 \times 10^{-n})$$

For instance, in the above example, if one iteration gives a value of $v(t_{i+1}) = 12.0133$ and the previous iteration was $v(t_i) = 12.0345$, the approximate error is

$$e_a = \left| \frac{12.0133 - 12.0345}{12.0133} \right| = 0.00176 = 0.176 \times 10^{-2} < 0.5 \times 10^{-n}$$

and the solution is being approximated to $n = 2$ significant figures.

1.8 Summary

In this chapter, we have introduced various concepts for translation of a physical problem into a mathematical expression. The mathematical expression is then simplified and approximated in order to be solved on a digital computer.

The numerical techniques to be implemented in the solution of such equations will be discussed in different chapters of this book. Particular attention is paid to conceptual understanding of the underlying mathematical principles and solution methods. The accuracy and applicability of each approximation method is also discussed. In order to fully grasp the concepts introduced, opportunities for both hand calculations as well as implementation of numerical algorithms on a digital computer will be presented.

Detection is, or ought to be, an exact science, and
should be treated in the same cold and unemotional
manner. You have attempted to tinge it with
romanticism, which produces much the same effect as if
you worked a love-story or an elopement into the fifth
proposition of Euclid

SIR ARTHUR CONAN DOYLE

CHAPTER 2

SINGLE NONLINEAR ALGEBRAIC EQUATION

2.1 Introduction

In this chapter we consider the problem of finding the root of a
single nonlinear algebraic *equation* of the form,

$$f(x) = 0 \qquad (2.1)$$

where $f(x)$ is a continuous function of x and the equation is
satisfied only at selected values of $x = r$, called the *roots*. The
equation can be a simple polynomial as we saw with the Peng-
Robinson equation of state in section 1.3.4 or a more complicated
function as in the multicomponent flash example discussed in
section 1.3.3. If the equation depends on other parameters, as is
often the case, we will represent them as:

$$f(x; p) = 0 \qquad (2.2)$$

where p represents a set of known parameter values. Clearly,
we can graph the function f vs. x for a range of values of x. The
objective of such an exercise is to graphically locate the values of
$x = r$ where the function crosses the x axis. While such a graphical approach has an intuitive appeal, it is difficult to generalize

such methods to higher dimensional systems. Hence we seek to construct computational algorithms that can be generalized and refined successively to handle a large class of nonlinear problems.

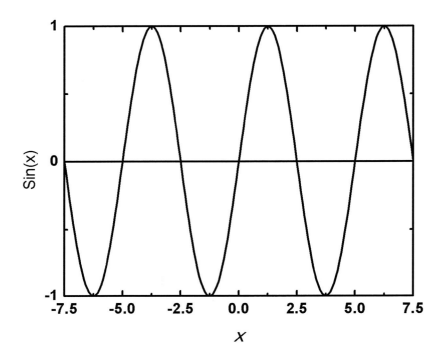

Figure 2.1: Graph of $f(x) = sin(x)$

Before we embark on such a task, some of the potential problems are illustrated with specific examples. In the general nonlinear case, there is no way to know *a priori*, how many values of r can be found that will satisfy the equation, particularly if the entire range of x in $(-\infty, \infty)$ is considered. For example, the simple equation

$$f(x) := \sin(x) = 0$$

has infinitely many solutions given by $r = n\pi$ where n is any integer. The graph of the function shown in figure 2.1 illustrates this clearly. Often, the physical description of the problem that gave rise to the mathematical function, will also provide information on the range of values of x that are of interest. For example, in the multicomponent flash equation, the problem was so formulated that the dependent variable had the physical interpretation of fraction of feed in vapor; hence this fraction must be between $(0, 1)$. Although the mathematical equation may have many other roots, outside of this range, they would lack any physical meaning and hence would not be of interest.

Algebraic theory tells us that the total number of roots of a polynomial is equal to the degree of the polynomial, but not all of them may be real roots. Furthermore, if the coefficients of the polynomial are all real, then any complex root must occur in pairs. Consider the three cubic equations given below:

$$f(x) := x^3 + 4\,x^2 + x - 6 = 0 \qquad r = -3, -2, 1$$

$$f(x) := x^3 + 3\,x^2 - 4 = 0, \qquad r = -2, -2, 1$$

$$f(x) := x^3 - x^2 + x - 1 = 0 \qquad r = 1$$

These are graphed in figures 2.2a,b,c respectively. In the first case there are three distinct roots. The function has a non-zero slope at each value of the root and such roots are called *simple* roots. In the second case we have a degeneracy or a non-simple root at $r = -2$. This problem manifests itself in a graphical representation with a zero slope of the function at the multiple root, $r = -2$. If the coefficients of the polynomial were slightly different, the curve could have moved slightly upward giving rise to two distinct roots or downwards yielding no roots in this region. Algebraically, we can see that the root is a multiple one with a multiplicity of 2 by factoring the function into $(x+2)(x+2)(x-1)$. In the third case there is only a single *real* root.

We begin by constructing some simple algorithms that have an intuitive appeal. They are easy to represent graphically and symbolically so that one can appreciate the connection between

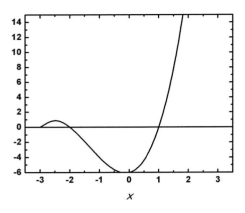

(a) $f(x) = x^3 + 4x^2 + x - 6$

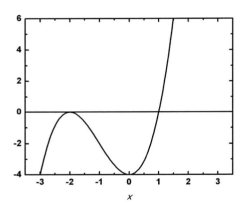

(b) $f(x) = x^3 + 3x^2 - 4$

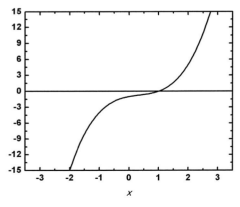

Figure 2.2:   Graphs   of
some simple functions

(c) $f(x) = x^3 - x^2 + x - 1$

the two representations. Subsequently we can refine the computational algorithms to meet the challenges posed by more difficult problems, while keeping the graphical representation as a visual aid.

There are essentially three key steps in any root finding algorithm. They are:

step 1: **Guess** one or more initial values for x.

step 2: **Iterate** using a scheme to improve the initial guess.

step 3: **Check convergence** - *i.e.*, has the improvement scheme of step 2 produced a result of desired accuracy?

The crux of the algorithm is often in the second step and the objective in devising various clever schemes is to get from the initial guess to the final result as quickly as possible.

2.2 Bisection method

The bisection algorithm is quite intuitive. A graphical illustration of this algorithm is shown in figure 2.3a.

In step 1, we make two guesses x_1 and x_2 and calculate the functions values $f_1 = f(x_1)$ and $f_2 = f(x_2)$. If the function values have opposite signs, it implies that it passes through zero somewhere between x_1 and x_2 and hence we can proceed to the second step of producing a better estimate of the root, x_3. If there is no sign change, it might imply that * there is no root between (x_1, x_2). So we have to make a set of alternate guesses. The scheme for producing a better estimate is also an extremely simple one of using the average of the two initial guesses, viz.

$$x_3 = \frac{x_1 + x_2}{2} \tag{2.3}$$

---

*What else might it imply?

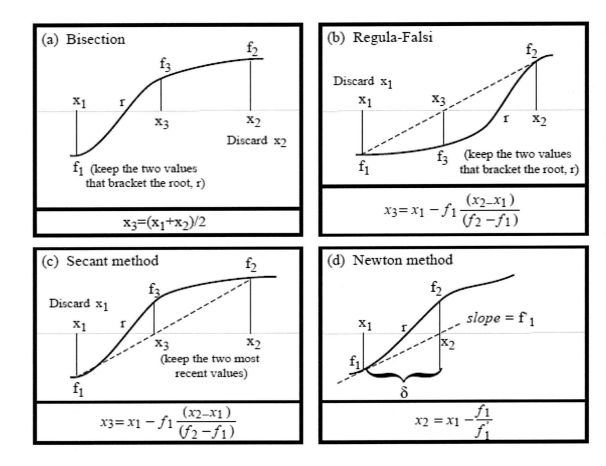

Figure 2.3: Graphical representation of some simple root finding algorithms

In figure 2.3a, (x_1, x_3) bracket the root r; hence we discard x_2, or better still, store the *value* of x_3 in the *variable* x_2 so that we are poised to repeat step 2. If the situation were such as the one shown in figure 2.3b, then we would discard x_1 or better still, store the *value* of x_3 in the *variable* x_1 and repeat step 2. In either case, (x_1, x_2) will have better guesses than the original values.

The final step is to check if we are close enough to the desired root r so that we can terminate the repeated application of step 2. One test might be to check if the absolute difference between two successive values of x is smaller than a specified tolerance*, *i.e.*,

$$|x_i - x_{i-1}| \leq \epsilon$$

When comparing values with different magnitudes, the percent relative error defined as

$$|\frac{x_i - x_{i-1}}{x_i}| \leq \epsilon \qquad x_i \neq 0$$

may be more useful. Another test might be to check if the absolute value of the function f_i at the end of every iteration is below a certain tolerance, *i.e.*,

$$|f(x_i)| \leq \epsilon$$

In addition, we might wish to place a limit on the number of times step 2 is repeated (*the maximum number of iterations*). A MATLAB function, constructed in the form of a *m-file*, is shown in figure 2.4.

EXAMPLE 2.1 (Multicomponent flash equation) *Let us consider the multicomponent, isothermal flash equation developed in section 1.3.3. The equation is*

$$\boxed{\sum_i^N \frac{(1 - K_i)z_i}{(K_i - 1)\psi + 1} = 0} \qquad (2.4)$$

where (K_i, z_i, N) are treated as known parameters and ψ is the unknown variable. Implementation of this function in MATLAB is shown the m-file *figure 2.5.*

---

*ϵ is a small number selected, *e.g.*, 10^{-3} or 10^{-6} for tight tolerance

```
function r=bisect(Fun,x,tol,trace)
%BISECT find the root of "Fun" using bisection scheme
%       Fun   - the name of the external function
%       x     - vector of length 2, (initial guesses)
%       tol   - error criterion
%       trace - print intermediate results
%
%    Usage   bisect('flash',[0,1])
%            flash is the name of the external function.
%                 [0,1] is the initial guess

%Check inputs
if nargin < 4, trace=0; end
if nargin < 3, tol=eps; trace=0; end
if (length(x) ~= 2)
 error('Please provide two initial guesses')
end

f = feval(Fun,x);   %Fun is assumed to accept a vector

if (prod(sign(f))) > 0,  %Check if roots are bracketed
 error('No sign change - no roots')
end;

for i = 1:100              %Set max limit on iterations
 x3 = (x(1) + x(2))/2;     %Update the guess
 f3 = feval(Fun,x3);       %Cal. f(x3)

%Check if x2 or x1 should be discarded
 if sign(f(1)*f3) < 0, x(2)=x3;  else x(1)=x3;  end;

 if abs(f3) < tol, r=x3; return; end  %Check convergence
 if trace, fprintf(1,'%3i %12.5f %12.5f\n', i,x3,f3); end
end
error('Exceeded maximum number of iterations')
```

Figure 2.4: MATLAB implementation of the bisection algorithm

```
function f=flash(psi)
% K is a vector of any length of equil ratios.
% z is the feed composition (same length as K)
% K, z are defined as global in main
% psi is the vapor fraction.

global K z
if ( length(K) ~= length(z) )
  error('Number of K values & compositions do not match')
end
n=length(psi);
for i = 1:n
 f(i)=sum( ((K-1).*z) ./ (1+(K-1)*psi(i)) );
end
```

Figure 2.5: Flash algorithm implementation

Observe that this function, while being concise, is fairly general to handle any number of components N and a vector of guesses psi *of any length and return a vector of function values, one corresponding to each element in the guessed variable* psi*. Assuming that you have such a function defined in a file named* flash.m*, you are encouraged to work through the following exercise using MATLAB.*

>> global K z
>> z=[.25 .25 .25 .25] %define a 4-component system
>> K=[2 1.5 0.5 0.1] %define equilibrium values
>> bisect('flash',[0,.1]) * %find the root using bisect
>> x=0:0.05:1; %create a vector of equally spaced data
>> y=flash(x); %evaluate the function
>> plot(x,y) %plot the function

In this section, we have developed and implemented the bi-

---

*ans=0.0434

section algorithm as a function in MATLAB and used it to solve an example problem from multicomponent flash. The function `bisect` can be used to solve any other root finding problem as long as you define the problem you want to solve as another MATLAB function along the lines of the example function `flash.m`.

While we managed to solve the problem, we did not concern ourselves with * questions such as, (i) how many iterations did it take to converge? and, (ii) can we improve the iteration scheme in step 2 to reduce the number of iterations? By design, the bisection scheme will always converge provided an acceptable set of initial guesses have been chosen. This method, however, converges rather slowly and we attempt to devise algorithms that improve the rate of convergence.

2.3   Regula-falsi method

Instead of using the average of the two initial guesses as we did with the bisection scheme, we can attempt to approximate the function $f(x)$ by straight line (a *linear* approximation) since we know two points on the function $f(x)$. This is illustrated graphically in figure 2.3b with the dashed line approximating the function. We can then determine the root, x_3 of this linear function, $\tilde{f}(\tilde{x})$. The equation for the dashed straight line in figure 2.3b is

$$\tilde{f}(\tilde{x}) := \frac{\tilde{x} - x_1}{\tilde{f} - f_1} = \frac{x_2 - x_1}{f_2 - f_1}$$

Now we can determine the value of $\tilde{x} = x_3$ where the linear function $\tilde{f} = 0$ in the above equation. This results in,

$$\boxed{x_3 = x_1 - f_1 \frac{x_2 - x_1}{f_2 - f_1}} \qquad (2.5)$$

---

*Is it always possible to find such a guess? Consider the pathological case of $r = -2$ in figure ??c!

which is used as the iterative equation in step 2. When we evaluate the original function at x_3, $f(x_3)$ clearly will not be zero (unless the scheme has converged) as shown in figure 2.3b; but x_3 will be closer to r than either x_1 or x_2. We can then retain x_3 and one of x_1 or x_2 in such a manner that the root r remains bracketed. This is achieved by following the same logic as in the bisection algorithm to discard the x value that does not bracket the root. Figure 2.6 shows the graphical depiction of the iterative steps in the Regula-Falsi method.

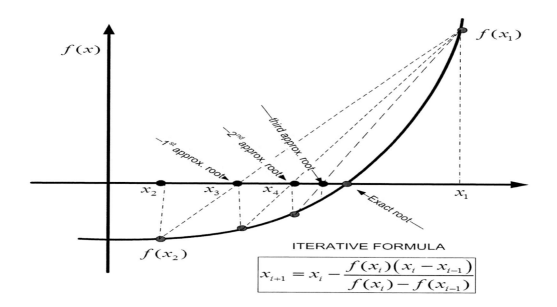

Figure 2.6: Regula-Falsi iterative steps

The MATLAB function `bisect` can be easily adapted to implement Regula-Falsi method by merely replacing equation (2.3) with equation (2.5) for step 2.

2.4   Newton's method

The Newton method is by far the most powerful and widely used algorithm for finding the roots of nonlinear equations. A graphical representation of the algorithm is shown in figure 2.3d. This algorithm also relies on constructing a linear approximation of the function; But this is achieved by taking the tangent to the function at a given point. Hence this scheme requires only one initial guess, x_1. The linear function $\tilde{f}(\tilde{x})$ shown by dashed line in figure 2.3d is,

$$\tilde{f}(\tilde{x}) := \frac{\tilde{f} - f_1}{\tilde{x} - x_1}$$

The root of this linear equation, is at $(\tilde{x} = x_2, \tilde{f} = 0)$. Under these conditions one can solve the above equation for x_2 as,

$$\boxed{x_2 = x_1 - \frac{f_1}{f_1'}} \tag{2.6}$$

which forms the iterative process (step 2). Note that this algorithm requires that the derivative of the function be evaluated at every iteration, which can be a computationally expensive operation.

While we have relied on the geometrical interpretation so far in constructing the algorithms, we can also derive Newton's scheme from a Taylor series expansion of a function. This is an instructive exercise, for it will enable us to generalize the Newton's scheme to higher dimensional (*i.e.*, more than two equations) systems as well as provide some information on the rate of convergence of the iterative scheme.

The Taylor series representation of a function around a reference point, x_i is,

$$f(x_i + \delta) = \sum_{k=0}^{\infty} \frac{f^{(k)}(x_i)}{k!} \delta^k \qquad (2.7)$$

where $f^{(k)}(x_i)$ is the $k - th$ derivative of the function at x_i and δ is a small displacement from x_i. While the infinite series expansion is an exact representation of the function, it requires all the higher order derivative of the function at the reference point. We can construct various levels of approximate representations of the function, $\tilde{f}$ by *truncating* the series at *finite* terms. For example a three term expansion $(k = 0, 1, 2)$ is

$$\tilde{f}(x_i + \delta) = f(x_i) + f'(x_i)\delta + f''(x_i)\frac{\delta^2}{2!} + \mathcal{O}(\delta^3)$$

where the symbol $\mathcal{O}(\delta^3)$ stands as a reminder of the higher order terms (three and above in this case) that have been neglected. The error introduced by such omission of higher order terms is called *truncation error*. In fact to derive the Newton scheme, we neglect the quadratic term $\mathcal{O}(\delta^2)$ also. In figure 2.3d, taking the reference point to be $x_i = x_1$, the displacement to be $\delta = x_{i+1} - x_i$, and recognising that $\tilde{f}(x_i + \delta) = 0$ we can rewrite the truncted two-term series as,

$$0 = f(x_i) + f'(x_i)(x_{i+1} - x_i) + \mathcal{O}(\delta^2)$$

which can be rearranged as

$$x_{i+1} = x_i - \frac{f(x_i)}{f'(x_i)}$$

This is the same as equation (2.6). The iterative steps are shown in Figure 2.7.

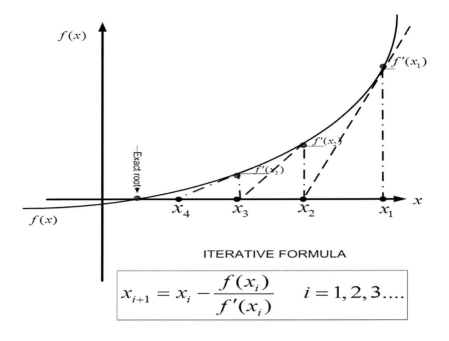

Figure 2.7: Newton's iterative steps

2.5   Secant method

In the secant method, two most recent estimates of the root are used to compute the derivative of the function f by linear approximation. Given two estimates x_2 and x_1, the derivative is computed as $f_1' = \frac{(f_2 - f_1)}{x_2 - x_1}$. Replacing the derivative in equation (2.6) with this and denoting the new root as x_3 we obtain:

$$x_3 = x_1 - \frac{f_1}{\frac{(f_2 - f_1)}{x_2 - x_1}}$$

the iterative procedure for the secant method becomes:

$$x_3 = x_1 - f_1 \left[\frac{x_2 - x_1}{f_2 - f_1} \right] \tag{2.8}$$

The secant formula looks exactly like the Requla Falsi formula in form. However, the two methods differ in implementation. For the secant method, the oldest value, x_1 is always discarded while the most recent value of x viz. x_2 and x_3 are retained. This simple change from the Regula-Falsi scheme produces a dramatic difference in the rate of convergence. A MATLAB implementation of the secant method is shown in figure 2.8. Figure 2.9 shows the graphical depiction of the iterative steps in the secant method.

```
function  r=secant(Fun,x,tol,trace)
%SECANT  find  the  root  of  a  function  "Fun"  using  secant  scheme
%        Fun    -  the  name  of  the  external  function
%        x      -  vector  of  length  2,  (initial  guesses)
%        tol    -  error  criterion
%        trace  -  print  intermediate  results
%
%    Usage    secant('flash',[0,1])
%             Here  flash  is  the  name  of  the  external  function.
%                  [0,1]  is  the  initial  guess
%Check  inputs
if  nargin  <  4,  trace=0;  end
if  nargin  <  3,  tol=eps;  trace=0;  end
if  (length(x)  ~=  2)
 error('Please  provide  two  initial  guesses')
end

f  =  feval(Fun,x);          %Fun  is  assumed  to  accept  a  vector

for  i  =  1:100             %Set  max  limit  on  iterations
 x3  =  x(1)  -  f(1)*(x(2)-x(1))/(f(2)-f(1))  ;  %Update(step  2)
 f3  =  feval(Fun,x3);       %Cal.  f(x3)

%Keep  the  last  two  values
 x(1)  =  x(2);f(1)  =  f(2);  x(2)  =  x3;  f(2)  =  f3;

 if  abs(f3)  <  tol,  r=x3;  return;  end  %Check  for  convergence
 if  trace,  fprintf(1,'%3i  %12.5f  %12.5f\n',  i,x3,f3);  end
end
error('Exceeded  maximum  number  of  iterations')
```

Figure 2.8: MATLAB implementation of the secant algorithm

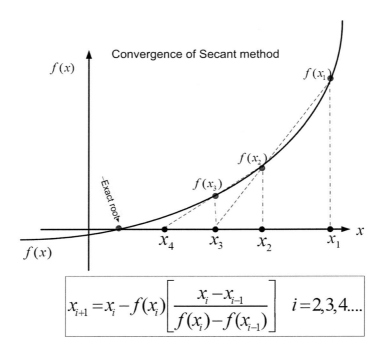

Figure 2.9: Secant iterative steps

2.6   Muller's method

This scheme can be thought of as an attempt to generalize secant method and is important at least from the point of illustrating such generalizations. Instead of making two guesses and constructing an approximate linear function as we did with the secant method, we can choose three inital guesses and construct a quadratic approximation to the original function and find the roots of the quadratic. A graphical representation of this is shown in figure 2.10. The three initial guesses are (x_0, x_1, x_2) and the corresponding function values are represented by (f_1, f_2, f_3) respectively. We construct a second degree polynomial as,

$$p_2(v) = av^2 + bv + c$$

where $v = (x - x_0)$. Note that the polynomial is represented as a function of a new independent variable v, which is merely a trans-

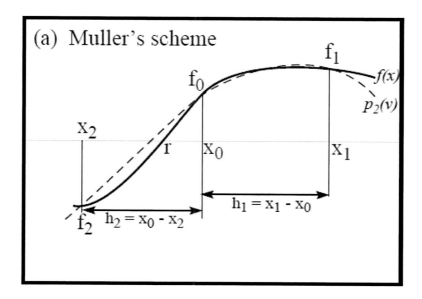

Figure 2.10: Graphical representation of Muller's scheme

lation of the original independent variable x by x_0. An alternate view is to regard v as the distances measured from reference point x_0, so that $v = 0$ at this new origin. (a, b, c) are the coefficients of the quadratic that must be determined in such a way that $p_2(v)$ passes through the three data points (x_0, f_0), (x_1, f_1) and (x_2, f_2). Defining $h_1 = (x_1 - x_0)$ and $h_2 = (x_0 - x_2)$ and requiring that the polynomial pass through the three points, we get,

$$\begin{aligned} p_2(0) = a(0)^2 + b(0) + c &= f_0 &\Rightarrow& \quad c = f_0 \\ p_2(h_1) = ah_1^2 + bh_1 + c &= f_1 \\ p_2(-h_2) = ah_2^2 - bh_2 + c &= f_2 \end{aligned}$$

The reason for coordinate shift should be clear by now. This enables c to be found directly. Solving the remaining two equations we obtain a and b as follows:

$$a = \frac{\gamma f_1 - f_0(1 + \gamma) + f_2}{\gamma h_1^2(1 + \gamma)}$$

$$b = \frac{f_1 - f_0 - ah_1^2}{h_1}$$

where $\gamma = h_2/h_1$. So far we have only constructed an approximate representation of the original function, $f(x) \approx p_2(v)$. The next step is to find the roots of this approximate function, $p_2(v) = 0$. These are given by,

$$v = \tilde{r} - x_0 = \frac{-b \pm \sqrt{b^2 - 4ac}}{a2}$$

This can be rearranged as,

$$\boxed{\tilde{r} = x_0 - \frac{2c}{b \pm \sqrt{b^2 - 4ac}}} \qquad (2.9)$$

Since $p_2(v)$ is a quadratic, there are clearly two roots $\tilde{r}$ in equation (2.9). In order the take the root closest to x_0 we choose the largest denominator in equation (2.9). In summary, the sequential procedure for implimenting Muller's scheme is as follows:

- Guess (x_0, x_1, x_2)

- Compute $(f_0 = f(x_0), f_1 = f(x_1), f_2 = f(x_2))$.

- Compute $h_1 = (x_1 - x_0)$, $h_2 = (x_0 - x_2)$, $\gamma = h_2/h_1$

- Compute $c = f(x_0)$.

- Compute $a = (\gamma f_1 - f_0(1 + \gamma) + f_2)/(\gamma h_1^2(1 + \gamma))$

- Compute $b = (f_1 - f_0 - ah_1^2)/(h_1)$.

- Compute the roots from equation (2.9).

- From (x_0, x_1, x_2) discard the point farthest from $\tilde{r}$ and substitue the new root in its place and repeat.

Note that Muller's method converges almost quadratically (as does Newton's scheme), but requires only one additional function evaluation at every iteration which is comparable to the computational load of the secant method. In particular derivative evaluation is not required, which is a major advantage as compared to Newton's method. Also, this scheme can converge to complex roots even while starting with real initial guesses as long as provision is made for handling complex arithmetic in the computer program. MATLAB handles complex arithmetic quite naturally.

2.7 Fixed point iteration

Another approach to construct an update scheme (for step 2) is to rearrange the given equation $f(x) = 0$ into a form,

$$x = g(x)$$

Then, starting with a guess x_i, we can evaluate $g(x_i)$ from the right hand side of the above equation and the result itself is regarded as a better estimate of the root, *i.e.*,

$$\boxed{x_{i+1} = g(x_i) \qquad i = 0, 1 \cdots} \tag{2.10}$$

Given, $f(x) = 0$ it is not difficult rewrite it in the form $x = g(x)$; nor is this process unique. For example, we can always let $g(x) = x + f(x)$. Such an iterative scheme need not always converge. Let us examine the possible behavior of the iterates with a specific example. In particular we will illustrate that different choices of $g(x)$ lead to different behavior. Consider the function

$$f(x) = x^2 - x - 6 = 0 \tag{2.11}$$

Iteration Number	Iterate
x_1	5.0000000
x_2	3.3166248
x_3	3.0523147
x_4	3.0087065
x_5	3.0014507
x_6	3.0002418
x_7	3.0000403
x_8	3.0000067
x_9	3.0000011
x_{10}	3.0000002

Table 2.1: The first ten iterates of $x_{i+1} = \sqrt{x_i + 6}$ starting with $x_0 = 5$

which has roots at $r = -2$ and $r = 3$. In the first case let us rewrite it as

$$x = \sqrt{x + 6}$$

A geometrical interpretation is that we are finding the intersection of two curves, $y = x$ (the left hand side) and $y = \sqrt{x + 6}$ (the right hand side). See figure 2.11 for a graphical illustration.

Starting with an initial guess, say $x_0 = 4$, we compute $x_1 = g(x_0) = \sqrt{x_0 + 6}$. This is tantamount to stepping between the $y = x$ and $y = g(x)$ curves as shown in figure 2.11a. It is clear that the sequence will converge monotonically to the root $r = 3$. The table 2.1 shows the first ten iterates, starting with an inital guess of $x_0 = 5$.

Observe that the slope of the function at the root is $g'(r = 3) < 1$. We will show shortly that the condition for convergence is indeed $|g'(r)| < 1$. As an alternate formulation consider rewritting equation (2.11) as $x = g(x) = 6/(x-1)$. Now, $g(x)$ has a singularity at $x = 1$. A graphical illustration is shown in figure 2.11b. Using this new $g(x)$, but starting at the same initial guess $x_0 = 4$ the sequence diverges initially in an oscillatory fashion around the root $r = 3$, but eventually is attracted to the other root at $r = -2$, also in an oscillatory fashion. Observe that the slopes at

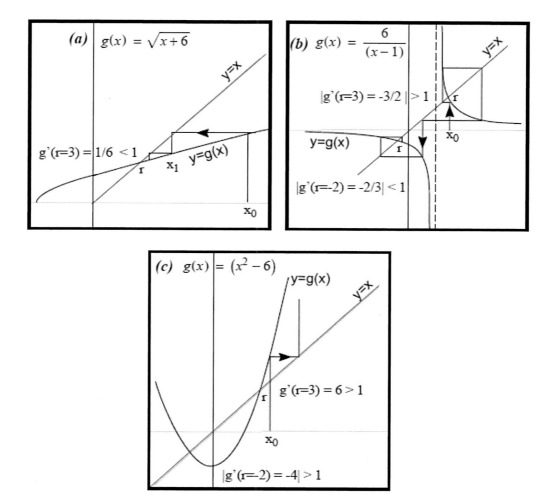

Figure 2.11: Graphical representation of fixed point scheme: a) convergence, b) divergence, c) divergence.

the two roots are: $g'(3) = -3/2$ and $g'(-2) = -2/3$. Both are negative and hence the oscillatory behavior. The one with absolute magnitude greater than unity diverges and the other with absolute magnitude less than unity converges. Finally consider the formulation $x = g(x) = (x^2 - 6)$. The behavior for this case is shown in figure 2.11c. For reasons indicated above, the sequence will not converge to either root! The following shows the MATLAB implementation for generating the iterative sequence for the first case. Enter this into a file called $g.m$.

```
function x=g(x)
for i=1:10
  fprintf(1,'%2i %12.5e\n',i,x);  %print the iterates
  x=sqrt(x+6);   %also try x=6/(x-1)  and x=(x^2-6) here
end
```

Invoke this function from within MATLAB with various initial guesses, *e.g.*, try initial guess of 5 by entering,

>> g(5)

2.8   Error analysis and convergence acceleration

2.8.1   Convergence of the bisection method

The speed of convergence of a given method relates to the number of iterations required to obtain a solution with desired accuracy. For the bisection method, starting with an initial interval between x_1 and x_2 which brackets the root, the next estimate is obtained by halving the interval. Defining the initial interval as $h_o = x_2 - x_1$, the error at each subsequent iteration may be obtained as :

error after the first iteration $\qquad e_1 = \dfrac{h_o}{2}$

error after the second iteration $\qquad e_2 = \dfrac{e_1}{2} = \dfrac{h_o}{2^2}$

error after the third iteration $\qquad e_3 = \dfrac{e_2}{2} = \dfrac{h_o}{2^3}$

$$\vdots$$

error after the nth iteration $\qquad e_n = \dfrac{e_{n-1}}{2} = \dfrac{h_o}{2^n}$

where n is the number of bisections. If we desire to know the root within an interval with width ϵ, we can calculate the number of iterations (bisections) required as

$$h_o 2^{-n} < \epsilon$$

taking the logarithim of both sides

$$\ln(h_o) - n \ln(2) < \ln \epsilon$$

we can see that the number of bisections to obtain an interval width (error) less than ϵ must be

$$\boxed{n > \frac{\ln(h_o) - \ln \epsilon}{\ln(2)}} \qquad (2.12)$$

Thus for example, if the initial interval width is $h_0 = 1$ and we desire an accuracy of $\epsilon = 10^{-8}$, then $n > 26.6 = 27$ since n is an integer.

2.8.2 Convergence of fixed point iteration method

A simple error analysis can be developed for the fixed point iterative scheme which will provide not only a criterion for convergence, but also clues for accelerating convergence with very little

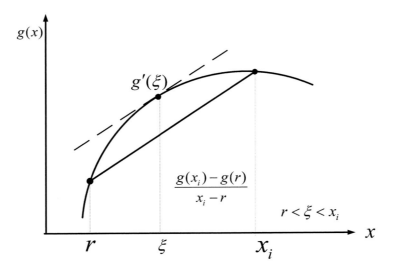

Figure 2.12: Graphical illustration of mean value theorem

additional computational effort. We are clearly moving away from the realm of intuition to the realm of analysis! Consider the fixed point iteration $x_{i+1} = g(x_i)$. After convergence to the root r we will have $r = g(r)$. Subtracting the two equations we get,

$$(x_{i+1} - r) = g(x_i) - g(r)$$

Multiplying and diving the right hand side by $(x_i - r)$,

$$(x_{i+1} - r) = \frac{g(x_i) - g(r)}{(x_i - r)}(x_i - r)$$

Now the difference $e_i = (x_i - r)$ can be interpreted as the error at iterative step i and hence the above equation can be written as,

$$\boxed{e_{i+1} = g'(\xi)\, e_i} \qquad (2.13)$$

where we have used the mean value theorem to replace slope of the chord by the tangent to the curve at some suitable value of $x = \xi$, i.e.,

$$\frac{(g(x_i) - g(r))}{(x_i - r)} = g'(\xi)$$

A geometrical interpretation of the mean value theorem is shown in figure 2.12. From equation (2.13), it is clear the error will decrease with every iteration if the slope $|g'(\xi)| < 1$; otherwise the error will be amplified at every iteration. Since the error in the current step is proportional to that of the previous step, we conclude that the rate of convergence of the fixed point iteration is linear. The development has been reasonably rigorous so far. We now take a more pragmatic step and assume that $g'(\xi) = K$ is a constant in the neighbourhodd of the root r. Then we have the sequence, *

$$ e_2 = K e_1, \qquad e_3 = K e_2 = K^2 e_1, \qquad e_4 = K e_3 = K^3 e_1 \qquad \cdots $$

and hence we can write a general error propagation solution as,

$$ \boxed{e_n = K^{n-1} e_1 \qquad \text{or} \qquad x_n - r = K^{n-1} e_1} \qquad (2.14) $$

It should be clear now that $e_n \to 0$ as $n \to \infty$ only if $|K| < 1$. †. We refer to equation (2.14) as the error propagation solution since it provides a solution of estimating the error at any step n, provided the error at the first step e_1 and K are known. We can now develop a generalized method for convergence acceleration.

2.8.3 Atkins method for convergence acceleration

We can develop a convergence acceleration scheme using the error solution (2.14) to estimate the three unknowns (r, K, e_1) in the second form of equation (2.14). Once we have generated three iterates, (x_n, x_{n+1}, x_{n+2}), we can use equation (2.14) to write down,

$$
\begin{aligned}
x_n &= r + K^{n-1} e_1 \\
x_{n+1} &= r + K^n e_1 \\
x_{n+2} &= r + K^{n+1} e_1
\end{aligned}
\qquad (2.15)
$$

---

*Will K be the same constant at every iteration?

†Well, if we know the error in the first step, none of this analysis would be necessary! $r = x_1 - e_1$ would do it!

Now we have three equations in three unkowns which can be solved to estimate r (and K, e_1 as well). If K were to remain a true constant with every iteration, r would be the correct root; since K is not a constant in general, r is only an *estimate* of the root, hopefully a better estimate than any of (x_n, x_{n+1}, x_{n+2}). Now let us proceed to construct a solution for r from the above three equations. We will define a first order forward difference operator Δ as,

$$\Delta x_n = x_{n+1} - x_n$$

Think of the symbol Δ as defining a new rule of operation just like a derivative operator $\frac{d}{dx}$ defines a rule. When Δ operates on x_n it is computed using the rule shown on the right hand side. Now, if we apply the operator Δ to x_{n+1} we should have,

$$\Delta x_{n+1} = x_{n+2} - x_{n+1}.$$

If we apply the Δ operator twice (which is equivalent to defining higher order derivatives), we should get,

$$\Delta(\Delta x_n) = \Delta^2 x_n = (\Delta x_{n+1}) - (\Delta x_n) = x_{n+2} - 2x_{n+1} + x_n.$$

You can verify that using equation (2.15) in the above definitions, we get,

$$\frac{(\Delta x_n)^2}{\Delta^2 x_n} = K^{n-1} e_1 = x_n - r$$

and hence r is given by,

$$r = x_n - \frac{(\Delta x_n)^2}{\Delta^2 x_n} = x_n - \frac{x_{n+1}^2 - 2x_n x_{n+1} + x_n^2}{x_{n+2} - 2x_{n+1} + x_n}$$

Thus the three iterates (x_n, x_{n+1}, x_{n+2}) can be plugged into the right hand side of the above equation to get a better estimate of r.

EXAMPLE 2.2 (Convergence acceleration) *Let us apply this convergence acceleration procedure to the first three iterates of table 2.1.*

$$x_1 = 5.0000000$$
$$x_2 = 3.3166248$$
$$x_3 = 3.0523147$$
$$\Delta x_1 = (x_2 - x_1) = -1.6833752$$
$$\Delta x_2 = (x_3 - x_2) = -0.26431010$$
$$\Delta^2 x_1 = (\Delta x_2 - \Delta x_1) = 1.41906510$$
$$r = x_1 - \frac{(\Delta x_1)^2}{\Delta^2 x_1} = 5.000000 - \frac{(-1.6833752)^2}{1.41906510} = 3.0030852$$

Compare this with the fourth iterate produce in the original sequence $x_4 = 3.0087065$.

2.8.4 Convergence of the Newton's scheme

The Newton scheme given by equation (2.6) can be thought of as a fixed point iteration scheme where $g(x)$ has been specified in a special manner as,

$$x_{n+1} = x_n - \frac{f(x_n)}{f'(x_n)} = g(x_n)$$

Hence,

$$g'(x) = 1 - \frac{(f')^2 - f f''}{(f')^2} = \left| \frac{f f''}{(f')^2} \right| < 1$$

Since $f(r) = 0$ by definition, $g'(r) = 0$ (barring any pathological situation such as $f'(r) = 0$) and the inequality should hold near the root r. Thus the Newton method is guaranteed to converge as long as we have a good initial guess. Having progressed this far, we can take the next step and ask the question about the rate of convergence of the Newton method. A Taylor series expansion of $g(x)$ around r is,

$$g(x_n) = g(r) + g'(r)(x_n - r) + \frac{g''(r)}{2}(x_n - r)^2 + \cdots$$

Recognizing that $e_{n+1} = x_{n+1} - r = g(x_n) - r$, $e_n = (x_n - r)$ and $g'(r) = 0$, the truncated Taylor series expansion can be rearranged as,

$$e_{n+1} = \frac{g''(r)}{2}e_n^2$$

which shows that the error at any step goes down as the square of the previous step - *i.e.*, quadratically! This manifests itself in the form of doubling accuracy at every iteration.

2.9   Deflation technique

Having found a root, r, of $f(x) = 0$, if we are interested in finding additional roots of $f(x) = 0$, we can start with a different initial guess and hope that the new initial guess lies within the region of attraction of a root different from r. Choosing a different initial guess does not guarantee that the iteration scheme will not be attracted to the root already discovered. In order to ensure that we stay away from the known root, r, we can choose to *deflate* the original function by constructing a modified function,

$$g(x) = f(x)/(x - r)$$

which does not have r as a root. For a single equation the concepts are best illustrated with a graphical example. Consider the illustration in figure 2.13a where the original function,

$$f(x) := (x - 2)\sin(2x)e^{-0.8x}$$

can be seen to have several roots including one at $r = 2$. A sketch of the deflated function, $g(x) = f(x)/(x - 2)$ is shown in figure

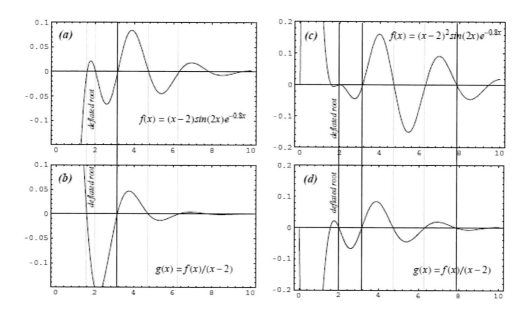

Figure 2.13: Graphical illustration deflation technique

2.13b. Since $r = 2$ turns out to be a *simple root* of $f(x) = 0$, the deflated function $g(x) = 0$ does not contain the already discovered root at $x = 2$. Hence starting with a different initial guess and applying an iterative method like the secant or Newton scheme on the function $g(x)$ will result in convergence to another root. This process can obviously be repeated by deflating successively found roots. For example if we know two roots r_1 and r_2 then a new function can be constructed as

$$h(x) = \frac{f(x)}{(x - r_1)(x - r_2)}.$$

The successive application of this approach is of course susceptible to propagation of round off errors. * For example if the roots r_1, r_2 are known to only a few significant digits, then the definition of the deflated function $h(x)$ will inherit these errors and hence the

---

*Can you think of a way to alleviate this problem?

roots of $h(x) = 0$ will not be as accurate as those of the original
equation $f(x) = 0$.

Another problem of the deflation technique pertains to non-
simple roots. A sketch of the function,

$$f(x) := (x - 2)^2 \sin(2x)e^{-0.8x}$$

is shown in figure 2.13c. It is immediately clear that $r = 2$ is a
double root - *i.e.*, occurs with a multiplicity of two. *Hence the
deflated function $g(x) = f(x)/(x - 2)$ still has $r = 2$ as a *simple
root* as seen in figure 2.13d.

2.10   Software tools

2.10.1   MATLAB

The MATLAB function for determining roots of a polynomial is
called **roots**. You can invoke it by entering,

>> **roots(c)**

where **c** is a vector containing the coefficients of the polynomial
in the form,

$$p_n(x) = c_1 x^n + c_2 x^{n-1} + \cdots + c_n x + c_{n+1}.$$

Let us consider the factored form of the polynomial $p_3(x) = (x +
2)(x+i)(x-i)$ so that we know the roots are at $(-2, \pm i)$. To check
whether MATLAB can find the roots of this polynomial we need
to construct the coefficients of the expanded polynomial. This
can be done with the convolve function **conv(f1,f2)** as follows.

---

*What computational problem might this pose?

```
>> f1 = [1 2] %Here we define coeff of (x+2) as [1 2]
>> f2 = [1 i] %Here we define coeff of (x+i) as [1 i]
>> f3 = [1 -i] %Here we define coeff of (x-i) as [1 -i]
>> c=conv(conv(f1,f2),f3) % c contains coeff of polynomial
>> r=roots(c) %returns roots of polynomial defined by c
```

Note that the function **roots** finds *all* of the roots of a polynomial, including complex ones.

The MATLAB function for finding a *real* root of any real, single nonlinear algebraic equation (not necessarily a polynomial) is called **fzero**. You can invoke it by entering,

> **>> fzero('fn',x)**

where **fn** is the name of a *m-file* that defines the function, **x** is the initial guess for the root. This **fzero** is not based on a very robust algorithm. If the function you want to solve has singularities, or multiple roots, the scheme fails to converge, often without producing any appropriate error or warning messages. Hence use with caution. After it produces an answer check that it is the correct result by evaluating the function at the root. As an example try the multicomponent flash problem considered previously. You are encouraged to try the following steps during a MATLAB session.

```
>>global K z;              % define K,z to be global
>>K=[2 1.5 0.5 0.2];       % define K values
>>z=[.25 .25 .25 .25];     % define z values
>>root=fzero('flash',.5)   % solve x0=0.5, ⇒ ans=0.0949
>>flash(root)              % check solution
>>root=fzero('flash',-.85) % solve x0=-0.85, ⇒ ans=-1.0000
>>flash(root)              % check solution
>>root=fzero('flash',1.85) % solve x0=1.85, ⇒ ans=1.6698
```

```
>>flash(root)              % check solution
>>root=fzero('flash',1.90)% solve x0=1.90, ⇒ ans=2.0
>>flash(root)              % check solution
```

*

2.11   Summary

The solution of non-linear equations using a computer will generally require some sort of iterative process. In this chapter, different methods for solving non-linear equations have been presented. The methods differ from simple to complicated, depending on the nature of the function and available infrmation. Simple methods such as bisection require the root to be bracketed and will find it if it exists, albeit at a slower pace. On the other hand, the Newton's method is quadratically convergent and will obtain the root with a minimum number iterations. However, the method may diverge if the slope of the function is close to zero.

Convergence accleration may be applied to improve the performance of root finding techniques.

---

*Note that the desired result is `root=0.0949203`. But starting with different initial guesses, MATLAB produces different results! Why? Try plotting the function over the range $\psi \in [-5, 5]$ in MATLAB and see if you can understand MATLAB behavior! (Clue: sign change)

2.12 Exercise problems

P2.1. The volume liquid methane in a spherical reactor of radius $r = 1m$ is related to the depth of the liquid (h) by the following equation:

$$V = \frac{\pi h^2(3r - h)}{3}$$

Determine the height of liquid (h) for a reactor with volume $V = 0.5m^3$ using:

(a) The bisection method.

(b) The secant method.

(c) The false position method.

NOTE: Perform only TWO iterations for each method. For all cases, start with $x_0 = 0.5m$ and $x_1 = 0.1m$

P2.2. Van der Waals Equation of State

The van der Waals equation relates pressure (P), the volume (V) and temperature (T) for real gases:

$$\left(P + \frac{n^2 a}{V^2}\right)(V - nb) = nRT$$

where n is the number of moles of gas present, R is the universal gas constant and a and b are van der Waals constants. You are required to find the volume (V) of 1 mole of chlorine gas at a temperature of $T = 313K$ and pressure $P = 2atm$, given the following parameters: $a = 6.29\frac{atm.Litre^2}{mole^2}$, $b = 0.0562\frac{Litre}{mole}$, $R = 0.08206\frac{atm.Litre}{mole.K}$.

(a) Based on Figure 2.14, estimate the volume of the chlorine gas.

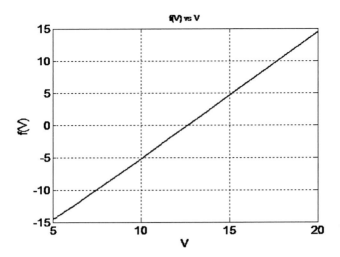

Figure 2.14: Plot of $f(V)$ vs. V for Chlorine gas at $T = 313K$ and $P = 2atm$

(b) Perform THREE iterations of the bisection method. Select a suitable bound based on the given graph (Figure 2.14).

(c) Perform THREE iterations of the Newton-Raphson method. Select an initial value based on the given graph.

(d) Assuming that the value of V obtained in part (c) is the most accurate (true value); calculate the percent error for part (a) and part (b).

P2.3. Ideal gas extension

The equation of state developed by Beattie and Bridgemann is an extension to the ideal gas law and can be represented as:

$$P = \frac{RT}{V} + \frac{a}{V^2} + \frac{b}{V^3} + \frac{c}{V^4}$$

where a, b and c are parameters specific to a given gas. Determine the specific volume (V) for a gas at $T = 293K$, $P = 25atm$ with $a = -0.106$, $b = 0.057$ and $c - 0.0001$

(a) Perform THREE iterations of the bisection method, using initial estimates of $V_1 = 0.001$ L/mol and $V_2 = 0.01$ L/mol.

(b) Perform TWO iterations of the Newton's method using an initial estimate of $V_1 = 0.001$ L/mol.

(c) If the exact value of the specific volume for the given parameters is 0.0018 L/mol, calculate the percent relative errors for the results in part (a) and (b).

P2.4. Multicomponent, isothermal flash model

A sketch of a multicomponent flash process is shown in figure 1.5.

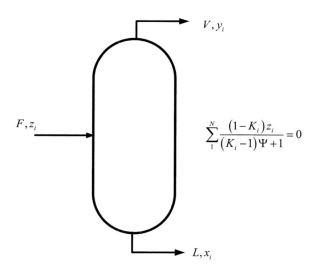

The following equation, which was derived in Chapter 1, models the multicomponent flash process. This is a single non-linear algebraic equation in the unknown ψ, which represents the fraction of feed that goes into the vapor phase.

$$\sum_{i=1}^{N} \frac{(1 - K_i)z_i}{(K_i - 1)\psi + 1} = 0 \qquad (2.16)$$

Component	i	z_i	K_i
Carbon dioxide	1	0.0046	1.650
Methane	2	0.8345	3.090
Ethane	3	0.0381	0.720
Propane	4	0.0163	0.390
Isobutane	5	0.0050	0.210
n-Butane	6	0.0074	0.175
Pentanes	7	0.0287	0.093
Hexanes	8	0.0220	0.065
Heptanes+	9	0.0434	0.036

Table 2.2: Feed composition & equilibrium ratio of a natural gas mixture

This equation has several roots, but not all of them have any physical meaning. Only the root for $\psi \in [0,1]$ is of interest. *For a bonus point you may choose to find the number of roots for the test data above!*

The test data in Table 2.2, (taken from Katz *et al.*) relate to the flashing of a natural gas stream at 1600 psia and $120^o F$. Determine the fraction ψ using the *secant* algorithm given in figure 2.8 and another root finding function that is provided in MATLAB named *fzero*.

P2.5. Determine the fraction of feed that goes into vapour when a multicompnent feed consisting of propane, n-butane and n-pentane with a composition if $Z_i = [0.3, 0.3, 0.4]$ is flashed at a temperature and pressure of $T = 750^o R, P = 400 psia$. Use equilibrium data from Holland (1963) in the form, $(K_i/T)^{1/3} = \sum_{j=1} a_{ij} T^{j-1}$, where the coefficients are given in the Table below. Determine the liquid and vapour composition (Ans:$\psi = 0.627$).

Recall that the flash equation is given by,

Component	a_{i1}	a_{i2}	a_{i3}	a_{i4}
Propane	-2.7980091E-1	1.1811943E-3	-1.0935041E-6	0.3518021E-9
n-Butane	-2.3203344E-1	0.83753226E-3	-0.61774360E-6	0.15243376E-9
n-Pentane	0.37103008E-1	-0.36257004E-3	0.99113800E-6	-0.54441110E-9

Table 2.3: Gas mixture for problem P2.2

$$ f(T, P, \psi) = \sum_{i=1}^{N} \frac{(1 - K_i)z_i}{(K_i - 1)\psi + 1} = 0 $$

(a) Use the **secant** and the **Muller** scheme. Include a listing of all the m-files that you write to complete the problem.

(b) Using only the **Muller** scheme, what should the temperature be in order to get 50% of the feed into vapour ? (Ans: T = 744.9569).

P2.6. Compressible flow in a pipe

In a fluid mechanics course you might come across the Weymouth equation, which is used for relating the pressure drop vs. flow rate in a pipeline carrying compressible gases. It is given by,

$$ Q_o = 433.54 \frac{T_o}{P_o} \left[\frac{(P_1^2 - P_2^2)}{L \, \sigma \, T} \right]^{0.5} d^{2.667} \eta \qquad (2.17) $$

where

Q_o is the gas flow rate = 2000000 SCFD
T_o is the standard temperature = $520^o R$
P_o is the standard pressure = 14.7 psia
P_1 is the upstream pressure, (?), psia

P_2 is the downstream pressure, (21.7), psia

L is the length of pipe $= 0.1894$ miles

σ is the specific gravity of gas (air$=1$) $= 0.7$

T is the actual gas temperature $= 530^o R$

d is the diameter of the pipe, $(?)$ inches

η is the efficiency $= 0.7$ (a fudge factor!)

(a) If the diameter of the pipe is 4.026 inches, determine the upstream pressure using the *secant* (initial guess of $[5, 45]$) and *fzero* (initial guess of 25) functions.

(b) Suppose the maximum pressure the pipeline can withstand is only 24.7 psia. Other conditions remaining the same as in previous part, determine the diameter of the pipe that should be used using the *secant* (initial guess of $[4, 8]$) and *fzero* (initial guess of 6) functions.

P2.7. A model for separation processes

Consider a stagewise separation process shown in the figure below:

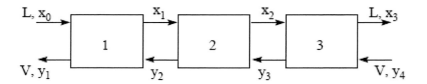

Figure 2.15: Stage separation process

A model for this process was developed in Chapter 1. The variables of interest are $(L, V, x_0, x_1, x_2, \cdots, x_n, y_1, y_2, y_3, \cdots, y_{n+1})$. Under the assumption of linear equilibrium model, $y_i = Kx_i$ it is possible to successively eliminate all of the variables and obtain the following single, analytical expression relating the input, (x_0, y_{n+1}), the output, x_n, the separation factor $S = L/KV$ and the number of stages n.

$$\frac{[x_0 - x_n]}{[x_0 - y_{n+1}/K]} = \frac{[(1/S)^{n+1} - (1/S)]}{[(1/S)^{n+1} - 1]} \qquad (2.18)$$

The equation is called the Kremser-Brown-Souders equation. We have a single equation relating six variables, viz. $(x_0, x_n, y_{n+1}, K, S, n)$. Given any five of these variables, we can solve for the 6th one. Your task is to formulate this problem as a root finding problem of the type

$$f(x; \boldsymbol{p}) = 0$$

where the unknown variable is associated with x and $\boldsymbol{p}$ is the parameter set consisting of the remaining five known values. Write an m-file to represent the function in the form

$$f(x; \boldsymbol{p}) = \frac{(x_0 - x_n)}{(x_0 - y_{n+1}/K)} - \frac{[(1/S)^{n+1} - (1/S)]}{[(1/S)^{n+1} - 1]} = 0$$

$$(2.19)$$

(a) In a typical *design problem* you might be given the flow rates, (say $L = 10, V = 10$), the inlet compositions (say, $x_0 = 0.8, y_{n+1} = 0$) and a specified recovery ($x_n = 0.1615$). Your task is to determine the number of stages (n) required to meet the specifications. Take the equilibrium ratio to be $K = 0.8$. Here the unknown variable x is associated with n and the others form the parameter set. Solve for n using *secant* and *bisection* methods using initial guesses of $[10, 30]$.

Report the number of iterations required for convergence to the MATLAB built-in convergence tolerance of $eps = 10^{-16}$. You can use the *secant.m* and *bisect.m* algorithms outlined in figures 2.8,2.4. You must construct a m-file to define the function represented by equation (2.19) in terms of the unknown. Here is a sample function for the first case.

```
function f=KBS1(x)
% Kremser-Brown-Souders equation
% number of stages is unknown i.e. solve for x=n
K=0.8; L=10; V=10;
x0 = 0.8; ynp1= 0; xn=0.1615; S=L/K/V; %Known values
m=length(x);
for i=1:m
 n=x(i);
 f(i) = (x0-xn)/(x0-ynp1/K) - ( (1/S)^(n+1) - (1/S))
    ...
/ ( (1/S)^(n+1) - 1);
end
```

Make sure that you understand what the above function does! In the next two parts you will have to modify this function to solve for a different unknown! Create a file named KBS1.m and enter the above function. Then to solve the problem from within MATLAB enter

>> secant('KBS1',[10,30],eps,1)

You may wish to plot the function to graphically locate the root using

>> x=10:1:30;
>> y=KBS1(x);
>> plot(x,y)

or, you can do the same in just one line using

>> **plot([10:1:30],KBS1(10:1:30))**

(b) In a *performance analysis* problem, you will be analyz-
ing an existing process with a known number of stages
(say, $n = 10$). Suppose $x_0 = 0.8, y_{n+1} = 0, L = 10, x_n =$
0.01488. Find the amount of gas V that can be processed. Use an initial guess of $[5, 20]$ and $[5, 30]$ with
both *secant* and *bisect* algorithms. Record and comment on your observations.

(c) In another variation of the *performance analysis* problem, the amount of gas to be processed ($V = 10$) may
be given. You will have to determine the exit composition x_n. Take $n = 20, x_0 = 0.8, y_{n+1} = 0, L = 10$.
Try initial guesses of $[0, .2]$ and $[0, 1]$ on both bisection
and secant algorithms. Record and comment on your
observations.

P2.8. Peng-Robinson Equation of State

The phase behavior of fluids can be predicted with the
help of equations of state. The one developed by Peng &
Robinson is particularly well tuned, accurate and hence is
widely used. The equation is given below.

$$P = \frac{RT}{(V - b)} - \frac{a(T)}{V(V + b) + b(V - b)} \tag{2.20}$$

where

$$a(T) = 0.45724 \frac{R^2 T_c^2}{P_c} \alpha(T_r, \omega), \qquad b = 0.0778 \frac{RT_c}{P_c},$$

$$\sqrt{\alpha} = 1 + m(1 - \sqrt{T_r}) \quad m = 0.37464 + 1.54226\omega - 0.26992\omega^2,$$

$$T_r = T/T_c, \text{ and} \qquad Z = PV/RT.$$

Whenever (P, T) are given it is convenient to write equation (2.20) as a cubic equation in Z

$$Z^3 - (1 - B)Z^2 + (A - 3B^2 - 2B)Z - (AB - B^2 - B^3) = 0 \tag{2.21}$$

where $A = aP/(R^2T^2)$, $B = bP/(RT)$.

Use equation (2.21) to compute the density of CO_2 in gmole/lit at $P = 20.684MPa$ and $T = 299.82^oK$. The critical properties required for CO_2 are $T_c = 304.2^oK$, $P_c = 7.3862MPa$ and $\omega = 0.225$, $R = 8314Pa\ m^3/kmol\ ^oK$.

a) Use the function *roots(c)* in MATLAB to find <u>all</u> the roots of the cubic equation (2.21) in terms of Z. In MATLAB, how does the function *roots* differ from the function *fzero*?

b) Use the *secant* method to find the *real* roots of the above equation.

c) After finding the compressibility Z from each of the above methods, convert it into molar density and compare with the experimental value of $20.814gmole/lit$

d) Consider the case where you are given (P, V) and you are asked to find T. Develop and implement the Newton iteration to solve for this case. Use the above equation to compute the temperature of CO_2 in ^oK at $P = 20.684 \times 10^6 Pa$ and $V = 0.04783lit/gmole$.

Compare the number of iterations required to obtain a solution to a tolerance of $||f|| < 10^{-15}$ using an initial guess of $T = 250$ by Newton method with that required by the **secant** method with an initial guess of $[200,310]$.

e) Suppose that you are given (T, V) and you are asked to find P, which form of equation will you choose? Eqn.

(2.20) or Eqn.(2.21)? What method of solution would you recommend?

P2.9. Transient heat conduction in semi-infinite slab

Many engineering problems can be cast in the form of determining the roots of a nonlinear algebraic equation. One such example arises in determining the time required to cool a solid body at a given point to a predetermined temperature level.

Consider a semi-infinite solid, initially at a temperature of $T_i = 200^oC$ and one side of it is suddenly exposed to an ambient temperature of $T_a = 70^oC$. The heat transfer coefficient between the solid and surroundings is $h = 525W/(m^2{}^oC)$. The thermal conductivity of the solid is $k = 215W/m^oC$ and the thermal diffusivity of the solid is $\alpha = 8.4 \times 10^{-5}m^2/s$. Determine the time required to cool the solid at a distance of $x = 4cm$ measured from the exposed surface, to $T = 120^oC$. The temperature profile as a function of time and distance is given by the following expression.

$$\theta = 1 - erf(\xi) - \left[e^{(hx/k+\tau)}\right]\left[1 - erf(\xi + \sqrt{\tau})\right]$$

where the dimensionless temperature, $\theta = \frac{(T-T_i)}{(T_a-T_i)}$, and $\xi = \frac{x}{2\sqrt{\alpha t}}$ and $\tau = \frac{h^2\alpha t}{k^2}$, t is the time, x is the distance and erf is the error function.

P2.10. Turbulent flow in a parallel pipeline system

Consider the flow of an incompressible ($\rho = 1000kg/m^3$), Newtonian fluid ($\mu = 0.001Pa \cdot s$) in a parallel pipe system shown in figure 2.16. The lengths, diameters, roughness for the pipes as well as the total flow rate are as shown in

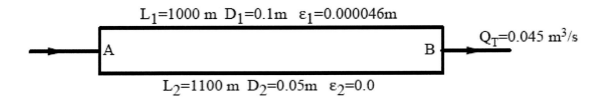

L_1=1000 m D_1=0.1m ε_1=0.000046m

Q_T=0.045 m³/s

A   B

L_2=1100 m D_2=0.05m ε_2=0.0

Figure 2.16: Turbulent flow in a parallel pipe

figure 2.16. Your task is to determine the individual flow rates in each of the pipe segments 1 and 2. The equation to be satisfied is obtained based on the fact that the pressure drop between points A and B is the same. The equation is

$$f_1(v_1)\frac{L_1}{D_1}\frac{v_1^2}{2} = f_2(v_2)\frac{L_2}{D_2}\frac{v_2^2}{2} \tag{2.22}$$

where v_1, v_2 are the velocities in the two pipes and f_1, f_2 are the friction factors given by the Churchill equation.

$$f_i(v_i) = 8 * \left[\left(\frac{8}{Re_i}\right)^{12} + \frac{1}{(A+B)^{1.5}}\right]^{1/12}$$

where

$$A = \left[2.457\ln\left(\frac{1}{(1/Re_i)^{0.9} + 0.27(\epsilon_i/D_i)}\right)\right]^{16}$$

$$B = \left[\frac{37530}{Re_i}\right]^{16}$$

and

$$Re_i = \frac{D_i v_i \rho}{\mu}$$

Finally the mass balance equation provides another constraint as,

$$\frac{\pi}{4}(D_1^2 v_1 + D_2^2 v_2) = Q_T$$

This problem can be formulated as two equation in two unknowns (v_1, v_2), but your task is to pose this as a single equation in one unknown, v_1, by rearranging equation 2.22 as,

$$F(v_1) = f_1(v_1)\frac{L_1}{D_1}\frac{v_1^2}{2} - f_2(v_2)\frac{L_2}{D_2}\frac{v_2^2}{2} = 0$$

i.e., for a given guess of v_1, write a m-file that will calculate $F(v_1)$. Then carryout the following calculations.

- Solve the problem using *secant* algorithm with initial guess of [4.5,5.5]. [Ans:$v_1 = 4.8703$]

- Suppose the total flow rate is increased to 0.09 m^3/s, what will be the new velocities in the pipes.

- Consider the case where $L_1 = 1000, L_2 = 900$ and $D_1 = 0.1, D_2 = 0.09$, other values being the same. Is there a flow rate Q_T for which the velocities in both pipes will be the same? If so what is it? [Ans:$Q_T = 0.0017$]

- Plot v_1 vs Q_T and v_2 vs Q_T for the case above over a suitable range of Q_T.

- Discuss the pros and cons of implementing the Newton method for this problem.

P2.11. Velocity profile of Non-Newtonian Fluid

The velocity profile for a non-Newtonian fluid flowing in a circular pipe is given by:

$$\frac{u}{u_m} = \left(\frac{3n+1}{n+1}\right)\left[1 - \left(\frac{r}{R}\right)^{\frac{n+1}{n}}\right]$$

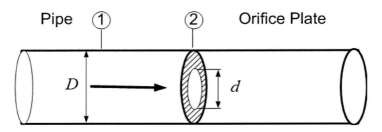

Figure 2.17: Flow through an orifice meter

where u_m is the mean velocity of the fluid, r is the radial position from the centre of the tube, R is the radius of the tube and n is a constant depending on the fluid properties (Newtonian fluid: n= 1, dilatant fluid: n = 3). Determine the value of n for a fluid with $\frac{u}{u_m} = 0.8$ at $\frac{r}{R} = 0.75$. Use $x_1 = 0.1$ and $x_2 = 0.9$ for your initial guesses.

(a) Bisection method.

(b) Regula-falsi method.

(c) Secant method.

(d) Newton's method (start with the lower bound, $x_1 = 0.1$).

(e) Use MATLAB method fzero.

(f) Use MATLAB method fminsearch. Compare and comment on the number of iterations required for each method.

P2.12. Discharge coefficient for an orifice

Orifice plates are widely used flow metering devices in the process industries. A typical orifice arrangement is shown in figure 2.17.

The volumetric flow rate $(m^3/s)$from an orifice is given by

$$Q = A_2 C_d \sqrt{\frac{2(P_1 - P_2)}{\rho(1 - \beta^4)}}$$

where A_2 is the orifice flow area, $\rho(kg/m^3)$ is the density of the fluid flowing in the pipe, $(P_1 - P_2)(kg/m.s^2)$ is the pressure differential and C_d is the discharge coefficient defined as

$$C_d = \frac{\text{actual discharge}}{\text{ideal discharge}}$$

A typical equation for the discharge coefficient is

$$C_d = 0.5959 + 0.031\beta^{2.1} - 0.184\beta^{8.0} + 91.71\beta^{2.5}/Re^{0.75}$$

where $\beta = d/D$ and Re is the Reynold's number for the flow.

Determine the value of β which gives a discharge coefficient of $C_d = 0.615$ at $Re = 2 \times 10^4$

(a) Solve using Muller's method using inital guesses of $x_0 = 0.1, x_1 = 0.8$ and $x_2 = 1.0$.

(b) Solve using MATLAB's fminsearch and fzero functions.

P2.13. Chemical Equilibrium

The equilibrium constant for a third order reversible chemical reaction given by

$$A + 2B \Leftrightarrow C$$

is given by

$$K = \frac{C_C}{C_A C_B^2}$$

where C_i is the concentration of species i. By performing mole balance and denoting the fractional conversion of species A as X_A, and the initial molar ratio $\varpi = \frac{C_{B0}}{C_{A0}}$, we can write

$$K = \frac{X_A}{C_{A0}^2(1 - X_A)(\varpi - X_A)^2}$$

Determine the fractional conversion for a system where $C_{A0} = 40 mol/m^3$, $C_{B0} = 25 mol/m^3$ and $K = 0.015$.

(a) Obtain the solution graphically

(b) Based on your answer above, solve for the conversion to within the tolerance error of $\epsilon_s = 0.5\%$

P2.14. Power for natural gas compressor

The total power requirement of a natural gas compressor for a given duty is the sum of the gas power and the friction power. For a centrifugal compressor, the gas power (in horsepower) is given by:

$$GHP = (0.004367)\frac{P_1}{V_1}\left(\frac{k}{k-1}\right)\left(\frac{P_2}{P_1^{(k-1)/k} - 1}\right)/CE$$

where P_1 is the inlet pressure [psia], V_1 is the inlet volume [ACFM], P_2 is the discharge pressure [psia], k is the ratio of specific heats and CE the compression efficiency.

Determine the discharge pressure when a 100hp compressor is fed with 100 ACFM natural gas assuming a compression efficiency of 0.85 and a heat capacity ratio of 1.2.

(a) The bisection method.

(b) The false position method.

(c) The Newton's method.

(d) The secant method.

Compare the results for the different methods and discuss your results.

P2.15. Specific heats

The specific heat capacity of Methane gas as a function of temperature is given by the following cubic polynomial:

$$C_P = 19.86 + 5.016 \times 10^{-2} \, \mathrm{T} + 1.27 \times 10^{-5} \, \mathrm{T}^2 - 10.99 \times 10^{-9} \, \mathrm{T}^3$$

Develop a plot of C_P vs. T for $\mathrm{T} \in [273 : 1500K]$ and use the bisection method to calculate the temperature corresponding to a specific heat value of $C_P = 2.5 kJ/kg.K$

P2.16. The Colebrook equation for friction factor

The Colebrook equation is an implicit equation that combines experimental results for turbulent flow in smooth and rough pipes to give:

$$\frac{1}{\sqrt{f}} = -2 \log \left(\frac{\epsilon}{3.7D} + \frac{2.51}{Re\sqrt{f}} \right)$$

where f is the Darcy friction factor, ϵ is the tube roughness, D the inside diameter of the conduit and Re is the Reynold's number for the flow, given as:

$$Re = \frac{\rho V D}{\mu}$$

with ρ as the fluid density, μ the fluid dynamic viscosity and V its velocity.

Determine the friction factor for air flowing in a tube with the following parameters: $D = 5mm$, $V = 35m/s$, $\rho = 1.52kg/m^3$, $\mu = 2.0N.s/m^2$ and $\epsilon = 0.002mm$.

P2.17. Transient heat conduction in semi-infinite slab

Many engineering problems can be cast in the form of determining the roots of a nonlinear algebraic equation. One such example arises in determining the time required to cool a solid body at a given point to a predetermined temperature level.

Consider a semi-infinite solid, initially at a temperature of $T_i = 200^oC$ and one side of it is suddenly exposed to an ambient temperature of $T_a = 70^oC$. The heat transfer coefficient between the solid and surroundings is $h = 525W/(m^2 {}^oC)$. The thermal conductivity of the solid is $k = 215W/m^oC$ and the thermal diffusivity of the solid is $\alpha = 8.4 \times 10^{-5}m^2/s$. Determine the time required to cool the solid at a distance of $x = 4cm$ measured from the exposed surface, to $T = 120^oC$. The temperature profile as a function of time and distance is given by the following expression.

$$\theta = 1 - erf(\xi) - \left[e^{(hx/k+\tau)}\right]\left[1 - erf(\xi + \sqrt{\tau})\right]$$

where the dimensionless temperature, $\theta = \frac{(T-T_i)}{(T_a-T_i)}$, and $\xi = \frac{x}{2\sqrt{\alpha t}}$ and $\tau = \frac{h^2\alpha t}{k^2}$, t is the time, x is the distance and erf is the error function.

CHAPTER 3

SYSTEM OF LINEAR ALGEBRAIC EQUATION

3.1 Introduction

Topics from linear algebra form the core of numerical analysis. Almost every conceivable problem, be it curve fitting, optimization, simulation of flow sheets or simulation of distributed parameter systems requiring solution of differential equations, require at some stage the solution of a system (often a large system!) of algebraic equations. MATLAB (acronym for MATrix LABoratory) was in fact conceived as a collection of tools to aid in the interactive learning and analysis of linear systems and was derived from a well known core of linear algebra routines written in FORTRAN called LINPACK.

In this chapter we provide a quick review of concepts from linear algebra. We make frequent reference to MATLAB implimentation of various concepts throughout this chapter. The reader is encouraged to try out these interactively during a MATLAB session. For a more complete treatment of topics in linear algebra see Hager and Barnett. The text by Amundson is also an excellent source with specific examples drawn from Chemical Engineering. For a more rigorous, axiomatic introduction within the frame work of linear opeartor theory see Ramakrishna and Amundson.

3.2   Matrix notation

We have already used the matrix notation to write a system of linear algebraic equations in a compact form in sections §1.3.1 and §1.3.2. While a matrix, as an object, is represented in bold face, its constituent elements are represented in index notation or as subscripted arrays in programming languages. For example the following are equivalent.

$$\boldsymbol{A} = [a_{ij}], \qquad i = 1, \cdots, m; \quad j = 1, \cdots, n$$

where $\boldsymbol{A}$ is an $m \times n$ matrix. a_{ij} represents an element of the matrix $\boldsymbol{A}$ in row i and column j position.

$$\boldsymbol{A} = [a_{ij}] = \begin{bmatrix} a_{11} & a_{12} & \cdots & a_{1,n-1} & a_{1,n} \\ a_{21} & a_{22} & \cdots & a_{2,n-1} & a_{2,n} \\ \vdots & \ddots & \ddots & \ddots & \vdots \\ a_{m-1,1} & a_{m-1,2} & \cdots & a_{m-1,n-1} & a_{m-1,n} \\ a_{m,1} & a_{m,2} & \cdots & a_{m,n-1} & a_{m,n} \end{bmatrix}$$

A vector can be thought of as an object with a single row or column. A row vector is represented by,

$$\boldsymbol{x} = [x_1 \ x_2 \cdots x_n]$$

while a column vector can be represented by,

$$\boldsymbol{y} = \begin{bmatrix} y_1 \\ y_2 \\ \vdots \\ y_m \end{bmatrix}$$

Note that these elements can be *real* or *complex*.

Having defined objects like vectors and matrices, we can extend the notions of basic arithmetic operations between scalar numbers to higher dimensional objects like vectors and matrices. The reasons for doing so are many. It not only allows us to express a large system of equations in a compact symbolic form, but a study of the properties of such objects allows us to develop and codify very efficient ways of solving and analysing large linear systems. A package such as MATLAB presents to us a vast array of such codified algorithms. As an engineer you should develop a conceptual understanding of the underlying principles and the skills to use such packages. But the most important task is to indentify each element of a vector or a matrix, which is tied closely to the physical description of the problem.

3.2.1 Review of basic operations

The arithmetic operations are defined both in symbolic form and using index notation. The later actually provides the algorithm for implementing the rules of operation using any programming language. The syntax of these operations in MATLAB are shown with specific examples.*

The addition operation between two matrices is defined as,

$$\text{addition:} \qquad \boldsymbol{A} = \boldsymbol{B} + \boldsymbol{C} \qquad \Rightarrow \qquad a_{ij} = b_{ij} + c_{ij}$$

---

*MATLAB illustrations have been tested with Ver 5. and higher

This implies an element-by-element addition of the matrices $\boldsymbol{B}$ and $\boldsymbol{C}$. Clearly all the matrices involved must have the same dimension. Note that the addition operation is *commutative* as seen easily with its scalar counter part. *i.e.*,

$$\boldsymbol{A} + \boldsymbol{B} = \boldsymbol{B} + \boldsymbol{A}$$

Matrix addition is also *associative*, *i.e.*, independent of the order in which it is carried out, *e.g.*,

$$\boldsymbol{A} + \boldsymbol{B} + \boldsymbol{C} = (\boldsymbol{A} + \boldsymbol{B}) + \boldsymbol{C} = \boldsymbol{A} + (\boldsymbol{B} + \boldsymbol{C})$$

The scalar multiplication of a matrix involves multiplying each element of the matrix by the scalar, *i.e.*,

scalar multiplication: $k\boldsymbol{A} = \boldsymbol{B}$ $\Rightarrow$ $k\, a_{ij} = b_{ij}$

Subtraction operation can be handled by combining addition and scalar multiplication rules as follwos:

The product between two matrices $\boldsymbol{A}$ (of dimension $n \times m$) and $\boldsymbol{B}$ (of dimension $m \times r$) is defined as, [*]

multiplication: C=AB $\Rightarrow$ $c_{ij} = \displaystyle\sum_{k=1}^{m} a_{ik}b_{kj}$ $\forall$ i, j

and the resultant matrix has the dimension $n \times r$. The operation indicated in the index notation is carried out for each value of the free indices $i = 1 \cdots n$ and $j = 1 \cdots r$. The product is defined only if the dimensions of $\boldsymbol{A}$, $\boldsymbol{B}$ are compatible - *i.e.*, number of *columns* in $\boldsymbol{A}$ should equal the number of *rows* in $\boldsymbol{B}$. This implies that while the product $\boldsymbol{A}\,\boldsymbol{B}$ may be defined, the product $\boldsymbol{B}\,\boldsymbol{A}$ may not even be defined! Even when they are dimensionally compatible, in general

$$\boldsymbol{AB} \neq \boldsymbol{BA}$$

i.e., matrix multiplication is not *commutative*.

---

[*]MATLAB syntax for the product operator between matrices is
`C=A*B`

EXAMPLE 3.1 (Matrix product) Consider the matrices A, B defined below.

$$A = \begin{bmatrix} 2 & 3 & 4 \\ 1 & 3 & 2 \end{bmatrix}, \qquad B = \begin{bmatrix} 1 & 2 \\ 3 & 1 \\ 4 & 1 \end{bmatrix}$$

In MATLAB they will be defined as follows:

```
>>A=[2 3 4;1 3 2] *% Define (2x3) matrix A.
>>B=[1 2; 3 1; 4 1]% Define (3x2) matrix B
>>C=A*B             % calculate the product
C=                  % Display the result
```

$$\begin{bmatrix} 27 & 11 \\ 18 & 7 \end{bmatrix}$$

Other useful products can also be defined between vectors and matrices. A Hadamard (or Schur) product is defined as [†]

$$C = A \circ B \qquad \Rightarrow \qquad c_{ij} = a_{ij}b_{ij} \qquad \forall \qquad i, j$$

Obviously, the dimension of A and B should be the same. The example below illustrates the Hadamard product, called the array product in MATLAB.

EXAMPLE 3.2 (The Hadamard product)

```
>>  A=[2 3 4;1 3 2];  % Define matrix A
>> C=A'.*B};          % Note the dimensions are made
>> C                  % the same by transpose of A
```

$$\begin{bmatrix} 2 & 2 \\ 9 & 3 \\ 16 & 2 \end{bmatrix}$$

[†]MATLAB syntax for the Hadamard product operator between matrices is `C=A.*B`

A Kronecker product is defined as [*]

$$C = A \otimes B \qquad \Rightarrow \qquad C = \begin{bmatrix} a_{11}B & a_{12}B & \cdots & a_{1m}B \\ a_{21}B & a_{22}B & \cdots & a_{2m}B \\ \vdots & & & \\ a_{n1}B & a_{n2}B & \cdots & a_{nm}B \end{bmatrix}$$

Multiplying a scalar number by unity leaves it unchanged. Extension of this notion to matrices results in the definition of *identity* matrix, [†]

$$I = \begin{bmatrix} 1 & 0 & \cdots & 0 \\ 0 & 1 & \cdots & 0 \\ \vdots & 0 & 1 & 0 \\ 0 & 0 & \cdots & 1 \end{bmatrix} \qquad \Rightarrow \qquad \delta_{ij} = \begin{cases} 1 & i = j \\ 0 & i \neq j \end{cases}$$

Multiplying any matrix A with an identity matrix I of appropriate dimension leaves the original matrix unchanged, *i.e.*,

$$AI = A$$

This allows us to generalize the notion of division with scalar numbers to matrices. [‡] Division operation can be thought of as the inverse of the multiplication operation. For example, given a number, say 2, we can define its inverse, x in such a way that the product of the two numbers produce unity. *i.e.*, $2 \times x = 1$ or $x = 2^{-1}$. In a similar way, given a matrix A, can we define the inverse matrix B such that

$$AB = I \qquad \text{or} \qquad B = A^{-1}$$

The task of developing an algorithm for finding the inverse of a matrix will be addressed later in this chapter.

---

[*]MATLAB function that generates the Kronecker product between matrices is C=kron(A,B)
[†]MATLAB function for producing an identity matrix of size N is I=eye(N)
[‡]MATLAB function for finding the inverse of a matrix A is B=inv(A)

For a square matrix, *powers* of a matrix $\boldsymbol{A}$ can be defined as,

$$\boldsymbol{A}^2 = \boldsymbol{A}\boldsymbol{A} \qquad \boldsymbol{A}^3 = \boldsymbol{A}\boldsymbol{A}\boldsymbol{A} = \boldsymbol{A}^2\boldsymbol{A} = \boldsymbol{A}\boldsymbol{A}^2$$

Note that $\boldsymbol{A}^p\boldsymbol{A}^q = \boldsymbol{A}^{p+q}$ for positve integers $\boldsymbol{p}$ and $\boldsymbol{q}$.* Having extended the definition of powers, we can extend the definition of *exponential* from scalars to square matrices as follows. † For a scalar $\boldsymbol{\alpha}$ it is,

$$e^\alpha = 1 + \alpha + \frac{\alpha^2}{2} + \cdots = \sum_{k=0}^{\infty} \frac{\alpha^k}{k!}$$

For a matrix $\boldsymbol{A}$ the *exponential matrix* can be defined as,

$$e^{\boldsymbol{A}} = \boldsymbol{I} + \boldsymbol{A} + \frac{\boldsymbol{A}^2}{2} + \cdots = \sum_{k=0}^{\infty} \frac{\boldsymbol{A}^k}{k!}$$

One operation that does not have a direct counter part in the scalar world is the *transpose* of a matrix. It is defined the result of exchanging the rows and columns of a matrix, *i.e.*,

$$\boldsymbol{B} = \boldsymbol{A}' \qquad \Rightarrow \qquad b_{ij} = a_{ji}$$

It is easy to verify that

$$(\boldsymbol{A} + \boldsymbol{B})' = \boldsymbol{A}' + \boldsymbol{B}'$$

Something that is not so easy to verify, nevertheless true, is

$$(\boldsymbol{A}\boldsymbol{B})' = \boldsymbol{B}'\boldsymbol{A}'$$

---

*MATLAB operator for producing the n-th power of a matrix A is, `A^n` while the syntax for producing element-by-element power is, `A.^n`. Make sure that you understand the difference between these two operations!

†MATLAB function
`exp(A)`
evaluates the exponential element-by-element while `expm(A)` evaluates the true matrix exponential.

3.3 Matrices with special structure

A *diagonal* matirx D has non-zero elements only along the diagonal.

$$
D = \begin{bmatrix}
d_{11} & 0 & \cdots & 0 \\
0 & d_{22} & \cdots & 0 \\
\vdots & 0 & \ddots & 0 \\
0 & 0 & \cdots & d_{nn}
\end{bmatrix}
$$

A *lower triangular* matrix L has non-zero elements on or below the diagonal,

$$
L = \begin{bmatrix}
l_{11} & 0 & \cdots & 0 \\
l_{21} & l_{22} & \cdots & 0 \\
\vdots & & \ddots & 0 \\
l_{n1} & l_{n2} & \cdots & l_{nn}
\end{bmatrix}
$$

A *upper triangular* matrix U has non-zero elements on or above the diagonal,

$$
U = \begin{bmatrix}
u_{11} & u_{12} & \cdots & u_{1n} \\
0 & u_{22} & \cdots & u_{2n} \\
0 & 0 & \ddots & \vdots \\
0 & 0 & \cdots & u_{nn}
\end{bmatrix}
$$

A *tridiagonal* matrix T has non-zero elements on the diagonal and one off diagonal row on each side of the diagonal

$$
T = \begin{bmatrix}
t_{11} & t_{12} & 0 & \cdots & & 0 \\
t_{21} & t_{22} & t_{23} & & 0 & 0 \\
0 & \ddots & \ddots & & \ddots & 0 \\
\vdots & 0 & t_{n-1,n-2} & t_{n-1,n-1} & t_{n-1,n} \\
0 & \cdots & & 0 & t_{n,n-1} & t_{n,n}
\end{bmatrix}
$$

A *sparse* matrix is a generic term to indicate those matrices without any specific strucutre such as above, but with a small number (typically 10 to 15 %) of non-zero elements.

3.4 Determinant

A determinant of a square matrix is defined in such a way that a scalar value is associated with the matrix that does not change with certain row or column operations on the matrix - *i.e.*, it is one of the scalar invariants of the matrix. In the context of solving a system of linear equations, the determinant is also useful in knowing whether the system of equations is solvable uniquely. The determinant is formed by summing *all* possible products formed by choosing *one and only one* element from each row and column of the matrix. The precise definition, taken from Amundson (1966), is

$$\boxed{det(A) = |A| = \sum(-1)^h (a_{1l_1} a_{2l_2} \cdots a_{nl_n})} \qquad (3.1)$$

Each term in the summation consists of a product of n elements selected such that only one element appears from each row and column. The summation involves a total of $n!$ terms accounted for as follows: for the first element l_1 in the product there are n choices, followed by $(n-1)$ choices for the second element l_2, $(n-2)$ choices for the third element l_3 *etc.* resulting in a total of $n!$ choices for a particular product. Note that in this way of counting, the set of second subscripts $\{l_1, l_2, \cdots l_n\}$ will contain all of the numbers in the range 1 to n, but they will not be in their natural order $\{1, 2, \cdots n\}$. hence, h is the number of permutations required to arrange $\{l_1, l_2, \cdots l_n\}$ in their natural order.*

This definition is neither intutive nor computationaly efficient. But it is instructive in understanding the following properties of determinants.

---

*MATLAB function for computing the determinant of a square matrix is `det(A)`

1. The determinant of a diagonal matrix D, is simply the product of all the diagonal elements, *i.e.*,

$$det(D) = \prod_{k=1}^{n} d_{kk}$$

   This is the only product term that is non-zero in equation (3.1).

2. A little thougtht should convince you that it is the same for lower or upper triangular matrices as well, viz.

$$det(L) = \prod_{k=1}^{n} l_{kk}$$

3. It should also be clear that if all the elements of any row or column are zero, then the determinant is zero.

4. If every element of any row or column of a matrix is multiplied by a scalar, it is equivalent to multiplying the determinant of the original matrix by the same scalar, *i.e.*,

$$\begin{vmatrix} ka_{11} & ka_{12} & \cdots & ka_{1n} \\ a_{21} & a_{22} & \cdots & a_{2n} \\ \vdots & & \ddots & \vdots \\ a_{n1} & a_{n2} & \cdots & a_{nn} \end{vmatrix} = \begin{vmatrix} a_{11} & a_{12} & \cdots & ka_{1n} \\ a_{21} & a_{22} & \cdots & ka_{2n} \\ \vdots & & \ddots & \vdots \\ a_{n1} & a_{n2} & \cdots & ka_{nn} \end{vmatrix} = k\, det(A)$$

5. Replacing any row (or column) of a matrix with a linear combination of that row (or column) and another row (or column) leaves the determinant unchanged.

6. A consequence of rules 3 and 5 is that if two rows (or columns) of a matrix are indentical the determinant is zero.

7. If any two rows (or columns) are interchanged, it results in a sign change of the determinant.

3.4.1   Laplace expansion of the determinant

A definition of determinant that you might have seen in an earlier linear algebra course is

$$
det(A) = |A| = \begin{cases} \sum_{k=1}^{n} a_{ik}A_{ik} & \text{for any} \quad i \\ \sum_{k=1}^{n} a_{kj}A_{kj} & \text{for any} \quad j \end{cases} \tag{3.2}
$$

where A_{ik}, called the *cofactor*, is given by,

$$
A_{ik} = (-1)^{i+k}M_{ik}
$$

and M_{ik}, called the *minor*, is the determinant of $(n-1) \times (n-1)$ submatrix of A obtained by deleting ith row and kth column of A. Note that the expansion in equation (3.2) can be carried out along any row i or column j of the original matrix A.

EXAMPLE 3.3 (✎ Calculating the determinant) Consider the matrix derived in Chapter 1 for the recycle example, viz. equation 1.8. Let us calculate the determinant of the matrix using the Laplace expansion algorithm around the first row.

$$
det(A) = \begin{vmatrix} 1 & 0 & 0.306 \\ 0 & 1 & 0.702 \\ -2 & 1 & 0 \end{vmatrix}
$$

$$
= \quad 1 \begin{vmatrix} 1 & 0.702 \\ 1 & 0 \end{vmatrix} + (-1)^{1+2} \times 0 \times \begin{vmatrix} 0 & 0.702 \\ -2 & 0 \end{vmatrix}
$$

$$
+ \qquad\qquad (-1)^{1+3} \times 0.306 \times \begin{vmatrix} 0 & 1 \\ -2 & 1 \end{vmatrix}
$$

$$
= \quad 1 \times (-0.702) + 0 + 0.306 \times 2 = -0.09
$$

A MATLAB implementation of this will be done as follows:

```
>>A=[1 0 0.306; 0 1 0.702; -2 1 0]  % Define matrix A
>>det(A)                            % calculate the determinant
```

3.5   Vector and matrix norms

Although matrices and vectors usually contain a number of elements, is some cases, we may wish to allocate a single value which represents the vector or matrix. This is called a norm of the vector or the matrix. The length of a vector is an example of a norm. The length of a vector (*Euclidean norm*) is defined as:

$$||\vec{x}||_2 = \sqrt{x_1^2 + x_2^2 + \cdots + x_n^2} \qquad (3.3)$$

This can be generalized to what is known as the p-norm of a vector:

$$||\vec{x}||_p = L_p = (x_1^p + x_2^p + \cdots + x_n^p)^{1/p} = \left\{ \sum_{i=1}^{n} |x_i|^p \right\}^{1/p} \qquad (3.4)$$

for p=1

$$||\vec{x}||_1 = L_1 = |x_1| + |x_2| + |x_2| + \cdots |x_n| = \left\{ \sum_{i=1}^{n} |x_i| \right\} \qquad (3.5)$$

Where a value of p=2 we have the length of a vector. For $p \to \infty$

$$||\vec{x}||_\infty = L_\infty \to max|x_i| \qquad (3.6)$$

Matrices can be considered as a collection of column vectors or row vectors. The definition of matrix norms is therefore move involved. We can follow the analogy with vectors and define:

$$||A||_p = \max_{x \neq 0} \frac{||A\vec{x}||_p}{||\vec{x}||_p} \tag{3.7}$$

In this text we will limit our discussions to the 1 and the ∞ norm of square matrices:

$$||A||_1 = \max_{x \neq 0} \frac{||A\vec{x}||_1}{||\vec{x}||_1} = \max_{1 \leq j \leq n} \sum_{i=1}^{n} |a_{ij}| \tag{3.8}$$

$$||A||_\infty = \max_{1 \leq i \leq n} \sum_{j=1}^{n} |a_{ij}| \tag{3.9}$$

The 1 norm is therefore the maximum column sum while the ∞ norm is the maximum row sum. Another metric which is frequently used is the spectral norm or spectral radius of a square matrix, defined as:

$$\rho(A) = \max_{1 \leq i \leq n} |\lambda_i| \tag{3.10}$$

where λ_i is the largest eigenvalue of the matrix A (see section 3.9 for the definition of eigenvalues).

EXAMPLE 3.4 (✎ **Calculating norms)** *(a) Vector Calculate* L_1, L_2 *and* L_∞ *for the following vector*

$$\vec{x} = \begin{bmatrix} 3 \\ 2 \\ -6 \end{bmatrix}$$

Solution:
Applying equation 3.4 we obtain

$$L_1 = \sum_{i=1}^{3} |x_i| = |3| + |2| + |-6| = 11$$

$$L_2 = \left\{ \sum_{i=1}^{2} x_i^2 \right\}^{1/2} = \left(3^2 + 2^2 + 6^2 \right)^{1/2} = 7$$

$$L_\infty = max|x_i| = max(|3|, |2|, |-6|) = 6$$

(b) Calculate L_1, L_∞ and the spectral radius for the matrix A given by

$$A = \begin{bmatrix} 1 & 0 & 0.306 \\ 0 & 1 & 0.702 \\ -2 & 1 & 0 \end{bmatrix}$$

$$||A||_1 = max\{|1| + |0| + |-2|, |0| + |1| + |1|, |0.306| + |0.702| + |0|\}$$
$$= max\{3, 2, 1.008\} = 3$$

$$||A||_\infty = max\{|1| + |0| + |0.306|, |0| + |1| + |0.702|, |-2| + |1| + |0|\}$$
$$= max\{1.306, 1.702, 3\} = 3$$

For the $||A||_2$ we need to calculate the spectral radius of A

$$\rho(A) = \max(\lambda_i)$$

$$\det(A - \lambda I) = \det\left(\begin{bmatrix} 1 & 0 & 0.306 \\ 0 & 1 & 0.702 \\ -2 & 1 & 0 \end{bmatrix} - \begin{bmatrix} \lambda & 0 & 0 \\ 0 & \lambda & 0 \\ 0 & 0 & \lambda \end{bmatrix} \right)$$

$$= \det\left(\begin{bmatrix} 1-\lambda & 0 & 0.306 \\ 0 & 1-\lambda & 0.702 \\ -2 & 1 & -\lambda \end{bmatrix} \right)$$

$$= (1 - \lambda)[-\lambda(1 - \lambda) - 0.702] + 0 + 0.306(1 - \lambda)$$

$$= \lambda^3 - 2\lambda^2 + 0.9100\lambda + 0.0900$$

The roots of the polynomial, whence the eigenvalues are $\lambda_1 = 1.0831$, $\lambda_2 = 1.0000$ and $\lambda_3 = -0.0831$, thus

$$||A||_2 = max\{|1.0831|, |1.0000|, |-0.0831|\} = 1.0831$$

3.6 Condition of a Matrix

A matrix A is said to be *ill conditioned* if there exists a matrix B for which small changes (pertubations) in the coefficients of A or B will produce large changes in $X = A^{-1}B$. The system of equations $AX = B$ is said to be ill-conditioned when A is ill conditioned. We can quantify the degree of conditioning of a system by using the condition of a number. To find the condition number of a matrix A, determine its inverse, A^{-1} then compute the norm of the matrix and the norm of the inverse. The product of the two may be used to determine the condition number of the matrix as:

$$cond(A) = ||A||.||A^{-1}|| \qquad (3.10)$$

Where $||A||$ is the norm of the matrix A as defined in the previous section. As there are many definitions for the norm, we shall stick to the 1 norm or the ∞ norm in this text. If we take the condition of an identity matrix as 1, a well-conditioned system will have a small condition number (close to 1), whereas a badly conditioned system will have a large condition number. Ill conditioning can occur when the determinant of A is close to zero (A is nearly singular !).

EXAMPLE 3.5 (Demonstrating ill-conditioning) *Consider two systems of equations with two unknowns x_1 and x_2*

$$System\ 1: \qquad (3.11)$$
$$x_1 + x_2 = 2$$
$$x_1 + 1.0001x_2 = 2.0001$$

Solution :$x_1 = 1, x_2 = 1$

$$\textit{System 2 :} \tag{3.12}$$

$$x_1 + x_2 = 2$$
$$x_1 + 1.0001x_2 = 2.0002$$

$$\tag{3.13}$$

Solution $:x_1 = 0, x_2 = 2$

Note that just a small change in the rightside of the second equation in the fifth decimal place causes a huge difference in the solution to the equations ! In order to examine how small changes in the elements of A *and* b *causes big changes in the solution* $x = A^{-1}b$.

For the above system we can write the coefficient matrix:

$$A = \begin{bmatrix} 1 & 1 \\ 1 & 1.0001 \end{bmatrix}$$

and the inverse

$$A^{-1} = 10^4 \begin{bmatrix} 1.0001 & -1 \\ -1 & 1 \end{bmatrix}$$

The condition number of this system based on the ∞ *norm is*

$$||A||_\infty = 2.0001, ||A^{-1}||_\infty = 10^4(2.0001) \tag{3.14}$$

thus

$$cond(A) = ||A||_\infty \cdot ||A^{-1}||_\infty = 40004.0001$$

The system is therefore ill-conditioned because the condition number is relatively high.

3.7 Solving a system of linear equations

3.7.1 Cramers rule

Consider a 2×2 system of equations,

$$a_{11}x_1 + a_{12}x_2 = b_1$$
$$a_{21}x_1 + a_{22}x_2 = b_2$$

in matrix form

$$\begin{bmatrix} a_{11} & a_{12} \\ a_{21} & a_{22} \end{bmatrix} \begin{bmatrix} x_1 \\ x_2 \end{bmatrix} = \begin{bmatrix} b_1 \\ b_2 \end{bmatrix}$$

Direct elimination of the variable x_2 results in

$$(a_{11}a_{22} - a_{12}a_{21})\, x_1 = a_{22}b_1 - a_{12}b_2 \tag{3.15}$$

but

$$(a_{11}a_{22} - a_{12}a_{21}) = \begin{vmatrix} a_{11} & a_{12} \\ a_{21} & a_{22} \end{vmatrix} = det(A)$$

and

$$a_{22}b_1 - a_{12}b_2 = \begin{vmatrix} b_1 & a_{12} \\ b_2 & a_{22} \end{vmatrix} = det(A(1))$$

Thus equation 3.15 can be written in an alternate form as,

$$det(A)\, x_1 = det(A(1))$$

where the matrix $A(1)$ is obtained from A after replacing the first column with the vector b. *i.e.*,

$$A(1) = \begin{vmatrix} b_1 & a_{12} \\ b_2 & a_{22} \end{vmatrix}$$

This generalizes to $n \times n$ system as follows,

$$x_1 = \frac{det(A(1))}{det(A)}, \quad \cdots \quad x_k = \frac{det(A(k))}{det(A)}, \quad \cdots \quad x_n = \frac{det(A(n))}{det(A)}.$$

where $A(\mathrm{k})$ is an $n \times n$ matrix obtained from A by replacing the kth column with the vector b. It should be clear from the above that, in order to have a unique solution, the determinant of A should be *non-zero*. If the determinant is zero, then such matrices are called *singular*.

EXAMPLE 3.6 (Solution using Cramer's rule) *Continuing with the re-cycle problem (equation (1.8) of Chapter 1), solution using Cramer's rule can be implemented with MATLAB as follows:*

$$A\,x = b \quad \Rightarrow \quad \begin{bmatrix} 1 & 0 & 0.306 \\ 0 & 1 & 0.702 \\ -2 & 1 & 0 \end{bmatrix} \begin{bmatrix} x_1 \\ x_2 \\ x_3 \end{bmatrix} = \begin{bmatrix} 101.48 \\ 225.78 \\ 0 \end{bmatrix}$$

```
>>A=[1 0 0.306; 0 1 0.702; -2 1 0];   % Define matrix A
>>b=[101.48 225.78 0]'                 % Define rhs vector b
>>A1=[b, A(:,[2 3])]                    % Define A(1)
>>A2=[A(:,1),b, A(:, 3)]               % Define A(2)
>>A3=[A(:,[1 2]), b ]                   % Define A(3)
>>x(1) = det(A1)/det(A)               % solve for component x(1)
>>x(2) = det(A2)/det(A)               % solve for component x(2)
>>x(3) = det(A3)/det(A)               % solve for component x(3)
>>norm(A*x'-b)                         % Check the residual
```

EXAMPLE 3.7 (Matrix norm and condition number) *Find the norms and condition number of the matrix given in example 3.6.*

```
>>A=[1 0 0.306; 0 1 0.702; -2 1 0];  % Define matrix A
>>norm(A,1)                            % (ans:   3)
>>norm(A,2)                            % (ans:   2.4496)
>>norm(A,inf)                          % (ans:   3)
>>cond(A)                              % (ans:   83.9429)
>>nu = eye(3)                          % define a 3x3 identity matrix
>>cond(nu)                             % (ans:   1 )
```

3.7.2   Matrix inverse

We defined the inverse of a matrix A as that matrix B which, when multiplied by A produces the identity matrix - *i.e.*, $AB = I$; but we did not develop a scheme for finding B. We can do so now by combining Cramer's rule and Laplace expansion for a determinant as follows. Using Laplace expansion of the determinant of $A(\text{k})$ around column k,

$$det A(k) = b_1 A_{1k} + b_2 A_{2k} + \cdots + b_n A_{nk} \qquad k = 1, 2, \cdots, n$$

where A_{ik} are the cofactors of A. The components of the solution vector, x are,

$$x_1 = (b_1 A_{11} + b_2 A_{21} + \cdots + b_n A_{n1})/det(A)$$
$$x_j = (b_1 A_{1j} + b_2 A_{2j} + \cdots + b_n A_{nj})/det(A)$$
$$x_n = (b_1 A_{1n} + b_2 A_{2n} + \cdots + b_n A_{nn})/det(A)$$

The right hand side of this system of equations can be written as a vector matrix product as follows,

$$\begin{bmatrix} x_1 \\ x_2 \\ \vdots \\ x_n \end{bmatrix} = \frac{1}{det(A)} \begin{bmatrix} A_{11} & A_{21} & \cdots & A_{n1} \\ A_{12} & A_{22} & \cdots & A_{n2} \\ \vdots & & \ddots & \vdots \\ A_{1n} & A_{2n} & \cdots & A_{nn} \end{bmatrix} \begin{bmatrix} b_1 \\ b_2 \\ \vdots \\ b_n \end{bmatrix}$$

or

$$x = B\, b$$

Premultiplying the original equation $A\, x = b$ by A^{-1} we get

$$A^{-1}Ax = A^{-1}b \quad \text{or} \quad x = A^{-1}b$$

Comparing the last two equations, it is clear that,

$$B = A^{-1} = \frac{1}{det(A)} \begin{bmatrix} A_{11} & A_{21} & \cdots & A_{n1} \\ A_{12} & A_{22} & \cdots & A_{n2} \\ \vdots & & \ddots & \vdots \\ A_{1n} & A_{2n} & \cdots & A_{nn} \end{bmatrix} = \frac{adj(A)}{det(A)}$$

The above equation can be thought of as the definition for the *adjoint* of a matrix. It is obtained by simply replacing each element with its cofactor and then transposing the resulting matrix.

Inverse of a diagonal matrix

Inverse of a diagonal matrix, D,

$$D = \begin{bmatrix} d_{11} & 0 & \cdots & 0 \\ 0 & d_{22} & \cdots & 0 \\ \vdots & 0 & \ddots & 0 \\ 0 & 0 & \cdots & d_{nn} \end{bmatrix}$$

is given by,

$$D^{-1} = \begin{bmatrix} \frac{1}{d_{11}} & 0 & \cdots & 0 \\ 0 & \frac{1}{d_{22}} & \cdots & 0 \\ \vdots & 0 & \ddots & 0 \\ 0 & 0 & \cdots & \frac{1}{d_{nn}} \end{bmatrix}$$

It is quite easy to verify using the definition of matrix multiplication that $DD^{-1} = I$.

Inverse of a triangular matrix

Inverse of a triangular matrix is also triangular. Suppose U is a given upper triangular matrix, then the elements of $V = U^{-1}$, can be found sequentially in an efficient manner by simply using the definition $UV = I$. This equation, in expanded form, is

$$\begin{bmatrix} u_{11} & u_{12} & \cdots & u_{1n} \\ 0 & u_{22} & \cdots & u_{2n} \\ 0 & 0 & \ddots & \vdots \\ 0 & 0 & \cdots & u_{nn} \end{bmatrix} \begin{bmatrix} v_{11} & v_{12} & \cdots & v_{1n} \\ v_{21} & v_{22} & \cdots & v_{2n} \\ & & \ddots & \vdots \\ v_{n1} & v_{n2} & \cdots & v_{nn} \end{bmatrix} = \begin{bmatrix} 1 & 0 & \cdots & 0 \\ 0 & 1 & \cdots & 0 \\ & & \ddots & \vdots \\ 0 & 0 & \cdots & 1 \end{bmatrix}$$

We can develop the algorithm (*i.e.*, find out the rules) by simply carrying out the matrix multiplication on the left hand side and equating it element-by-element to the right hand side. First let us convince ourself that V is also upper triangular, *i.e.*,

$$\boxed{v_{ij} = 0 \qquad i > j}$$
(3.16)

Consider the element $(n, 1)$ which is obtained by summing the product of each element of n-th row of U (consisting mostly of zeros!) with the corresponding element of the 1-st column of V. The only non-zero term in this product is

$$u_{nn} v_{n1} = 0$$

Since $u_{nn} \neq 0$ it is clear that $v_{n1} = 0$. Carrying out similar arguments in a sequential manner (in the order $\{i = n \cdots j - 1, j = 1 \cdots n\}$ - *i.e.*, decreasing order of i and increasing order of j) it is easy to verify equation (3.16) and thus establish that V is also upper triangular.

The non-zero elements of V can also be found in a sequential manner as follows. For each of the diagonal elements (i, i) summing the product of each element of i-th row of U with the corresponding element of the i-th column of V, the only non-zero term is,

$$\boxed{v_{ii} = \frac{1}{u_{ii}} \qquad i = 1, \cdots, n}$$
(3.17)

Next, for each of the upper elements (i, j) summing the product of each element of i-th row of U with the corresponding element of the j-th column of V, we get,

$$u_{ii} v_{ij} + \sum_{r=i+1}^{j} u_{ir} v_{rj} = 0$$

and hence we get,

$$v_{ij} = -\frac{1}{u_{ii}} \sum_{r=i+1}^{j} u_{ir} v_{rj} \qquad j = 2, \cdots, n; \; j > i; \; i = j-1, 1$$

(3.18)

Note that equation (3.18) should be applied in a specific order, as otherwise, it may involve unknown elements v_{rj} on the right hand side. First, all of the diagonal elements of V (viz. v_{ii}) must be calcualted from equation (3.17) as they are needed on the right hand side of equation (3.18). Next the order indicated in equation (3.18), viz. increasing j from 2 to n and for each j decreasing i from $(j - 1)$ to 1, sould be obeyed to avoid having unknowns values appearing on the right hand side of (3.18).

A MATLAB implementation of this algorithm is shown in figure 3.1 to illustrate precisely the order of the calculations. Note that the built-in, general purpose MATLAB inverse function (viz. `inv(U)`) does not take into account the special structure of a triangular matrix and hence is computationally more expensive than the `invu` funcion of figure 3.1. This is illustrated with the following example.

EXAMPLE 3.8 *Consider the upper triangular matrix,*

$$U = \begin{bmatrix} 1 & 2 & 3 & 4 \\ 0 & 2 & 3 & 1 \\ 0 & 0 & 1 & 2 \\ 0 & 0 & 0 & 4 \end{bmatrix}$$

Let us find its inverse using both the built-in MATLAB function `inv(U)` *and the function* `invu(U)` *of figure 3.1 that is applicable sepcifically for an upper triangular matrix. You can also compare the floating point operation count for each of the algorithm. Work through the following example using MATLAB. Make sure that the function* invu *of figure 3.1 is in the search path of MATLAB.*

```
>> U=[1  2  3  4;  0  2  3  1;0  0   1  2;  0  0  0  4]

U =
     1       2       3       4
     0       2       3       1
     0       0       1       2
     0       0       0       4

>> tic  %initialize  the  counter
>> V=inv(U)
V =
    1.0000     -1.0000           0    -0.7500
         0      0.5000     -1.5000     0.6250
         0           0      1.0000    -0.5000
         0           0           0     0.2500
>> toc    %print  elapsed  time
Elapsed  time  is  0.000211  seconds

>> tic;ch3_invu(U),toc   %initialize  time  count,  then  invert
ans =
    1.0000     -1.0000           0    -0.7500
         0      0.5000     -1.5000     0.6250
         0           0      1.0000    -0.5000
         0           0           0     0.2500
Elapsed  time  is  0.000211  seconds
```

```
function  v=invu(u)
%  Invert  upper  triangular  matrix
%   u  -  (nxn)  matrix
%   v  -  inv(a)

n=size(u,1);    %  get  number  of  rows  in  matrix  a

for  i=2:n
 for  j=1:i-1
   v(i,j)=0;
 end
end

for  i=1:n
 v(i,i)=1/u(i,i);
end
```

```
for j=2:n
  for i=j-1:-1:1
    v(i,j) = -1/u(i,i)*sum(u(i,i+1:j)*v(i+1:j,j));
  end
end
```

Figure 3.1: MATLAB implementation of inverse of an upper triangular matrix

3.7.3   Gaussian elimination

Gaussian elimination is one of the most efficient algorithms for solving a large system of linear algebraic equations. It is based on a systematic generalization of a rather intuitive elimination process that we routinely apply to a small, say, (2×2) systems. *e.g.*,

$$10x_1 + 2x_2 = 4$$

$$x_1 + 4x_2 = 3$$

From the first equation we have $x_1 = (4 - 2x_2)/10$ which is used to *eliminate* the variable x_1 from the second equation, viz. $(4-2x_2)/10+4x_2 = 3$ which is solved to get $x_2 = 0.6842$. In the second phase, the value of x_2 is *back substituted* into the first equation and we get $x_1 = 0.2632$. We could have reversed the order and eliminated x_1 from the first equation after rearranging the second equation as $x_1 = (3 - 4x_2)$. Thus there are two phases to the algorithm: (a) forward elimination of one variable at a time until the last equation contains only one unknown; (b) back substitution of variables. Also, note that we have used two rules during the elimination process: (i) two equations (or two rows) can be interchanged as it is merely a matter of book keeping and it does not in any way alter the problem formulation, (ii) we can replace any equation with a linear combination of itself with another equation.

Consider the system $Ax = b$ in expanded matrix form

$$\begin{bmatrix} a_{11} & a_{12} & \cdots & a_{1n} \\ a_{21} & a_{22} & \cdots & a_{2n} \\ \vdots & \ddots & \ddots & \vdots \\ a_{n1} & a_{n2} & \cdots & a_{nn} \end{bmatrix} \begin{bmatrix} x_1 \\ x_2 \\ \vdots \\ x_n \end{bmatrix} = \begin{bmatrix} b_1 \\ b_2 \\ \vdots \\ b_n \end{bmatrix}$$

In the solution of the equation $Ax = b$, it is more efficient to store all the coefficients in an array of dimension $n(n+1)$, with the constant coeffcient b being stored in the column $n+1$ of the array. Each row then contains all the coefficients representing the equation. If the *augumented matrix* $C = A|B$ and the linear system may be represented as

$$C = A|B = \begin{bmatrix} a_{11} & a_{12} & \cdots & a_{1n} & b_1 \\ a_{21} & a_{22} & \cdots & a_{2n} & b_2 \\ \vdots & \ddots & \ddots & \vdots & \vdots \\ a_{n1} & a_{n2} & \cdots & a_{nn} & b_n \end{bmatrix} \tag{3.19}$$

The system $Ax = b$ solved by performing row operations on the augumented matrix $C = A|B$.

EXAMPLE 3.9 (✎ **Gauss elimination)** *Consider the following* 3×3 *system*

$$2x_1 - x_2 + x_3 = 4$$
$$4x_1 + 3x_2 - x_3 = 6$$
$$3x_1 + 2x_2 + 2x_3 = 15$$

The coefficient matrix

$$A = \begin{bmatrix} 2 & -1 & 1 \\ 4 & 3 & -1 \\ 3 & 2 & 2 \end{bmatrix}$$

and the constant vector

$$b = \begin{bmatrix} 4 \\ 6 \\ 15 \end{bmatrix}$$

are combined to form the augumented matrix

$$C = \begin{bmatrix} 2 & -1 & 1 & 4 \\ 4 & 3 & -1 & 6 \\ 3 & 2 & 2 & 15 \end{bmatrix}$$

Manipulate

$$C = \begin{bmatrix} 2 & -1 & 1 & 4 \\ 4 & 3 & -1 & 6 \\ 3 & 2 & 2 & 15 \end{bmatrix} \begin{matrix} \\ row2 - (4/2)row1 \\ row3 - (3/2)row1 \end{matrix} \Rightarrow \begin{bmatrix} 2 & -1 & 1 & 4 \\ 0 & 5 & -3 & -2 \\ 0 & 7/2 & 1/2 & 9 \end{bmatrix}$$

$$\begin{bmatrix} 2 & -1 & 1 & 4 \\ 0 & 5 & -3 & -2 \\ 0 & 7/2 & 1/2 & 9 \end{bmatrix} \begin{matrix} \\ \\ row3 - (7/10)row2 \end{matrix} \Rightarrow \begin{bmatrix} 2 & -1 & 1 & 4 \\ 0 & 5 & -3 & -2 \\ 0 & 0 & 13/5 & 52/9 \end{bmatrix}$$

Thus the matrix equation becomes

$$\begin{bmatrix} 2 & -1 & 1 \\ 0 & 5 & -3 \\ 0 & 0 & 13/5 \end{bmatrix} \begin{bmatrix} x_1 \\ x_2 \\ x_3 \end{bmatrix} = \begin{bmatrix} 4 \\ -2 \\ 52/5 \end{bmatrix}$$

The coefficent matrix has been converted to upper triangular form. We can now perform back-substitution to obtain the solution:

$$13/5x_3 = 52/5 \Rightarrow 13x_3 = 52 \ or \ x_3 = 4$$

Substitute in the second equation

$$5x_2 - 3x_3 = 2 \Rightarrow x_2 - 3(3) = 10 \ or \ x_2 = 2$$

finally, the first equation may be solved for x_1

$$2x_1 - x_2 + x_3 = 4 \rightarrow 2x_1 - 2 + (4) = 4 \Rightarrow 2x_1 = 2 \; or \; x_1 = 1$$

Thus the unknown vector $\vec{x}$ has been found

$$\vec{x} = \begin{bmatrix} x_1 \\ x_2 \\ x_3 \end{bmatrix} = \begin{bmatrix} 1 \\ 2 \\ 4 \end{bmatrix}$$

A conceptual description of a naive Gaussian elimination algorithm is shown in figure 3.2. All of the arithmetic operations needed to eliminate one variable at a time are identified in the illustration.

We call it a naive scheme as we have assumed that none of the diagonal elements are zero, although this is not a requirement for existence of a solution. The reason for avoiding zeros on the diagonals is to avoid division by zeros in step 2 of the illustration 3.2. If there are zeros on the diagonal, we can interchange two equations in such a way the diagonals do not contain zeros. This process is called *pivoting.* Even if we organize the equations in such a way that there are no zeros on the diagonal, we may end up with a zero on the diagonal during the elimination process (likely to occur in step 3 of illustration 3.2). If that situation arises, we can continue to exchange that particular row with another one to avoid division by zero. If the matrix is *singular* we will eventually end up with an unavoidable zero on the diagonal. This situation will arise if the original set of equations is not *linearly independent*; in other words the *rank* of the matrix $\boldsymbol{A}$ is less than $\boldsymbol{n}$. Due to the finite precision of computers, the floating point operation in step 3 of illustration 3.2 will not result usually in an exact zero, but rather a very small number. Loss of precision due to round off errors is a common problem with direct methods involving large system of equations since any error introduced at one step corrupts all subsequent calcualtions.

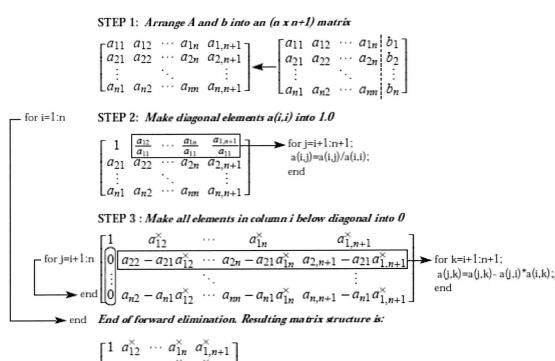

Figure 3.2: Naive Gaussian elimination scheme

A MATLAB implementation of the algorithm is given in figure 3.3 through the function `gauss.m`. *

---

*Note that it is merely for illustrating the concepts involved in the elimination process; MATLAB `backslash`, \ operator provides a much more elegant solution to solve $A x = b$ in the form $x = A \backslash b$.

```
function x=gauss(a,b)
% Naive Gaussian elimination. Cannot have zeros on diagonal
%   a - (nxn) matrix
%   b - column vector of length n

m=size(a,1);    % get number of rows in matrix a
n=length(b);    % get length of b
if (m ~= n)
  error('a and b do not have the same number of rows')
end

%Step 1: form (n,n+1) augmented matrix
a(:,n+1)=b;

for i=1:n
%Step 2: make diagonal elements into 1.0
a(i,i+1:n+1) = a(i,i+1:n+1)/a(i,i);

%Step 3: make all elements below diagonal into 0
 for j=i+1:n
   a(j,i+1:n+1) = a(j,i+1:n+1) - a(j,i)*a(i,i+1:n+1);
 end
end
%Step 4: begin back substitution
for j=n-1:-1:1
 a(j,n+1) = a(j,n+1) - a(j,j+1:n)*a(j+1:n,n+1);
end

%return solution
x=a(:,n+1)
```

Figure 3.3: MATLAB implementation of naive Gaussian elimination

EXAMPLE 3.10 *Let us continue with the recycle problem (equation (1.8) of Chapter 1). First we obtain solution using the built-in MATLAB linear equation solver (viz.* $x = A \backslash b$ *and record execution time* (in seconds) using the* tic toc *routine. Then we solve with the Gaussian elimination function* **gauss** *and compare the time. Note that in order to use the naive Gaussian elimination function, we need to switch the 2nd and 3rd equations to avoid division by zero.*

**NOTE: The execution time may vary from system to system

```
>>A=[1 0 0.306;        % matrix entry continues on next two lines
>>-2 1 0;
>>0 1 0.702];          % Definition of matrix A complete
>>b=[101.48 0 225.78]' ; % Define right hand side column vector b
>>A\b                  % solution is :   [23.8920 47.7840 253.5556]
>>tic;A\b;toc          % examine execution time (ans:  0.000039s)
>>tic;gauss(A,b);toc   % examine execution time (ans:  0.000042s]
>>tic;inv(A)*b;toc     % examine execution time (ans:  0.000089s)
```

EXAMPLE 3.11 - loss of accuracy & need for pivoting

The need for pivoting can be illustrated with the following simple example.

$$\epsilon x_1 + x_2 = 1$$

$$x_1 + x_2 = 2$$

where ϵ is a small number. In matrix form it will be,

$$\begin{bmatrix} \epsilon & 1 \\ 1 & 1 \end{bmatrix} \begin{bmatrix} x_1 \\ x_2 \end{bmatrix} = \begin{bmatrix} 1 \\ 2 \end{bmatrix}$$

In using naive Gaussian elimination without rearranging the equations, we first make the diagonal into unity, which results in

$$x_1 + \frac{1}{\epsilon} x_2 = \frac{1}{\epsilon}$$

Next we eliminate the variable x_1 from the 2nd equation which resutls in,

$$\left(1 - \frac{1}{\epsilon}\right) x_2 = 2 - \frac{1}{\epsilon}$$

Rearranging this and using back substitution we finally get x_2 and x_1 as,

$$x_2 = \frac{2 - \frac{1}{\epsilon}}{1 - \frac{1}{\epsilon}}$$

$$x_1 = \frac{1}{\epsilon} - \frac{x_2}{\epsilon}$$

The problem in computing x_1 as $\epsilon \to 0$ should be clear now. As ϵ crosses the threshold of finite precision of the computation (hardware or software), taking the difference of two large numbers of comparable magnitude, can result in significant loss of precision. Let us solve the problem once again after rearranging the equations as,

$$x_1 + x_2 = 2$$

$$\epsilon x_1 + x_2 = 1$$

and apply Gaussian elimination once again. Since the diagonal element in the first equation is already unity, we can eliminate x_1 from the 2nd equation to obtain,

$$(1 - \epsilon)x_2 = 1 - 2\epsilon \qquad or \qquad x_2 = \frac{1 - 2\epsilon}{1 - \epsilon}$$

Back substitution yields,

$$x_1 = 2 - x_2$$

Both these computations are well behaved as $\epsilon \to 0$.
We can actually demonstrate this using the MATLAB function gauss *shown in figure 3.3 and compare it with the MATLAB built-in function $A\backslash b$ which does use pivoting to rearrange the equations and minimize the loss of precision. The results are compared in table 3.1 for ϵ in the range of 10^{-15} to 10^{-17}. Since MATLAB uses double precision, this range of ϵ is the threshold for loss of precision. Observe that the naive Gaussian elimination produces incorrect results for $\epsilon < 10^{-16}$.*

3.7.4 Thomas algorithm

Many problems such as the stagewise separation problem we saw in section §1.3.1 or the solution of differential equations that we

ϵ	Naive elimination without pivoting gauss(A,b)	Built-in MATLAB $A \backslash b$
1×10^{-15}	[1 1]	[1, 1]
1×10^{-16}	[2 1]	[1, 1]
1×10^{-17}	[0 1]	[1, 1]

Table 3.1: Loss of precision and need for pivoting

will see in later chapters involve solving a system of linear equations $\boldsymbol{Tx} = \boldsymbol{b}$ with a *tridiagonal* matrix structure.

$$
\boldsymbol{T} = \begin{bmatrix}
d_1 & c_1 & 0 & \cdots & 0 \\
a_1 & d_2 & c_2 & \cdots & 0 \\
 & & \ddots & & \\
0 & 0 & a_{n-2} & d_{n-1} & c_{n-1} \\
0 & \cdots & 0 & a_{n-1} & d_n
\end{bmatrix}
$$

$$
\boldsymbol{x} = \begin{bmatrix} x_1 \\ x_2 \\ \vdots \\ x_{n-1} \\ x_n \end{bmatrix}
\qquad
\boldsymbol{b} = \begin{bmatrix} b_1 \\ b_2 \\ \vdots \\ b_{n-1} \\ b_n \end{bmatrix}
$$

Since we know where the zero elements are, we do not have to carry out the elimination steps on those entries of the matrix $\boldsymbol{T}$; but the essential steps in the algorithm remain the same as in the Gaussian elimination scheme and are illustrated in figure 3.4. MATLAB implementation is shown in figure 3.5.

Given

$$\begin{bmatrix} d_1 & c_1 & 0 & 0 & & \vdots & b_1 \\ a_1 & d_2 & c_2 & 0 & & \vdots & b_2 \\ 0 & \ddots & \ddots & \ddots & 0 & \vdots & \\ 0 & 0 & a_{n-2} & d_{n-1} & c_{n-1} & \vdots & b_{n-1} \\ & & & a_{n-1} & d_n & \vdots & b_n \end{bmatrix}$$

STEP 1: *Eliminate lower diagonal elements*

for j=2:n

$$\begin{bmatrix} d_1 & c_1 & 0 & 0 & & \vdots & b_1 \\ 0 & \boxed{d_2^*} & c_2 & 0 & & \vdots & \boxed{b_2^*} \\ 0 & \ddots & \ddots & \ddots & 0 & \vdots & \\ 0 & 0 & 0 & d_{n-1}^* & c_{n-1} & \vdots & b_{n-1}^* \\ & & & 0 & d_n^* & \vdots & b_n^* \end{bmatrix}$$

end

$d(j) = d(j) - \{a(j\text{-}1)/d(j\text{-}1)\}^*c(j\text{-}1)$
$b(j) = b(j) - \{a(j\text{-}1)/d(j\text{-}1)\}^*b(j\text{-}1)$

STEP 2: *Back substitution*

$$\begin{bmatrix} d_1 & c_1 & 0 & 0 & & b_1 \\ 0 & \boxed{d_2^* \quad c_2} & 0 & & \boxed{b_2^*} \\ 0 & \ddots & \ddots & \ddots & 0 & \\ 0 & 0 & 0 & d_{n-1}^* & c_{n-1} & b_{n-1}^* \\ & & & 0 & \boxed{d_n^*} & \boxed{b_n^*} \end{bmatrix}$$

for i=n-1:-1:1
 $b(i) = \{b(i) - c(i)^*b(i+1)\}/d(i);$
end

$b(n) = b(n)/d(n)$

Solution is stored in b

Figure 3.4: Thomas algorithm

```
function x=thomas(a,b,c,d)
% Thomas algorithm for tridiagonal systems
%   d - diagonal elements, n
%   b - right hand side forcing term,  n
%   a - lower diagonal elements, (n-1)
%   c - upper diagonal elements, (n-1)

na=length(a); % get length of a
nb=length(b); % get length of b
nc=length(c); % get length of c
nd=length(d); % get length of d
if (nd ~= nb | na ~= nc | (nd-1) ~= na)
  error('array dimensions not consistent')
end
n=length(d);
%Step 1: forward elimination
```

```
for i=2:n
  fctr=a(i-1)/d(i-1);
  d(i) = d(i) - fctr*c(i-1);
  b(i) = b(i) - fctr*b(i-1);
end

%Step 2: back substitution
b(n) = b(n)/d(n);
for j=n-1:-1:1
 b(j) = (b(j) - c(j)*b(j+1))/d(j);
end

%return solution
x=b;
```

Figure 3.5: MATLAB implementation of Thomas algorithm

3.7.5   Gauss-Jordan elimination

This is an extension of the gauss elimination method. In Gauss elimination, the coefficient matrix is reduced to an upper triangular matrix. Back-substitution is therefore required in order to obtain the unknowns. In the Gauss-Jordan method, all the off diagonal elements (above and below the main diagonal) are reduced to zero. The need for back-substitution is therefore eliminated.

EXAMPLE 3.12 (✎ Gauss Jordan method) *Consider the following* **3 × 3** *system*

$$3x_1 - 6x_2 + 7x_3 = 3$$
$$9x_1 - 5x_3 = 3$$
$$5x_1 - 8x_2 + 6x_3 = -4$$

The coefficient matrix

$$A = \begin{bmatrix} 3 & -6 & 7 \\ 9 & 0 & -5 \\ 5 & -8 & 6 \end{bmatrix}$$

and the constant vector

$$b = \begin{bmatrix} 3 \\ 3 \\ -4 \end{bmatrix}$$

are combined to form the augumented matrix

$$C = \begin{bmatrix} 3 & -6 & 7 & 3 \\ 9 & 0 & -5 & 3 \\ 5 & -8 & 6 & -4 \end{bmatrix}$$

With Gauss Jordan elimination, we reduce the original coefficient matrix to an identity matrix
pivot row 1, divide by pivot element $a_{11} = 3$

$$C = \begin{bmatrix} 3 & -6 & 7 & 3 \\ 9 & 0 & -5 & 3 \\ 5 & -8 & 6 & -4 \end{bmatrix} \quad \boldsymbol{row1/3} \quad \Rightarrow \begin{bmatrix} 1 & -2 & 2.33 & 1 \\ 9 & 0 & -5 & 3 \\ 5 & -8 & 6 & -4 \end{bmatrix}$$

Eliminate row 2 and 3 using row 1

$$\begin{bmatrix} 1 & -2 & 2.33 & 1 \\ 9 & 0 & -5 & 3 \\ 5 & -8 & 6 & -4 \end{bmatrix} \quad \begin{matrix} \boldsymbol{row2 - 9row1} \\ \boldsymbol{row3 - 5row1} \end{matrix} \Rightarrow \begin{bmatrix} 1 & -2 & 2.33 & 1 \\ 0 & 18 & -26 & -6 \\ 0 & 2 & -5.65 & -9 \end{bmatrix}$$

pivot row 2, divide by pivot element $a_{22} = 18$

$$\begin{bmatrix} 1 & -2 & 2.33 & 1 \\ 0 & 18 & -26 & -6 \\ 0 & 2 & -5.65 & -9 \end{bmatrix} \quad \boldsymbol{row2/18} \quad \Rightarrow \begin{bmatrix} 1 & -2 & 2.33 & 1 \\ 0 & 1 & 1.44 & -0.33 \\ 0 & 2 & -5.65 & -9 \end{bmatrix}$$

Eliminate row 1 and 3 using row 2

$$\begin{bmatrix} 1 & -2 & 2.33 & 1 \\ 0 & 1 & 1.44 & -0.33 \\ 0 & 2 & -5.65 & -9 \end{bmatrix} \quad \begin{matrix} \boldsymbol{row1 + 2row2} \\ \\ \boldsymbol{row3 - 2row2} \end{matrix} \Rightarrow \begin{bmatrix} 1 & 0 & -0.55 & 0.33 \\ 0 & 1 & 1.44 & -0.33 \\ 0 & 0 & -2.77 & -8.33 \end{bmatrix}$$

pivot row 3, divide by pivot element $a_{33} = -2.77$

$$\begin{bmatrix} 1 & 0 & -0.55 & 0.33 \\ 0 & 1 & 1.44 & -0.33 \\ 0 & 0 & -2.77 & -8.33 \end{bmatrix} \quad \boldsymbol{row3/(-2.77)} \Rightarrow \begin{bmatrix} 1 & 0 & -0.55 & 0.33 \\ 0 & 1 & 1.44 & -0.33 \\ 0 & 0 & 1 & 3.01 \end{bmatrix}$$

Eliminate row 1 and 2 using row 3

$$\begin{bmatrix} 1 & 0 & -0.55 & | & 0.33 \\ 0 & 1 & 1.44 & | & -0.33 \\ 0 & 0 & 1 & | & 3.01 \end{bmatrix} \begin{matrix} row1 + 0.55row3 \\ row2 - 1.44row3 \end{matrix} \Rightarrow \begin{bmatrix} 1 & 0 & 0 & | & 1.99 \\ 0 & 1 & 0 & | & 4.00 \\ 0 & 0 & 1 & | & 3.01 \end{bmatrix}$$

Thus the matrix equation becomes

$$\begin{bmatrix} 1 & 0 & 0 \\ 0 & 1 & 0 \\ 0 & 0 & 1 \end{bmatrix} \begin{bmatrix} x_1 \\ x_2 \\ x_3 \end{bmatrix} = \begin{bmatrix} 1.99 \\ 4.00 \\ 3.01 \end{bmatrix}$$

The coefficent matrix has been converted into identity form. Thus the unknown vector $\vec{x}$ has been found without back-substitution !

$$\vec{x} = \begin{bmatrix} x_1 \\ x_2 \\ x_3 \end{bmatrix} = \begin{bmatrix} 1.99 \\ 4.00 \\ 3.01 \end{bmatrix}$$

3.7.6   Gaussian elimination - *Symbolic representaion*

Given a square matrix A of dimension $n \times n$ it is possible to write it is as the product of two matrices B and C, *i.e.*, $A = BC$. This process is called *factorization* and is in fact not at all unique - *i.e.*, there are inifnitely many possiblilities for B and C. This is clear with a simple counting of the unknowns - viz. there are $2 \times n^2$ unknown elements in B and C while only n^2 equations can be obtained by equating each element of A with the corresponding element from the product BC.

The extra degrees of freedom can be used to specify any specific structure for B and C. For example we can require $B = L$ be a lower triangular matrix and $C = U$ be an upper triangular matrix.This process is called LU factorization or decomposition. Since each triangular matrix has $n \times (n + 1)/2$ unknowns, we still have a total of $n^2 + n$ unknowns. The extra n degrees of freedom is often used in one of three ways:

- *Doolitle* method assigns the diagonal elements of L to be unity, *i.e.*, $l_{ii} = 1$.

- *Crout* method assigns the diagonal elements of U to be unity, *i.e.*, $u_{ii} = 1$.

- *Cholesky* method assigns the diagonal elements of L to be equal to that of U - *i.e.*, $l_{ii} = u_{ii}$.

While a simple degree of freedom analysis, indicates that it is possible to factorize a matrix into a product of lower and upper triangular matrices, it does not tell us how to find out the unknown elements.

3.7.7 LU decomposition

Consider the product of L and U as shown in the expanded form below. All of the elements of L and U are unkonwn. By carrying out the matrix product on the left hand side and equating element-by-element to the right hand side, we can develop sufficient number of equations to find out all of the unkown elements on the left hand side. The trick, however is, (as we did with inverting a triangular matrix) to carry out the calculations in a particualr sequence so that no more than one unknown appears in each equation.

$$
\begin{bmatrix}
l_{11} & 0 & 0 & \cdots & 0 \\
l_{21} & l_{22} & 0 & \cdots & 0 \\
l_{31} & l_{32} & l_{33} & \cdots & 0 \\
\vdots & \vdots & \vdots & \ddots & 0 \\
l_{n1} & l_{n2} & l_{n3} & \cdots & l_{nn}
\end{bmatrix}
\begin{bmatrix}
1 & u_{12} & u_{13} & \cdots & u_{1n} \\
0 & 1 & u_{23} & \cdots & u_{2n} \\
0 & 0 & 1 & \cdots & u_{3n} \\
\vdots & \vdots & \vdots & \ddots & \vdots \\
0 & 0 & 0 & \cdots & 1
\end{bmatrix}
=
\begin{bmatrix}
a_{11} & a_{12} & \cdots & a_{1n} \\
a_{21} & a_{22} & \cdots & a_{2n} \\
a_{31} & a_{32} & \cdots & a_{3n} \\
\vdots & \vdots & \cdots & \vdots \\
a_{n1} & a_{n2} & \cdots & a_{nn}
\end{bmatrix}
$$

Let us first consider elements in column 1 of L. Carrying out the multiplication and equating we obtain,

$$l_{i1} = a_{i1} \qquad i = 1, \cdots, n \tag{3.20}$$

* Next focusing on the elements in the first row of U we get,

$$u_{1j} = a_{1j}/l_{11} \qquad j = 2, \cdots, n \tag{3.21}$$

Next we alternate between a column of L and a row of U. The general expression for any element i in column j of L is,

$$l_{ij} = a_{ij} - \sum_{k=1}^{j-1} l_{ik}u_{kj} \qquad j = 2, \cdots, n \quad i = j, \cdots, n \tag{3.22}$$

Similarly the general expression for any element i in row j of U is,

$$u_{ji} = \frac{\left[a_{ji} - \sum_{k=1}^{j-1} l_{jk}u_{ki} \right]}{l_{jj}} \qquad j = 2, \cdots, n \quad i = j+1, \cdots, n \tag{3.23}$$

Equations (3.20-3.23) form the basic algorithm for LU decomposition. In order to illustrate the implementation of equations (3.20-3.23) as an algorithm, a MATLAB function called LU.m is shown in figure 3.6. Note that MATLAB provides a built-in function for LU decomposition called lu(A).

EXAMPLE 3.13 (✎LU factors from Gauss elimination)

Recall example 3.9 where the given equations were solved by gauss elimination. In this case, we want to keep a record of all operations which are done when reducing the coefficient matrix to upper triangular form.

---

*It would be inefficient to proceed to the 2nd column of L. Why?

The coefficient matrix

$$A = \begin{bmatrix} 2 & -1 & 1 \\ 4 & 3 & -1 \\ 3 & 2 & 2 \end{bmatrix}$$

*We will construct **L** from an identity matrix of the same size placed placed on the left of the given matrix.*

$$A = \begin{bmatrix} 1 & 0 & 0 \\ 0 & 1 & 0 \\ 0 & 0 & 1 \end{bmatrix} \begin{bmatrix} 2 & -1 & 1 \\ 4 & 3 & -1 \\ 3 & 2 & 2 \end{bmatrix}$$

To reduce the matrix to lower triangular, starting with the first column, row 2 is multiplied by 1/2 and then subtracted from row1; and row 3 is multiplied by 2/3 and then subtracted from row 1. These factors are recorded in the respective positions in column 1

$$A = \begin{bmatrix} 1 & 0 & 0 \\ 1/2 & 1 & 0 \\ 3/2 & 0 & 1 \end{bmatrix} \begin{bmatrix} 2 & -1 & 1 \\ 0 & 5 & -3 \\ 0 & 7/2 & 1/2 \end{bmatrix}$$

Row 2 is used to eliminate elements in column 2 below the diagonal of the second factor in the above product. Multiplier m2 = 7/10 is subtracted from row three and the multiplier recorded in the identity matrix. We now have the lower and upper triangular matrices as desired

$$A = \begin{bmatrix} 1 & 0 & 0 \\ 1/2 & 1 & 0 \\ 3/2 & 13/5 & 1 \end{bmatrix} \begin{bmatrix} 2 & -1 & 1 \\ 0 & 5 & -3 \\ 0 & 0 & 13/5 \end{bmatrix}$$

We can verify that $A = LU$ by multiplying the two matrices, L and U to obtain A.

```
function [L,U]=LU(a)
% Naive LU decomposition
%   a     - (nxn) matrix
%   L,U   - are (nxn) factored matrices
% Usage [L,U]=LU(A)

n=size(a,1);    % get number of rows in matrix a

%Step 1: first column of L
L(:,1)=a(:,1);

%Step 2: first row of U
U(1,:)=a(1,:)/L(1,1);

%Step 3: Alternate between column of L and row of U
for j=2:n
  for i = j:n
    L(i,j) = a(i,j) - sum(L(i,1:j-1)'.*U(1:j-1,j));
  end
  U(j,j) = 1;
  for i=j+1:n
    U(j,i)=(a(j,i) - sum(L(j,1:j-1)'.*U(1:j-1,i) ) )/L(j,j);
  end
end
```

Figure 3.6: MATLAB implementation of LU decomposition algorithm

Recognizing that A can be factored into the product LU, one can implement an efficient scheme for solving a system of linear algebraic equations $Ax = b$ repeatedly, particularly when the matrix A remains unchanged, but different solutions are required for different forcing terms on the right hand side, b. The equation

$$Ax = b$$

can be written as

$$LUx = b \qquad let \qquad Ux = z$$

and hence

$$Lz = b$$

which can be solved for z:

$$z = L^{-1}b$$

and finally back substitution to obtain x:

$$x = U^{-1}z$$

The operations required for forward elimination and back substitution are stored in the LU factored matrix and as we saw earlier it is relatively efficient to invert triangular matrices. Hence two additional vector-matrix products provide a solution for each new value of b.

EXAMPLE 3.14 *Work through the following exercise in MAT-LAB to get a feel for the built-in MATLAB implementation of LU factorization with that given in figure 3.6. Before you work through the exercise make sure that the file* LU.m *that contains the function illustrated in figure 3.6 is in the MATLAB path. Also, be aware of the upper case function* LU *of figure 3.6 and the lower case* lu *which is the built-in function.*

```
>>A=[1 0 0.306; 0 1 0.702; -2 1 0];   % Define matrix A
>>b=[101.48 225.78 0]'                 % Define right hand vector b
>>tic                                  % initialize time
>>x=A\b                                % solve using built-in solver
>>toc                                  %
>>tic                                  % re-initialize time
>>[l,u]=LU(A)                          %Use algorithm in figure 3.6
>>toc                                  %
>>x=inv(u)*(inv(l)*b)                  % Solve linear system
>>toc                                  %
>>tic                                  %
>>[L,U]=lu(A)                          %use built-in function
>>toc                                  %
```

```
>>x=inv(U)*(inv(L)*b)          % Solve linear system
>>toc                          %
```

3.8   Iterative algorithms for systems of linear equations

The direct methods discussed in section §3.7 have the advantage of producing the solution in a finite number of calculations. They suffer, however, from loss of precision due to accumulated round off errors. This problem is particulary severe in large dimensional systems (more than 10,000 equations). Iterative methods, on the other hand, produce the result in an asymptotic manner by repeated application of a simple algorithm. Hence the number of floating point operations required to produce the final result cannot be known *a priori*. But they have the natural ability to eliminate errors at every step of the iteration.

Iterative methods rely on the concepts developed in Chapter 2. They are extended naturally from a single equation (one-dimensional system) to a system of equations (n-dimensional system). The development parallels that of section §2.7 on fixed point iterations schemes. Given an equation of the form, $\boldsymbol{A}\,\boldsymbol{x} = \boldsymbol{b}$ we can rearrange it into a form,

$$\boxed{\boldsymbol{x}^{(p+1)} = \boldsymbol{G}(\boldsymbol{x}^{(p)}) \qquad \boldsymbol{p} = 0, 1, \cdots} \qquad (3.24)$$

Here we can view the vector $\boldsymbol{x}$ as a point in a $\boldsymbol{n}$-dimensional vector space and the above equation as an iterative map that maps a point $\boldsymbol{x}^{(p)}$ into another point $\boldsymbol{x}^{(p+1)}$ in the $\boldsymbol{n}$-dimensional vector space. Starting with an initial guess $\boldsymbol{x}^{(0)}$ we calculate successive iterates $\boldsymbol{x}^{(1)}, \boldsymbol{x}^{(2)} \cdots$ until the sequence converges. The only difference from chapter 2 is that the above iteration is applied to a higher dimensional system of ($\boldsymbol{n}$) equations. Note that $\boldsymbol{G}(\boldsymbol{x})$ is also vector. Since we are dealing with a linear system, $\boldsymbol{G}$ will be a linear function of x which is constructed from the given A matrix. G can typically be represented as

$$x^{(p+1)} = G(x^{(p)}) = Tx^{(p)} + c. \qquad (3.25)$$

In section §2.7 we saw that a given equation $f(x) = 0$ can be rearranged into the form $x = g(x)$ in several different ways. In a similar manner, a given equation $Ax = b$ can be rearranged into the form $x^{(p+1)} = G(x^{(p)})$ in more than one way. Different choices of G results in different iterative methods. In section §2.7 we also saw that the condition for convergence of the sequence $x_{i+1} = g(x_i)$ is $g'(r) < 1$. Recognizing that the derivative of $G(x^{(p)})$ with respect to $x^{(p)}$ is a matrix, $G' = T$ a convergence condition similar to that found for the scalar case must depend on the properties of the matrix T. Another way to demonstrate this is as follows. Once the sequence $x^{(1)}, x^{(2)} \cdots$ converges to, say, r equation (3.25) becomes,

$$r = Tr + c.$$

Subtracting equation (3.25) from the above,

$$(x^{(p+1)} - r) = T(x^{(p)} - r).$$

Now, recognizing that $(x^{(p)} - r) = \epsilon^{(p)}$ is a measure of the error at iteration level p, we have

$$\epsilon^{(p+1)} = T\epsilon^{(p)}.$$

Thus, the error at step $(p + 1)$ depend on the error at step (p). If the matrix T has the property of amplifying the error at any step, then the iterative sequence will diverge. The property of the matrix T that determines this feature is called the *spectral radius*. The *spectral radius* is defined as the largest eigenvalue in magnitude of T. For convenience of the iterative sequence the *spectral radius* of T should be less than unity,

$$\boxed{\rho(T) < 1} \qquad (3.26)$$

3.8.1   Jacobi iteration

The Jacobi iteration rearranges the given equations in the form,

$$x_1^{(p+1)} = \frac{1}{a_{11}}(b_1 - a_{12}x_2^{(p)} - a_{13}x_3^{(p)} - \cdots - a_{1n}x_n^{(p)})$$

$$x_j^{(p+1)} = \frac{1}{a_{jj}}\left[b_j - \sum_{k=1}^{j-1} a_{jk}x_k^{(p)} - \sum_{k=j+1}^{n} a_{jk}x_k^{(p)}\right] \qquad (3.27)$$

$$x_n^{(p+1)} = \frac{1}{a_{nn}}(b_n - a_{n1}x_1^{(p)} - a_{n2}x_2^{(p)} - \cdots - a_{n,n-1}x_{n-1}^{(p)})$$

where the variable x_j has been extracted form the $j - th$ equation and expressed as a function of the remaining variables. The above set of equations can be applied repetitively to update each component of the unknown vector $x=(x_1, x_2, \cdots , x_n)$ provided an inital guess is known for x.

Residual form

We can obtain an equivalent and more convenient form of equation 3.27 by adding and subtracting $x_j^{(p)}$ from the right side of the equation to yield

$$x_j^{(p+1)} = x_j^{(p)} + \frac{1}{a_{jj}}\left[b_j - \sum_{k=1}^{n} a_{jk}x_k^{(p)}\right] \qquad (3.28)$$

Equation 3.28 can further be written in a general form as

$$x_j^{(p+1)} = x_j^{(p)} + \frac{R_j^{(p)}}{a_{jj}} \qquad j = 1, 2, 3, \cdots n \qquad (3.29)$$

$$R_j^{(p)} = b_j - \sum_{k=1}^{n} a_{jk}x_k^{(p)}$$

Where $R_j^{(p)}$ is called the residual form of equation j. The residuals are the net values of the equations evaluated for the approximate solution vector x^p.

Matrix form

Equation 3.27 can also be written in matrix form as, *

$$Lx^{(p)} + Dx^{(p+1)} + Ux^{(p)} = b$$

where the matrices D, L, U are defined in term of components of A as follows.

$$D = \begin{bmatrix} a_{11} & 0 & \cdots & 0 \\ 0 & a_{22} & \cdots & 0 \\ \vdots & 0 & \ddots & 0 \\ 0 & 0 & \cdots & a_{nn} \end{bmatrix}$$

$$L = \begin{bmatrix} 0 & 0 & \cdots & 0 \\ a_{21} & 0 & \cdots & 0 \\ \vdots & & \ddots & 0 \\ a_{n1} & a_{n2} & \cdots & 0 \end{bmatrix} \qquad U = \begin{bmatrix} 0 & a_{12} & \cdots & a_{1n} \\ 0 & 0 & \cdots & a_{2n} \\ 0 & 0 & \ddots & \vdots \\ 0 & 0 & \cdots & 0 \end{bmatrix}$$

which can be rearranged as,

$$x^{(p+1)} = D^{-1}(b - (L+U)x^{(p)}) \tag{3.30}$$

and hence $G(x^{(p)}) = -D^{-1}(L+U)x^{(p)} + D^{-1}b$ and $G' = T = -D^{-1}(L+U)$.

This method has been shown to be convergent as long as the original matrix A is diagonally dominant, *i.e.*,

$$\boxed{a_{ii} > \sum_{j=1, j \neq i}^{n} a_{ij} \qquad i = 1, \cdots, n} \tag{3.31}$$

---

*Note that MATLAB functions
`diag`
`tril`
`triu`
are useful in extracting parts of a given matrix A

An examination of equation (3.27) reveals that none of the diagonal elements can be zero. If any is found to be zero, one can easily exchange the positions of any two equations to avoid this problem. Equation (3.27) is used in actual computational implementation, while the matrix form of the equation (3.30) is useful for conceptual description and convergence analysis. Note that each element in the equation set (3.27) can be updated independent of the others in any order because the right hand side of equation (3.27) is evaluated at the p-th level of iteration. This method requires that $x^{(p)}$ and $x^{(p+1)}$ be stored as two separate vectors until all elements of $x^{(p+1)}$ have been updated using equation (3.27). A minor variation of the algorithm which uses a new value of the element in $x^{(p+1)}$ as soon as it is available is called the Gauss-Seidel method. It has the dual advantage of faster convergence than the Jacobi iteration as well as reduced storage requirement for only one array x.

3.8.2   Gauss-Seidel iteration

In the Gauss-Seidel iteration we rearrange the given equations in the form,

$$
x_1^{(p+1)} = \frac{1}{a_{11}}(b_1 - a_{12}x_2^{(p)} - a_{13}x_3^{(p)} - \cdots - a_{1n}x_n^{(p)})
$$

$$
x_j^{(p+1)} = \frac{1}{a_{jj}}\left[b_j - \sum_{k=1}^{j-1} a_{jk}x_k^{(p+1)} - \sum_{k=j+1}^{n} a_{jk}x_k^{(p)} \right] \tag{3.32}
$$

$$
x_n^{(p+1)} = \frac{1}{a_{nn}}(b_n - a_{n1}x_1^{(p+1)} - a_{n2}x_2^{(p+1)} - \cdots - a_{n,n-1}x_{n-1}^{(p+1)})
$$

Observe that known values of the elements in $x^{(p+1)}$ are used on the right hand side of the above equations (3.32) as soon as they are available within the same iteration. We have used the superscripts p and $(p+1)$ explicitly in equation (3.32) to indicate where the newest values occur. In a computer program there is no need to assign separate arrays for p and $(p+1)$ levels of iteration. Using just a single array for x will automatically propagate the newest values as soon as they are updated.

Residual form

Equation 3.32 can be written in terms of the residuals R_j by adding and subtracting $x_j^{(p)}$ from the right hand side of the equation and rearranging to obtain

$$x_j^{(p+1)} = x_k^{(p)} + \frac{R_j^{(p)}}{a_{jj}} \qquad j = 1, 2, 3, \cdots, n \quad (3.33)$$

$$R_j^{(p)} = b_j - \sum_{k=1}^{j-1} a_{jk} x_k^{(p+1)} - \sum_{k=1}^{n} a_{jk} x_k^{(p)}$$

Matrix form

The Gauss-Seidel equation can also be written symbolically in matrix form as,

$$Lx^{(p+1)} + Dx^{(p+1)} + Ux^{(p)} = b$$

where the matrices D, L, U are defined as before. Factoring $x^{(p+1)}$ we get,

$$x^{(p+1)} = (L + D)^{-1}(b - Ux^{(p)}) \qquad (3.34)$$

and hence $G(x^{(p)}) = -(L + D)^{-1}Ux^{(p)} + (L + D)^{-1}b$ and $G' = T = -(L + D)^{-1}U$. Thus the convergence of this scheme depends on the spectral radius of the matrix, $T = -(L + D)^{-1}U$. This method has also been shown to be convergent as long as the original matrix A is diagonally dominant.

MATLAB implementation of the Gauss-Seidel algorithm is shown in figure 3.7.

```
function x=GS(a,b,x,tol,max)
% Gauss-Seidel iteration
%   a  - (nxn) matrix
%   b  - column vector of length n
%   x  - initial guess vector x
%   tol - convergence tolerance
%   max - maximum number of iterations
%         Usage x=GS(A,b,x)

m=size(a,1);    % get number of rows in matrix a
n=length(b);    % get length of b
if (m ~= n)
  error('a and b do not have the same number of rows')
end
if nargin < 5, max=100; end
if nargin < 4, max=100; tol=eps; end
if nargin == 2
  error('Initial guess is required')
end
count=0;

while (norm(a*x-b)  > tol & count < max),
  x(1) = ( b(1) - a(1,2:n)*x(2:n) )/a(1,1);
 for i=2:n-1
   x(i) = (b(i) - a(i,1:i-1)*x(1:i-1) - ...
                a(i,i+1:n)*x(i+1:n) )/a(i,i);
 end
  x(n) = ( b(n) - a(n,1:n-1)*x(1:n-1) )/a(n,n);
  count=count+1;
end

if (count >= max)
 fprintf(1,'Maximum iteration %3i exceeded\n',count)
 fprintf(1,'Residual is %12.5e\n ',norm(a*x-b) )
end
```

Figure 3.7: MATLAB implementation of Gauss-Seidel algorithm

3.8.3 Successive over-relaxation (SOR) scheme

The relaxation scheme can be thought of as a convergence acceleration scheme that can be applied to any of the basic iterative methods like Jacobi or Gauss-Seidel schemes. We introduce an extra parameter, ω often called the *relaxation parameter* and choose its value in such a way that we can either speed up convergence by using $\omega > 1$ (called *over-relaxation*) or in some difficult problems with poor initial guess we can attempt to enlarge the region of convergence using $\omega < 1$ (called *under-relaxation*). Let us illustrate the implementation with the Gauss-Seidel scheme. The basic Gauss-Seidel scheme is:

$$t := x_j^{(p+1)} = \frac{1}{a_{jj}} \left[b_j - \sum_{k=1}^{j-1} a_{jk} x_k^{(p+1)} - \sum_{k=j+1}^{n} a_{jk} x_k^{(p)} \right]$$

Instead of accepting the value of $x_j^{(p+1)}$ computed from the above formula as the current value, we store it in a temporary variable t and form a better (or accelerated) estimate of $x_j^{(p+1)}$ from,

$$x_j^{(p+1)} = x_j^{(p)} + \omega \left[t - x_j^{(p)} \right]$$

Observe that if $\omega = 1$, the method remains the same as Gauss-Seidel scheme. For $\omega > 1$, then the difference between two successive iterates (the term in the square brackets) is amplified and added to the current value $x_j^{(p)}$.

The equation can be written in residual form as

$$x_j^{(p+1)} = x_k^{(p)} + \omega \frac{R_j^{(p)}}{a_{jj}} \qquad j = 1, 2, 3, \cdots, n \quad (3.35)$$

$$R_j^{(p)} = b_j - \sum_{k=1}^{j-1} a_{jk} x_k^{(p+1)} - \sum_{k=1}^{n} a_{jk} x_k^{(p)}$$

And the symbolic matrix form as,

$$x^{(p+1)} = x^{(p)} + \omega [\{ D^{-1} (b - Lx^{(p+1)} - Ux^{(p)}) \} - x^{(p)}]$$

where the term in braces represent the Gauss-Seidel scheme. After extracting $x^{(p+1)}$ from the above equation, it can be cast in the standard iterative from of equation (3.25) as,

$$x^{(p+1)} = (D+\omega L)^{-1}[(1-\omega)D - \omega U]x^{(p)} + \omega(D+\omega L)^{-1}b$$
$$(3.36)$$

Thus the convergence of the relaxation method depends on the spectral radius of the matrix $T(\omega) := (D+\omega L)^{-1}[(1-\omega)D - \omega U]$. Since this matrix is a function of ω we have gained a measure of control over the convergence of the iterative scheme. It has been shown [58] that the SOR method is convergent for $0 < \omega < 2$ and that there is an optimum value of ω which results in the maximum rate of convergence. The optimum value of ω is very problem dependent and often difficult to determine precisely. For linear problems, typical values in the range of $\omega \approx 1.7 \sim 1.8$ are used.

EXAMPLE 3.15 (✎ Jacobi and Gauss Seidel) *To illustrate the iterative methods, lets solve the following system of equations with initial values* $x^{(0)} = [0 \ \ 0 \ \ 0]^T$

$$3x_1 + x_2 - 2x_3 = 9 \qquad (3.37)$$
$$-x_1 + 4x_2 - 3x_3 = -8$$
$$x_1 - x_2 + 4x_3 = 1$$

a) Jacobi method
Equations 3.37 can be rearranged to yield the residuals, R_j

$$R_1 \ \ = 9 - 3x_1 - x_2 + 2x_3 \qquad (3.38)$$
$$R_2 \ = -8 + x_1 - 4x_2 + 3x_3$$
$$R_3 \ \ = 1 - x_1 + x_2 - 4x_3$$

Substituting the initial values $x^{(0)} = [0 \ \ 0 \ \ 0]^T$

$$R_1 = 9$$
$$R_2 = -8$$
$$R_3 = 1$$

Substituting these values into the updating equation

$$x_j^{(p+1)} = x_j^{(p)} + \frac{R_j^{(p)}}{a_{jj}}$$

Step 1, p =0 , j $= 1, 2, 3$

$$x_1^{(1)} = x_1^{(0)} + \frac{R_1^{(0)}}{a_{11}} = 0 + \frac{9}{3} = 3.0000$$

$$x_2^{(1)} = x_1^{(0)} + \frac{R_2^{(0)}}{a_{22}} = 0 + \frac{-8}{4} = -2.0000$$

$$x_3^{(1)} = x_1^{(0)} + \frac{R_3^{(0)}}{a_{33}} = 0 + \frac{1}{4} = 0.2500$$

Step 2, p =1 , j $= 1, 2, 3$ *and*
$x^{(1)} = [3.0000 \ -2.0000 \ 0.2500]^T$

$$R_1^{(1)} = 2.5$$
$$R_2^{(1)} = 3.75$$
$$R_3^{(1)} = -5$$

giving

$$x_1^{(1)} = 3.0000 + \frac{2.5}{3} = 3.8333$$

$$x_2^{(1)} = -2.0000 + \frac{3.75}{4} = -1.0025$$

$$x_3^{(1)} = 0.2500 + \frac{-5}{4} = -1.0000$$

The above can be repeated until a specified convergence criterion has been met, e.g.,

$$\left| \frac{x_j^{p+1} - x_j^p}{x_j^{p+1}} \right| \leq \epsilon_S$$

or a specified norm

$$\left\| x_j^{p+1} - x_j^p \right\|_2 \leq \epsilon_S$$

Table below shows 10 iterations of the method

Jacobi iteration results

p	x_1	x_2	x_3	L_2
0	0.0000	0.0000	0.0000	
1	3.0000	-2.0000	0.2500	3.6142
2	3.8333	-1.0625	-1.0000	1.7708
3	2.6875	-1.7917	-0.9740	1.3584
4	2.9479	-2.0586	-0.8698	0.3872
5	3.1063	-1.9154	-1.0016	0.2510
6	2.9707	-1.9746	-1.0054	0.1481
7	2.9879	-2.0114	-0.9863	0.0449
8	3.0129	-1.9928	-0.9998	0.0340
9	2.9977	-1.9966	-1.0014	0.0158
10	2.9979	-2.0016	-0.9986	0.0057

b) Gauss Seidel

Table below shows 10 iterations carried out for the same problem using Gauss Seidel. The superiority of the Gauss Seidel method over Jacobi is seen here whereby Jacobi method has converged to 1×10^{-5} in 10 iterations while the Jacobi has has only reached 5.7×10^{-3}. More iterations are required for the Jacobi for the same level of convergence.

Gauss Seidel iteration results

p	x_1	x_2	x_3	L_2
0	0.0000	0.0000	0.0000	
1	3.0000	-1.2500	-0.8125	3.3500
2	2.8750	-1.8906	-0.9414	0.6653
3	3.0026	-1.9554	-0.9895	0.1510
4	2.9921	-1.9941	-0.9966	0.0407
5	3.0003	-1.9973	-0.9994	0.0093
6	2.9995	-1.9997	-0.9998	0.0025
7	3.0000	-1.9998	-1.0000	5.7698e-004
8	3.0000	-2.0000	-1.0000	1.5805e-004
9	3.0000	-2.0000	-1.0000	3.6483e-005
10	3.0000	-2.0000	-1.0000	1.0037e-005

3.9 Gram-Schmidt orthogonalization procedure

Given a set of n linearly independent vectors, $\{x_i \mid i = 1, \cdots, n\}$ that are not necessarily orthonormal, it is possible to produce an orthonormal set of vectors $\{u_i \mid i = 1, \cdots, n\}$. We begin by normalizing the x_1 vector using the norm $||x_1|| = \sqrt{x_1 \cdot x_1}$ and call it u_1.

$$u_1 = \frac{x_1}{||x_1||}$$

Subsequently we construct other vectors orthogonal to u_1 and normalize each one. For example we construct u_2' by subtracting u_1 from x_2 in such a way that u_2' contains no components of u_1 - *i.e.*,

$$u_2' = x_2 - c_0\, u_1$$

In the above c_0 is to be found in such a way that u_2' is orthogonal to u_1.

$$u_1^T \cdot u_2' = 0 = u_1^T \cdot x_2 - c_0 \quad \text{or} \quad c_0 = u_1^T \cdot x_2$$

Similarly we have,

$$u_3' = x_3 - c_1\, u_1 - c_2\, u_2$$

Requiring orthogonality with respect to both u_1 and u_2

$$u_1^T \cdot u_3' = 0 = u_1^T \cdot x_3 - c_1 \quad \text{or} \quad c_1 = u_1^T \cdot x_3$$

$$u_2^T \cdot u_3' = 0 = u_2^T \cdot x_3 - c_2 \quad \text{or} \quad c_2 = u_2^T \cdot x_3$$

$$u_3' = x_3 - (u_1^T \cdot x_3)\, u_1 - (u_2^T \cdot x_3)\, u_2$$

In general we have,

$$\boxed{\; u_s' = x_s - \sum_{j=1}^{s-1}(u_j^T \cdot x_s)\, u_j \qquad u_s = \frac{u_s'}{||u_s'||} \qquad s = 2, \cdots n; \;}$$

$$(3.15)$$

```
function u=GS_orth(x)
%Gram-Schmidt procedure applied on input x
%   x is a matrix of nxn.
%   Each x(:,j) represents a vector
n=length(x);
if rank(x) ~= n
 error('vectors in x are not linearly independent')
end
u(:,1) = x(:,1)/norm(x(:,1));
for s=2:n
   sum = zeros(n,1);
   for j=1:s-1
```

```
      sum = sum + (u(:,j)'*x(:,s)) * u(:,j);
  end
  uprime = x(:,s) - sum;
  u(:,s) = uprime/norm(uprime);
end
```

Figure 3.8: Illustration of Gram-Schmidt algorithm

The Gram-Schmidt algorithm is illustrated in figure 3.8. Note that MATLAB has a built-in function Q=orth(A) which produces an orthonormal set from A. Q spans the same space as A and the number of columns in Q is the rank of A.

3.10   The eigenvalue problem

A square matrix, A, when operated on certain vectors, called eigenvectors, x, leaves the vector unchanged excpet for a scaling factor, λ. This fact can be represented as,

$$Ax = \lambda x \qquad (3.16)$$

The problem of finding such eignvectors and eigenvalues is addressed by rewritting equation (3.16) as,

$$(A - \lambda I)\, x = 0$$

which represents a set of homogeneous equations that admit non-trivial solutions only if

$$det(A - \lambda I) = 0.$$

i.e., only certain values of λ will make the above determinant zero. This requirement produces an n-th degree polynomial in λ, called the *characteristic polynomial.* Fundamental results from algebra tell us that this polynomial will have exactly n roots, $\{\lambda_j | j = 1 \cdots n\}$ and corresponding to each root, λ_j we can determine an eigenvector, x_j from

$$(A - \lambda_j I)\, x_j = 0.$$

Note that if, x_j satisfies the above equation, then ax_j will also satsify the same equation. Viewed alternately, since the $det(A - \lambda_j I)$ is zero, x_j can be determined only up to an unknown constant - *i.e.*, only the direction of the eignvector can be determined, its magnitude being arbitrary.

The MATLAB built-in function [V,D]=eig(A) computes all of the eigenvalues and the associated eigenvectors.

EXAMPLE 3.16 *Eigenvalues and eigenvectors*

Determine the eigenvalues and eigenvectors of the matrix A defined below.

$$A = \begin{bmatrix} 2 & 4 & 3 \\ 4 & 4 & 3 \\ 3 & 3 & 5 \end{bmatrix}$$

A typical MATLAB session follows.

```
>> A=[2 4 3;4  4 3;3 3 5]   %Define the matrix

A =

     2      4      3
     4      4      3
     3      3      5
%Compute the eigenvalues (in D) and the eigenvectors (in V)
>> [V,D]=eig(A)

V =

    0.8197    -0.2674     0.5066
   -0.5587    -0.5685     0.6039
   -0.1265     0.7780     0.6154

D =

   -1.1894         0          0
         0    1.7764          0
         0         0    10.4130
%compute the coefficients of the characteric polynomial (in c)
>> c=poly(A)
```

```
c =

    1.0000   -11.0000     4.0000    22.0000

%compute the eigenvalues (in r) and compare against the marix D
>> r=roots(c)

r =

   10.4130
    1.7764
   -1.1894
```

Note that in the above example, the coefficients of the characteristic polynomial, contained in the vector c, are defined as follows.

$$p_n(\lambda) = c_1\lambda^n + c_2\lambda^{n-1} + \cdots + c_{n+1}$$

3.10.1 Left and right eigenvectors

The eigenvector x, defined in equation (3.16), is called the right eigenvector, since the matrix product operation is performed from the right. Consider the operation with a vector y

$$y'A = y'\lambda \qquad (3.17)$$

Since equation (3.17) can be written as

$$y'(A - \lambda I) = 0$$

the criterion for admitting nontrivial solutions is still the same, viz.

$$det(A - \lambda I) = 0.$$

Thus the eigenvalues are the same as those defined for the right eigenvector. If A is symmetric, then taking the transpose of equation (3.17) leads to equation (3.16) pointing out that the distinction between the left and right eigenvectors disappear. However for a nonsymmetric matrix, A there is a set of left

$\{x_i | i = 1 \cdots n\}$ and right $\{y_j | j = 1 \cdots n\}$ eigenvectors that are distinct and form a *bi-orthogonal* set as shown below.

3.10.2   Bi-orthogonality

As long as the eigenvalues are distinct, the left and right eigenvectors form a bi-orthogonal set. To demonstrate this, take the left product of equation (3.16) with y'_j and the right product of equation (3.17) with x_i. These lead respectively to

$$y'_j A x_i = \lambda_i y'_j x_i$$

$$y'_j A x_i = \lambda_j y'_j x_i$$

Subtracting one from the other, we get,

$$0 = (\lambda_i - \lambda_j) y'_j x_i.$$

Since λ_i and λ_j are distinct, we get

$$\boxed{y'_j x_i = 0 \qquad \forall i \neq j}$$

which is the condition for bi-orthogonality.

3.10.3   Power iteration

A simple algorithm to find the largest eigenvalue and its associated eigenvector of a matrix A is the power iteration scheme. Conceptually the algorithm works as follows. Starting with any arbitrary vector, $z^{(0)}$, produce a sequence of vectors from

$$y^{(p+1)} = A z^{(p)}$$

$$y^{(p+1)} = k^{(p+1)} z^{(p+1)} \qquad p = 0, 1, \cdots$$

The second step above is merely a scaling operation to keep the vector length $z^{(p)}$ bounded. The vector $z^{(p)}$ converges to the eigenvector x_1 corresponding to the largest eigenvalue as $p \rightarrow \infty$.

The reason why it works can be understood, by begining with a spectral representation of the arbitrary vector, $z^{(0)}$ and tracing the effect of each operation, *i.e.*,

$$z^{(0)} = \sum_i \alpha_i x_i$$

$$y^{(1)} = Az^{(0)} = \sum_i \alpha_i Ax_i = \sum_i \alpha_i \lambda_i x_i$$

$$y^{(2)} = Az^{(1)} = A\frac{y^{(1)}}{k^{(1)}} = \frac{1}{k^{(1)}} \sum_i \alpha_i \lambda_i Ax_i = \frac{1}{k^{(1)}} \sum_i \alpha_i \lambda_i^2 x_i$$

Repeating this process we get,

$$y^{(p+1)} = Az^{(p)} = \frac{1}{\prod_j^p k^{(j)}} \sum_i \alpha_i \lambda_i^{p+1} x_i$$

Factoring the largest eigenvalue, λ_1,

$$y^{(p+1)} = Az^{(p)} = \frac{\lambda_1^{p+1}}{\prod_j^p k^{(j)}} \sum_i \alpha_i \left(\frac{\lambda_i}{\lambda_1}\right)^{p+1} x_i$$

Since $(\lambda_i/\lambda_1) < 1$ for $i > 1$ only the first term in the summation survives as $p \rightarrow \infty$. Thus $y^{(p)} \rightarrow x_1$, the eigenvector corresponding to the largest eigenvalue.

Several other features also become evident from the above analysis.

- The convergence rate will be faster, if the largest eigenvalue is well separated from the remaining eigenvalues.

- If the largest eigenvalue occurs with a multiplicity of two, then the above sequence will not converge, or rather converge to a subspace spanned by the eigenvectors corresponding to the eigenvalues that occur with multiplicity.

- If the initial guess vector does not contain any component in the direction of x_1, then the sequence will converge to the next largest eigenvalue. This can be acheived by making the guess vector, $z^{(0)}$, orthogonal to the known eigenvector, x_1.

```
function [Rayleigh_Q,V] = Power(T,MaxIt)
%Power iteration to find the largest e.value of T

if nargin < 2,
   MaxIt = 100;
end

n=length(T);              %Find the size of T
z_old=rand(n,1);          %Generate random vector, z
z_new=z_old/norm(z_old);  %Scale it
Check_sign=1; count = 0;  %Initialize
while (norm(z_old-z_new) > 1.e-10 & count < MaxIt),
   count = count + 1;
   z_old=z_new*Check_sign;
   z_new=T*z_new;
   z_new=z_new/norm(z_new);
   Check_sign=sign((z_new'*(T*z_new))/(z_new'*z_new));
end
if (count >= MaxIt)
   error('Power iteration failed to converge')
end
%Compute the Rayliegh quotient
V=z_new;
Rayleigh_Q=(z_new'*(T*z_new))/(z_new'*z_new);
```

Figure 3.9: MATLAB implementation of power iteration

3.10.4   Inverse iteration

To find the smallest eigenvalue of a given a matrix A, the power iteration could still be applied, but on the inverse of matrix A. Consider the original eigenvalue problem

$$A x_i = \lambda_i x_i.$$

Premultiply by A^{-1} to get,

$$A^{-1} A x_i = \lambda_i A^{-1} x_i$$

which can be rewritten as,

$$\frac{1}{\lambda_i} x_i = A^{-1} x_i.$$

Hence it is clear that the eigenvalues, μ_i of A^{-1} viz.

$$\mu_i x_i = A^{-1} x_i$$

are related to eigenvalues, λ_i of A through,

$$\lambda_i = \frac{1}{\mu_i}.$$

Although the illustration below uses the inverse of the matrix, in reality there is no need to find A^{-1} since power iteration only requires computation of a new vector y from a given vector z using,

$$y^{(p+1)} = A^{-1} z^{(p)}.$$

This can be done most effectively by solving the linear system

$$A y^{(p+1)} = z^{(p)}$$

using LU factorization, which needs to be done only once.

3.10.5 Shift-Inverse iteration

To find the eigenvalue closest to a selected point, σ, the power iteration could be applied to the matrix $(A - \sigma I)^{-1}$, which is equivalent to solving the eigenvalue problem

$$(A - \sigma I)^{-1} x_i = \mu_i x_i.$$

This can be rewritten as,

$$\frac{1}{\mu_i} x_i = (A - \sigma I) x_i = A x_i - \sigma x_i = (\lambda_i - \sigma) x_i.$$

Hence it is clear that the eigenvalues, μ_i of $(A - \sigma I)^{-1}$ are related to eigenvalues, λ_i of A through,

$$\lambda_i = \frac{1}{\mu_i} + \sigma.$$

As in the previous section, there is no need to find the inverse since power iteration only requires computation of a new vector y from a given vector z using,

$$y^{(p+1)} = (A - \sigma I)^{-1} z^{(p)}.$$

This can be done most effectively by solving the linear system

$$(A - \sigma I)y^{(p+1)} = z^{(p)}$$

using LU factorization of $(A - \sigma I)$, which needs to be done only once.

EXAMPLE 3.17 *Determine the largest and smallest eigenvalues of the matrix T defined below using the power iteration.*

$$T = \begin{bmatrix} 2 & -1 & 0 & 0 \\ -2 & 2 & -1 & 0 \\ 0 & -2 & 2 & -1 \\ 0 & 0 & -2 & 2 \end{bmatrix}$$

A typical MATLAB session follows.

```
>> T=trid(2,-1,-2,4)    %generate the matrix

T =

        2       -1        0        0
       -2        2       -1        0
        0       -2        2       -1
        0        0       -2        2

>>[d,v]=ch3_poweri(T) %apply power iteration
```

```
d =

    4.2882

v =

   -0.2012
    0.4603
   -0.6510
    0.5690

>>max(eig(T)) %Find the largest e-value from ``eig'' function

ans =

    4.2882

%Find the smallest e. value
>>mu=ch3_poweri(inv(T));
>>lambda=1/mu

lambda =

   -0.2882
>>min(eig(T))

ans =

   -0.2882

>>%Find the e.value closest to 2.5
>>sigma=2.5;
>>mu=ch3_poweri(inv(T-sigma*eye(4)))

mu =

    2.6736

>>lambda=sigma+1/mu

lambda =

    2.8740
%verfiy using ``eig''
>>eig(T)

ans =
```

```
-0.2882
 4.2882
 2.8740
 1.1260
```

3.11 Summary

In this chapter, we have developed methods for efficiently solving systems of linear algebraic equations. We have reviewed matrix operations and special matrices and introduced vector and matrix norms for use to understand matrix ill conditioning and susceptibility of matrices to round of errors. The direct methods for dealing with matrices including Cramer's method, Gauss elimination and LU factorization are discussed. Iterative solution schemes and their convergence characteristics are also introduced and analysed.

Convergence of linear iterative schemes using eigenvalue analysis has carried out. Finally, we have also developed the Gram-Schmidt process, which can generate an orthonormal set from a linearly independent set.

3.12 Exercise Problems

P3.1. Matrix determinant, condition and norm.

Consider the following matrix

$$A = \begin{bmatrix} 4 & -1 & 2 \\ 4 & -8 & 2 \\ -2 & 1 & 6 \end{bmatrix}$$

Determine

(a) the determinant of the matrix A.

(b) the inverse of the matrix A.

(c) the condition number $cond(A)$ using column sum norm.

P3.2. Matrix condition

A continuous function is to be approximated using a fourth degree polynomial. This can be done by calculating the following linear system:

$$Hx = b$$

where H is the Hilbert matrix defined as

$$H_{i,j} = \frac{1}{i + j - 1}$$

and b is given by

$$b = b1 = [4.0000; 2.8400; 2.2514; 1.8771; 1.6140]$$

(a) Calculate the condition of H based on the ∞ norm.

(b) Solve the linear system.

(c) If new measurements are made such that $b = b2 = [4.009; 2.8402; 2.2512; 1.8773; 1.6142]$, solve for the new system.

(d) Compute $\frac{||\delta b||}{||b||}$ and $\frac{||\delta x||}{||x||}$

(e) How does the small pertubation in the measurements impact the solution? Explain.

P3.3. Consider the system

$$H = \begin{bmatrix} 1 & 1/2 & 1/3 \\ 1/2 & 1/3 & 1/4 \\ 1/3 & 1/4 & 1/5 \end{bmatrix} ; b = \begin{bmatrix} 1 \\ -1 \\ 1 \end{bmatrix}$$

where H is Hilbert matrix which is severely ill- conditioned. Solve the system using

(a) Gauss-Jordan elimination.

(b) exact computations.

(c) rounding off each number to 3 figures.

Perform 3 iterations each by

(a) Jacobi method.

(b) Gauss- Seidel method.

(c) Successive over-relaxation method with $\omega = 1.6$.

Use initial guess $x^{(0)} = [111]^T$ and compare in each case how close to the $x^{(3)}$ is to the exact solution. (Use 2-norm for comparison).

P3.4. Consider the following system of linear equations

$$
\begin{aligned}
x_1 - x_2 + 2x_3 + x_4 &= 7 \\
2x_1 - 4x_2 + x_3 + 3x_4 &= 10 \\
-x_1 + 3x_2 - 4x_3 + 2x_4 &= -14 \\
2x_1 + 4x_2 + 3x_3 - 2x_4 &= 1
\end{aligned}
$$

Solve the above problem using

(a) Cramer's rule.

(b) Naive Gauss elimination.

(c) Gauss- Jordan elimination.

(d) Crout LU factorization.

P3.5. Solve the following system of equations using Gauss Seidel method

$$
\begin{aligned}
12x_1 + x_2 + 7x_3 &= 27 \\
x_1 + 12x_2 + 3x_3 &= -24 \\
7x_1 + 3x_2 + 12x_3 &= 3
\end{aligned}
$$

P3.6. Consider the following system of tridiagonal equations

$$2x_1 + x_2 = 4$$
$$x_1 + 2x_2 + x_3 = 8$$
$$x_2 + 2x_3 + x_4 = 12$$
$$+x_3 + 2x_4 = 11$$

Solve the above problem using

(a) Thomas algorithm.

(b) Jacobi iteration.

(c) Gauss- Seidel iteration.

(d) SOR mthod with $\omega = 1.3$.

P3.7. Consider the following system of tridiagonal equations

$$\begin{bmatrix} 3 & 2 & 0 & 0 \\ 2 & 3 & 2 & 0 \\ 0 & 2 & 3 & 2 \\ 0 & 0 & 2 & 3 \end{bmatrix} \begin{bmatrix} x_1 \\ x_2 \\ x_3 \\ x_4 \end{bmatrix} = \begin{bmatrix} 12 \\ 17 \\ 14 \\ 7 \end{bmatrix}$$

Solve the above problem using

(a) Jacobi iteration.

(b) Gauss- Seidel iteration.

(c) SOR mthod with $\omega = 1.4$.

P3.8. It is desired to solve the system $\boldsymbol{Ax} = \boldsymbol{b}$ where $\boldsymbol{A}$ is given by:

$$\boldsymbol{A} = \begin{bmatrix} 1 & 2 & 3 \\ 2 & 1 & 4 \\ 3 & 1 & 5 \end{bmatrix} ; \boldsymbol{A} = \begin{bmatrix} 2 & 4 & -4 \\ 2 & 2 & 2 \\ 3 & 3 & 1 \end{bmatrix}$$

If Jacobi and Gauss-Seidel iteration schemes are used, will the converge? Justify your answers.

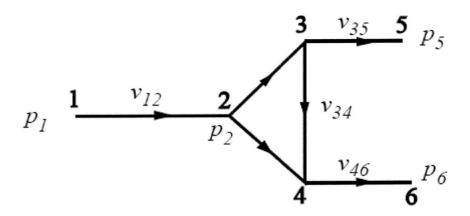

Figure 3.10: Laminar flow in a pipe network

P3.9. Consider the following system

$$A = \begin{bmatrix} 1 & 1 + \epsilon \\ 1 & 1 \end{bmatrix}$$

Calculate A^{-1} and $det(A)$ for different values of $\epsilon = 0.01, 0.001$ and 0.0001.

P3.10. Laminar flow through a pipeline network

Consider laminar flow through the network shown in figure 4.3. The governing equations are the pressure drop equations for each pipe element $i - j$ and the mass balance equation at each node.

The pressure drop between nodes i and j is given by,

$$p_i - p_j = \alpha_{ij} v_{ij} \qquad \text{where} \qquad \alpha_{ij} = \frac{32\mu l_{ij}}{d_{ij}^2} \quad (3.18)$$

The mass balance at node 2 is given, for example by,

$$d_{12}^2 v_{12} = d_{23}^2 v_{23} + d_{24}^2 v_{24} \qquad (3.19)$$

Similar equations apply at nodes **3** and **4**. Let the unknown vector be

$$\underline{x} = \begin{bmatrix} p_2 & p_3 & p_4 & v_{12} & v_{23} & v_{24} & v_{34} & v_{35} & v_{46} \end{bmatrix}$$

There will be six momentum balance equations, one for each pipe element, and three mass balance (for incompressible fluids volume balance) equations, one at each node. Arrange them as a system of nine equations in nine unknowns and solve the resulting set of equations. Take the viscosity of the fluid, $\mu = 0.1 Pa \cdot s$. The dimensions of the pipes are given below.

Table 1

Element no	12	23	24	34	35	46
d_{ij} (m)	0.1	0.08	0.08	0.10	0.09	0.09
l_{ij} (m)	1000	800	800	900	1000	1000

a) Use MATLAB to solve this problem for the specified pressures of $p_1 = 300 kPa$ and $p_5 = p_6 = 100 kPa$. You need to assemble the system of equations in the form $\boldsymbol{A}\,\boldsymbol{x} = \boldsymbol{b}$. Report the time for each execution. When reporting the time, report only for that particular operation - *i.e.*, initialize the counter using `tic` before every operation.

- Compute the determinant of $\boldsymbol{A}$.
- Compute the $\boldsymbol{LU}$ factor of $\boldsymbol{A}$ using built-in function `lu`. Report the time. What is the structure of $\boldsymbol{L}$?

Explain. The function `LU` provided in the lecture notes will fail on this matrix. Why?

- Compute the solution using `inv(A)*b`.
- Compute the rank of A.

b) Find out the new velocity and pressure distributions when p_6 is changed to $150kPa$.

c) Suppose the forcing (column) vector in part (a) is $b1$ and that in part (b) is $b2$, report and explain the difference in time for the following two ways of obtaining the two solutions using the sparse matrix. Note that in the first case both solutions are obtained simultaneously.

> $b = [b1, b2];\text{tic};x = S\backslash b,\text{toc}$
> $\text{tic};x1 = S\backslash b1, x2 = S\backslash b2,\text{toc}$

Repeat the above experiment with the full matrix, A and report the execution time.

d) Comment on how you would adopt the above problem formulation if a valve on line **34** is shut so that there is no flow in that line **34**.

P3.11. The equations governing conduction heat transfer through a fin can be discretized to get a tridiagonal system. Consider the case with $N = 4$, so that there are five equations in the form $Ax = b$ as given below.

$$\begin{bmatrix} d & 1 & 0 & 0 & 0 \\ 1 & d & 1 & 0 & 0 \\ 0 & 1 & d & 1 & 0 \\ 0 & 0 & 1 & d & 1 \\ 0 & 0 & 0 & 2 & d \end{bmatrix} \begin{bmatrix} \theta_1 \\ \theta_2 \\ \theta_3 \\ \theta_4 \\ \theta_5 \end{bmatrix} = \begin{bmatrix} -1 \\ 0 \\ 0 \\ 0 \\ 0 \end{bmatrix}$$

Here, $d = -(2 + (mL)^2 h^2)$ is the diagonal element. Use $mL = 1$. Do the following using MATLAB. Feel free to use the *help* command with each of the ***MATLAB*** functions to find out about their syntax and usage.

a) Solve the system of equations using the matrix inverse function, ***inv***

b) Solve the system using left matrix division $A \backslash b'$

c) compute the determinant of A using the function ***det***.

d) Find the ***LU*** factors of A using the function ***lu***.

e) Compute the product of the determinants of L and U and verify that it is the same as in (c).

f) Find the rank of A using the function ***rank***.

g) Verify that $inv(A) * A = I$

h) Calculate the *eigenvalues* of A using the function ***eig***.

i) Find the *characteristic polynomial* of A using the function ***poly***.

j) Calculate the *roots of the characteristic polynomial* of A using the function ***roots*** and verify that they are the same as the eigenvalues of A.

P3.12. The following equations have been obtained in the analysis of an engineering system

$$3x_1 - x_2 - x_4 = -3$$
$$-x_1 + 3x_2 - x_3 = 2$$
$$-x_2 + 4x_3 - x_4 = 6$$
$$-x_1 - x_3 + 4x_4 = 12$$

Solve the above problem using

(a) Gauss elimination.

(b) Jacobi method.

(c) Gauss- Seidel method.

(d) SOR method.

(e) the Matlab backslash operator.

(f) Matlab built function using inv(A) * b

Compare the CPU execution time and/or the number of iterations required for each method

P3.13. Reactor system

The following system of equations is designed to determine the conncentration C in a series of coupled reactors as the function of the amount of mass input to each reactor

$$
\begin{aligned}
20C_1 - C_2 - C_3 &= 424 \\
-5C_1 + 21C_2 - 2C_3 &= 200 \\
-5C_1 - 5C_2 + 22C_3 &= -24
\end{aligned}
$$

(a) set up the problem in matrix form

(b) perform 2 iterations of the Jacobi method (by hand). Verify that the Jacobi method will converge by computing the spectral radius.

(c) perform two iterations of the Gauss-Seidel method

(d) Perform two iterations of the SOR method with $\omega = 1.5$.

(e) Solve the problem using MATLAB and any method of your choice.

P3.14. Equilibrium stage process for extraction

The mass balance for a stage extraction process can be written as follows:

$$
P_1 y_{i-1} + P_2 x_{i+1} = P_1 y_i + P_2 x_i
$$

When equilibrium has been established, we can write

$$x_i = Ky_i$$

where K is the distribution coefficient. The two equations can be combined to yield:

$$y_{i-1} - \left(1 + \frac{P_2}{P_1}K\right)y_i + \frac{P_2}{P_1}Kx_{i+1} = 0$$

If $P_1 = 500kg/h$, $P_2 = 900kg/h$, $x_{in} = 0$, $y_{in} = 0.1$ and $K = 4$, determine the values of x_{out} and y_{out} for a five stage separation system.

(a) Clearly set up the system matrix and the right hand side vector

(b) Solve the problem using the Jacobi method and calculate the spectral radius.

(c) Solve the problem using the Gauss-Seidel method.

P3.15. Balancing chemical reactions

Background on chemical reactions as matrix equations

Consider the following chemical reaction

$$O_2 + 2H_2 \rightarrow 2H_2O \tag{3.20}$$

where each atom balance can be written in a matrix form as

$$\begin{matrix} O: \\ H: \end{matrix} \begin{bmatrix} 2 \\ 0 \end{bmatrix} \begin{bmatrix} 0 \\ 4 \end{bmatrix} \begin{bmatrix} 2 \\ 4 \end{bmatrix}$$

this can be represented as a matrix equation

$$\sum \nu_i A_i = 0 \tag{3.21}$$

where ν_i are the stoichiometric coeffciients (negative for products and positive for reactants) and A_i the specie molecules present. We can therefore write reaction 3.20 in the form of 3.21 as:

$$-1O_2 - 2H_2 + 2H_2O = 0$$

rewriting the molecular formulae with the corresponding matrices

$$-1\begin{bmatrix} 2 \\ 0 \end{bmatrix} - 2\begin{bmatrix} 0 \\ 4 \end{bmatrix} + 2\begin{bmatrix} 2 \\ 4 \end{bmatrix} = \begin{bmatrix} 0 \\ 0 \end{bmatrix}$$

which can be written in matrix form as

$$\begin{bmatrix} 2 & 0 & 2 \\ 0 & 4 & 4 \end{bmatrix} \begin{bmatrix} -1 \\ -2 \\ 2 \end{bmatrix} = \begin{bmatrix} 0 \\ 0 \end{bmatrix}$$

which can be writen in compact form as

$$A\nu = 0$$

which is a null matrix. By solving the null matrix equation we can obtain the stoichimetric coefficients and therefor balance the chemical reactions.

Problem - Balancing chemical reactions

The catalytic hydrgenation of carbon monoxide to methane (also called the Sabatier reaction) is an important reaction which could have future applicatins in astronaut life support systems in manned space colonization adventures. The process is described as:

$$CO_2 + H_2 \Rightarrow CH_4 + H_2O$$

Determine the smallest positive integer to balance the equation.

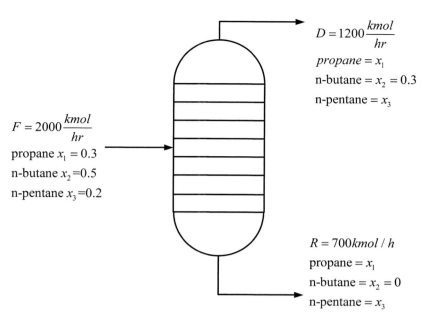

Figure 3.11: Distillation column for problem **P3.16**.

P3.16. Distillation unit

A hydrocarbon feed consisting of a mixture of propane, nbutane and isopentane is fractionated at a rate of 2000 kmol/hr int a distillate which contains 70% of all the propane in the feed. The mol fraction of nbutane in the distilatte is 0.3. Given that the output rate from the distilate is 1400 kmol/hr and feed from the bottom is 600 kmol/hr, determine the concentrations of the components in the leaving streams.

P3.17. Distillation train

Based on the figure below, find the mass flow rates P,Q and R from column outlets.

P3.18. Grahm-Schmidt procedure

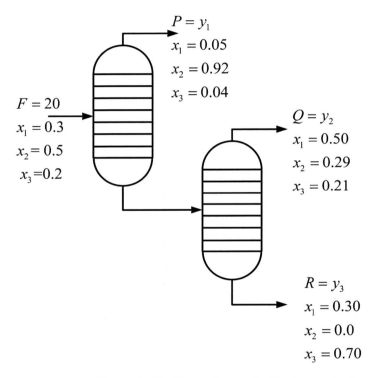

Figure 3.12: Two column distillation train for problem **P3.17**.

Consider the vectors

$$x_1 = [1234] \qquad (3.22)$$
$$x_2 = [1212] \qquad (3.23)$$
$$x_3 = [2131] \qquad (3.24)$$
$$x_4 = [2154] \qquad (3.25)$$

- Check if they form a linearly independent set.
- Construct an orthonormal set using the Grahm-Schmidt procedure.

P3.19. Power iteration

Consider the matrix, A given below.

A =

```
2.0 + 4.0i  -1.0 - 2.0i        0              0
-2.0 - 4.0i   2.0 + 4.0i   -1.0 - 2.0i        0
     0       -2.0 - 4.0i    2.0 + 4.0i   -1.0 - 2.0i
     0            0        -2.0 - 4.0i    2.0 + 4.0i
```

Use the power iteration algorithmn given in Fig. 3.9 to solve the following problems.

- Find the largest eigenvalue. [Ans: 4.2882 + 8.5765i]
- Find the smallest eigenvalue. [Ans: -0.2882 - 0.5765i]
- Find the eigenvalue closest to $\sigma = (1 + 2i)$. [Ans: 1.1260 + 2.2519i]

Let knowledge grow from more to more, But more of reverence in us dwell; That mind and soul, according well, May make one music as before.

— ALFRED TENNYSON

CHAPTER 4

SYSTEMS OF NONLINEAR ALGEBRAIC EQUATIONS

In this chapter we extend the concepts developed in Chapter 2 - viz. finding the roots of a system of nonlinear algebraic *equations* of the form,

$$\boldsymbol{f}(\boldsymbol{x}) = \boldsymbol{0} \tag{4.1}$$

where $\boldsymbol{f}(\boldsymbol{x})$ is a vector function of $\boldsymbol{x}$ - *i.e.*, there are n equations which can be written in expanded or component form as,

$$f_1(x_1, x_2, \cdots, x_n) = 0$$

$$f_2(x_1, x_2, \cdots, x_n) = 0$$

$$\cdots$$

$$f_n(x_1, x_2, \cdots, x_n) = 0$$

As with the scalar case, the equation is satisfied only at selected values of $\boldsymbol{x} = \boldsymbol{r} = [r_1, r_2, \cdots, r_n]$, called the *roots*. The separation process model discussed in section §1.3.1 (variations 2 and 3, in particular) and the reaction sequence model of section §1.3.5 are two of the many examples in chemical engineering that give rise to such non-linear system of equations. As with the scalar case, the equations often depend on other parameters, and we will represent them as

$$f(x; p) = 0 \qquad (4.2)$$

where p represents a set of known parameter values. In such cases it may be required to construct solution families for ranges of values of p - *i.e.*, $x(p)$. This task is most efficiently achieved using continuation methods.

4.1 Newton's method

For a scalar equation a geometrical interpretation of the Newton scheme is easy to develop as shown in figure 2.2d. This is difficult to visualize for higher dimensional systems. The algorithm developed in section §2.5 can, however, be generalized easily to higher dimensional systems. The basic concept of linearizing a nonlinear function remains the same as with a scalar case. We need to make use of the multivariate form of the Taylor series expansion. We will illustrate the concepts with a two-dimensional system of equations written in component form as,

$$f_1(x_1, x_2) = 0$$

$$f_2(x_1, x_2) = 0$$

Thus the vectors $f(x) = [f_1(x_1, x_2), f_2(x_1, x_2)]$ and $x = [x_1, x_2]$ contain two elements. Let the *roots* be represented by $r = [r_1, r_2]$ - *i.e.*, $f(r) = 0$.

Suppose $x^{(0)}$ be some known *initial guess* for the solution vector x and let the root be at a small displacement δ from $x^{(0)}$ - *i.e.*,

$$r = x^{(0)} + \delta$$

If we can device a scheme to estimate δ then we can apply such a scheme repeatedly to get closer to the root r. Variations in the function value $f_1(x_1, x_2)$ can be caused by variations in either components x_1 or x_2. Recognizing this, a bi-variate Taylor series expansion around $\boldsymbol{x}^{(0)}$ can be written as,

$$f_1(x_1^{(0)} + \delta_1, x_2^{(0)} + \delta_2) = f_1(x_1^{(0)}, x_2^{(0)}) +$$

$$\underbrace{\left.\frac{\partial f_1}{\partial x_1}\right|_{[x_1^{(0)}, x_2^{(0)}]} \delta_1}_{\text{variation due to } x_1} + \underbrace{\left.\frac{\partial f_1}{\partial x_2}\right|_{[x_1^{(0)}, x_2^{(0)}]} \delta_2}_{\text{variation due to } x_2} + \mathcal{O}(\boldsymbol{\delta}^2)$$

$$f_2(x_1^{(0)} + \delta_1, x_2^{(0)} + \delta_2) = f_2(x_1^{(0)}, x_2^{(0)}) +$$

$$\underbrace{\left.\frac{\partial f_2}{\partial x_1}\right|_{[x_1^{(0)}, x_2^{(0)}]} \delta_1}_{\text{variation due to } x_1} + \underbrace{\left.\frac{\partial f_2}{\partial x_2}\right|_{[x_1^{(0)}, x_2^{(0)}]} \delta_2}_{\text{variation due to } x_2} + \mathcal{O}(\boldsymbol{\delta}^2)$$

Since $\boldsymbol{\delta}$ is supposed to be small, we can neglect higher order terms $\mathcal{O}(\boldsymbol{\delta}^2)$ in the above equations and this step is the essence of the linearization process. Since $\boldsymbol{x}^{(0)} + \boldsymbol{\delta} = \boldsymbol{r}$ and $\boldsymbol{f}(\boldsymbol{r}) = \boldsymbol{0}$, the left hand sides of the above equations are zero. Thus we get,

$$0 = f_1(x_1^{(0)}, x_2^{(0)}) + \left.\frac{\partial f_1}{\partial x_1}\right|_{[x_1^{(0)}, x_2^{(0)}]} \delta_1 + \left.\frac{\partial f_1}{\partial x_2}\right|_{[x_1^{(0)}, x_2^{(0)}]} \delta_2$$

$$0 = f_2(x_1^{(0)}, x_2^{(0)}) + \left.\frac{\partial f_2}{\partial x_1}\right|_{[x_1^{(0)}, x_2^{(0)}]} \delta_1 + \left.\frac{\partial f_2}{\partial x_2}\right|_{[x_1^{(0)}, x_2^{(0)}]} \delta_2$$

These are two linear equations in two unknowns $[\delta_1, \delta_2]$. Note that the two functions $[f_1, f_2]$ and their four partial derivatives are required to be evaluated at the guess value of $[x_1^{(0)}, x_2^{(0)}]$. The above equations can be arranged into matrix form as,

$$\begin{bmatrix} 0 \\ 0 \end{bmatrix} = \begin{bmatrix} f_1 \\ f_2 \end{bmatrix} + \begin{bmatrix} \frac{\partial f_1}{\partial x_1} & \frac{\partial f_1}{\partial x_2} \\ \frac{\partial f_2}{\partial x_1} & \frac{\partial f_2}{\partial x_2} \end{bmatrix} \begin{bmatrix} \delta_1 \\ \delta_2 \end{bmatrix}$$

or in symbolic form

$$\boldsymbol{0} = \boldsymbol{f}^{(0)} + \boldsymbol{J}^{(0)} \boldsymbol{\delta}$$

where $J^{(0)}$ is called the Jacobian matrix and the superscript is a reminder that quantities are evaluated using the current guess value of $x^{(0)}$. Thus, the displacement vector δ is obtained by solving the linear system,

$$\delta = -J^{-1}f$$

In general then, given $x^{(0)}$, the algorithm consists of (i) evaluating the function and the Jacobian at the current iterate $x^{(k)}$, (ii) solving the linear system for the displacement vector $\delta^{(k)}$ and (iii) finding the new estimate for the iterate $x^{(k+1)}$ from the equations

$$\delta^{(k)} = -[J^{(k)}]^{-1}f^{(k)} \qquad x^{(k+1)} = x^{(k)} + \delta^{(k)} \qquad k = 0, 1, \cdots$$

$$(4.3)$$

Convergence check

The final step is to check if we are close enough to the desired root r so that we can terminate the iteration. One test might be to check if the absolute difference between two successive values of x is smaller than a specified tolerance. This can be done by computing the norm of δ

$$||\delta|| \le \epsilon$$

Another test might be to check if the absolute value of the function f at the end of every iteration is below a certain tolerance. Since we are dealing with vectors, once again a norm of f must be calculated.

$$||f|| \le \epsilon$$

In addition to the above convergence tests, we might wish to place a limit on the number of times the iteration is repeated. A MATLAB function, constructed in the form of a *m-file*, is shown in figure 4.1. Note that this MATLAB function requires an initial

guess as well as two external functions for computing the function
values and the Jacobian.

```
function x=newton(Fun,Jac,x,tol,trace)
% Newton method for a system of nonlinear  equations
%       Fun   - name of the external function to compute f
%       Jac   - name of the externan function to compute J
%       x     - vector of initial guesses
%       tol   - error criterion
%       trace - print intermediate results
%
%    Usage   newton('Fun','Jac',x)

%Check inputs
if nargin < 5, trace=0; end
if nargin < 4, tol=eps; trace=0; end

max=25;
n=length(x);
count=0;
f=1;

while (norm(f)  > tol & count < max), %check convergence
  f = feval(Fun,x);       %evaluate the function
  J = feval(Jac,x);       %evaluate Jacobian
  x = x -J\f;             %update the guess
  count=count+1;
  if trace,
    fprintf(1,'Iter.# = %3i  Resid = %12.5e\n', count,norm(f));
  end
end

if (count >= max)
 fprintf(1,'Maximum iteration %3i exceeded\n',count)
 fprintf(1,'Residual is %12.5e\n ',norm(f) )
end
```

Figure 4.1: MATLAB implementation of Newton scheme

EXAMPLE 4.1 (Reactors in series) *This example is from section §1.3.5 and consists of a system of nonlinear equations that model a series of continuously stirred tank reactors. A sketch is shown in figure 1.6*

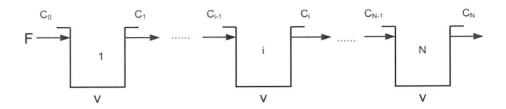

Recall that the model equations are given by,

$$f_i := \beta C_i^2 + C_i - C_{i-1} = 0 \qquad i = 1 \cdots n \qquad (4.4)$$

As discussed in section §1.3.5, there are n equations and $(n + 2)$ variables in total. Hence we have two degrees of freedom. We consider a design situation where inlet and outlet concentrations are specified as, say, $C_0 = 5.0, C_n = 0.5$ mol/lit. The unknown vector consists of n variable elements,

$$x = \{C_1, C_2 \cdots C_{n-1}, \beta\}$$

We are required to determine the volume of each reactor for a given number n. The volume is given by the expression $\beta = kV/F$. The rate constant is $k = 0.125$ lit/(mol min) and the feed rate is $F = 25$ lit/min. In solving the above equations we are primarily interested in β, but we also get all of the intermediate concentrations. Before we can invoke the algorithm of figure 4.1 we need to write two functions for evaluation the function values and the Jacobian.

The Jacobian is given by,

$$
J = \begin{bmatrix}
\frac{\partial f_1}{\partial x_1} & 0 & 0 & \cdots & \frac{\partial f_1}{\partial x_n} \\
\frac{\partial f_2}{\partial x_1} & \frac{\partial f_2}{\partial x_2} & 0 & \cdots & \frac{\partial f_2}{\partial x_n} \\
0 & \frac{\partial f_3}{\partial x_2} & \frac{\partial f_3}{\partial x_3} & \cdots & \frac{\partial f_3}{\partial x_n} \\
\vdots & 0 & \ddots & \ddots & \vdots \\
0 & \cdots & 0 & \frac{\partial f_n}{\partial x_{n-1}} & \frac{\partial f_n}{\partial x_n}
\end{bmatrix}
$$

$$
= \begin{bmatrix}
2x_n x_1 + 1 & 0 & 0 & \cdots & x_1^2 \\
-1 & 2x_n x_2 + 1 & 0 & \cdots & x_2^2 \\
0 & -1 & 2x_n x_3 + 1 & \cdots & x_3^2 \\
\vdots & 0 & \ddots & \ddots & \vdots \\
0 & \cdots & 0 & -1 & a_n^2
\end{bmatrix} \quad (4.5)
$$

```
function f=cstrF(x)
% Reactor in series model, the function
% x=[C(1),C(2), .., C(n-1),beta]
% f(i) = beta C(i)^2 + C(i) - C(i-1)
n=length(x);
C0=5.0; Cn=0.5;  %define parameters in equation
f(1) = x(n)*x(1)^2 + x(1) - C0;
for i = 2:n-1
 f(i)= x(n)*x(i)^2 + x(i) - x(i-1);
end
f(n) = x(n)*Cn^2 + Cn - x(n-1);
f=f';

function J=cstrJ(x)
% Reactor in series model, the Jacobian
% x=[C(1),C(2), .., C(n-1),beta]
n=length(x);
C0=5.0; Cn=0.5;  %define parameters in equation
J(1,1) = x(n)*2*x(1) + 1;
J(1,n) = x(1)^2;
for i = 2:n-1
 J(i,i) = x(n)*2*x(i) + 1;
 J(i,i-1) = -1;
 J(i,n) = x(i)^2;
end
J(n,n) = Cn^2;
J(n,n-1) = -1;
```

Figure 4.2: CSTR in series example - function & Jacobian evaluation

The MATLAB functions to compute the function in equation (4.4) and the Jacobian in equation (4.5) are shown in figure 4.2. Work through the following example after ensuring that the three m-files `newton.m`, `cstrF.m` *and* `cstrJ.m` *are the MATLAB search path.*

```
>>x=[1 .5 .2 .1 0]'            % Initial guess for n=5
>>r=newton('cstrF','cstrJ',x,1.e-10,1) % call Newton scheme
Iter.# = 1 Resid = 4.06325e+00
Iter.# = 2 Resid = 1.25795e+01
Iter.# = 3 Resid = 2.79982e+00
Iter.# = 4 Resid = 4.69658e-01
Iter.# = 5 Resid = 2.41737e-01
Iter.# = 6 Resid = 4.74318e-03
Iter.# = 7 Resid = 1.61759e-06
Iter.# = 8 Resid = 1.25103e-12

r =

    2.2262
    1.2919
    0.8691
    0.6399
    0.5597

>>V=r(5)*25/.125              % compute V (ans:111.9427)
>>x=[1:-.1:.1]'               % repeat solution for n=10
>>r=newton('cstrF','cstrJ',x,1.e-10,1) % call Newton scheme
>>V=r(10)*25/.125             % compute V (ans:44.9859)
```

In the above example, observe first that the number of reactors is defined implicitly by the length of the vector x. Secondly observe the quadratic convergence of the iteration sequence - viz. the residual goes down from 10^{-3} in iteration number 6 to 10^{-6} in iteration number 7 and 10^{-12} in iteration number 8. In other words the number of significant digits of accuracy doubles with every iteration once the iteration reaches close to the root.

EXAMPLE 4.2 *The trajectories of two comets are given by* $x^2 +$
$2x + 2y^2 = 26$ *and* $x^3 - y^2 + 4*y - 19$ *respectively. Using MATLAB*
built in function FSOLVE to determine the point where the comets
will colide. Start with an initial guess of $[1, 1]$
Define the function

```
function F = fun(x)
F(1) = x(1)^2 + 2*x(1) + 2*x(2)^2 - 26;
F(2) = x(1)^3 - x(2)^2 + 4*x(2) - 19;
end


Solve


>> X = fsolve(@fun,[1,1])


X =

    2.4943    2.7194
```

4.2 summary

In this chapter, we have extended the concepts of solving non-linear equations for single equations to multiple non-linear equations. The Newton method is well suited for this task. Other techniques for non-linear equatins such as the fixed point iteration method may also be used for multiple equations.

MATLAB has a built in function for solving nonlinear function of several variables, namely FSOLVE. It is easy to implement and will calculate the Jacobian internally.

4.3   Exercise Problems

P4.1. Non linear equations

The trajectories of two comets are given by $x^2 + 2x + 2y^2 = 26$ and $x^3 - y^2 + 4y - 19$ respectively. Using Newtons method to determine the point where the comets will colide. Start with an initial guess of $[1, 1]$. Carry out two iterations.

P4.2. Determine the point of intersection for two curves given by

$$
\begin{aligned}
f(x, y) &= & x^4 + 2x + xy - 5 \\
g(x, y) &= & x^3 - 8y^2 + 10y - 11
\end{aligned}
$$

Carry out two Newton's iterations with an initial guess of $[0, 0]$.

P4.3. Turbulent flow through a pipeline network

Consider turbulent flow through the network shown in figure 4.3. The governing equations are the pressure drop equations for each pipe element $i - j$ and the mass balance equation at each node. The pressure drop between nodes i and j is given by,

$$
p_i - p_j = \alpha_{ij} v_{ij}^2 \qquad \text{where} \qquad \alpha_{ij} = \frac{2 f \rho l_{ij}}{d_{ij}^2} \qquad (4.5)
$$

In general the friction factor f is given by the Moody chart or its equivalent Churchill correlation. In fully developed turbulent flow it is relatively insensitive to changes in Re. Hence take it to be a constant $f = 0.005$.

The unknown vector is,

$$
\underline{x} = [p_2 \ p_3 \ p_4 \ v_{12} \ v_{23} \ v_{24} \ v_{34} \ v_{35} \ v_{46}]
$$

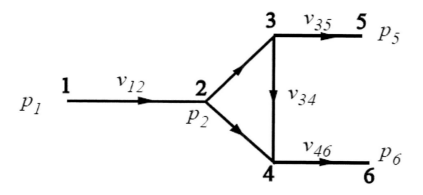

Figure 4.3: Pipe network

There will be six momentum balance equations, one for each pipe element, and three mass balance (for incompressible fluids volume balance) equations, one at each node. Arrange them as a system of nine equations in nine unknowns and solve the resulting set of equations. Take the viscosity of the fluid, $\mu = 0.1 Pa \cdot s$ and the density as $\rho = 1000 kg/m^3$. The dimensions of the pipes are given below.

Table 1

Element no	12	23	24	34	35	46
d_{ij} (m)	0.1	0.08	0.08	0.10	0.09	0.09
l_{ij} (m)	1000	800	800	900	1000	1000

a) Use MATLAB to solve this problem using Newton method for the specified pressures of $p_1 = 300kPa$ and $p_5 = p_6 = 100kPa$. Report the number of iterations.

b) Implement the Jacobi iteration to solve this problem. Report the number of iterations.

c) Implement the Gauss-Seidel iteration to solve this problem. Report the number of iterations.

d) Implement the Successive-relaxation iteration to solve this problem. Report the number of iterations.

e) Find out the new velocity and pressure distributions when p_6 is changed to $150 kPa$.

f) Comment on how you would adopt the above problem formulation if a valve on line 34 is shut so that there is no flow in that line 34.

P4.4. CSTR in series - a system of nonlinear equations

An example from chemical engineering process that gives rise to a system of nonlinear equations is that of a continuously stirred tank reactor in series.

Consider an isothermal, irreversible second order reaction. The reaction rate expression is given by,

$$r = kVC_{Ai}^2 \tag{4.5}$$

where C_{Ai} is the exit concentration of component A from the $i-th$ reactor. A material balance on the $i-th$ reactor gives,

$$kVC_i^2 = F(C_{Ai-1} - C_{Ai}) \tag{4.5}$$

Letting $\beta = kV/F$, we have the following n-simultaneous nonlinear equations.

$$f_i := \beta C_{Ai}^2 + C_{Ai} - C_{Ai-1} = 0 \qquad i = 1 \cdots N \tag{4.5}$$

Consider the case when the volume of the reactor is an unknown, but the required conversion (i.e., C_{AN}) is given. Then the unknown vector will be $\underline{x} = [C_{A1}, C_{A2}, \cdots, C_{AN-1}, \beta]$. Write a program that will accept values of $[C_{A0}, C_{AN}, k, F, N]$, a convergence tolerance, an upper limit for the number of iterations and a vector of initial estimate for the unknowns. The program should then implement the Newton scheme to compute and print values of the unknown vector. Adopt the Thomas algorithm to solve efficiently the linearized equations at each Newton step.

a) Determine the volume of each reactor as well as the total cumulative volume for each of the following cases: $[N = 5, 10, 20, 50, 200]$. - [Ans. for N=10, V=224.9].

b) How does the cumulative volume required to achieve the desired conversion change as the number of reactors in series is increased?

Use the following set of data to test your program

- inlet concentration, $C_{A0} = 2.0$ mol/lit
- exit concentration, $C_{AN} = 0.2$ mol/lit
- rate constant, $k = 0.075$ lit/mol.min
- flow rate, $F = 30$ lit/min

P4.5. The following reactions are taking place in a constant volume gas-phase batch reactor:

$$A + B \Leftrightarrow C + D$$
$$B + C \Leftrightarrow R + S$$
$$A + R \Leftrightarrow T$$

The above equilibrium reactions can be represented as a system of algebraic equations, whereas non-linear relations from equilibrium:

$$K_{C1} = \frac{C_C C_D}{C_A C_D}$$

$$K_{C2} = \frac{C_R C_S}{C_B C_C}$$

$$K_{C2} = \frac{C_T}{C_A C_S}$$

and linear relationships from the stoichiometry of each equation.

$$C_A = C_{A0} - C_D - C_T$$

$$C_B = C_{B0} - C_D - C_S$$

$$C_C = C_D - C_S$$

$$C_S = C_R - C_T$$

Solve for the equilibrium concentrations give only initial species concentrations of $C_{A0} = C_{B0} = 2.0$ and o assumed that the equilibrium constants $K_{C1} = 1.05$, $K_{C2} = 2.6$ and $K_{C3} = 5$

Use three different starting initial estimates

a) $C_D = C_R = C_T = 0$

a) $C_D = C_R = C_T = 1$

a) $C_D = C_R = C_T = 10$

CHAPTER 5

FUNCTIONAL APPROXIMATIONS

In previous chapters we have developed algorithms for solving systems of linear and nonlinear *algebraic* equations. Before we undertake the development of algorithms for *differential* equations, we need to develop some basic concepts of *functional approximations*. In this respect, the present chapter is a bridge between the realms of *lumped parameter* models and *distributed* and/or *dynamic* models.

There are at least two kinds of *functional approximation* problems that we encounter frequently. In the first class of problem, a known function $f(x)$ is approximated by another function, $P_n(x)$ for reasons of computational necessity or expediency. As modelers of physical phenomena, we often encounter a second class of problem in which there is a need to represent an experimentally observed, discrete set of data of the form $\{x_i, f_i | i = 1, \cdots n\}$ as a function of the form $f(x)$ over the domain of the independent variable x.

Part I

Approximate Representation of Functions

5.1   Approximate representation of functions

5.1.1   Series expansion

As an example of the first class of problem, consider the evaluation of the *error function* given by,

$$erf(x) = \frac{2}{\sqrt{\pi}} \int_0^x e^{-\xi^2} \, d\xi$$

Since the integral does not have a closed form expression, we have to use a series expansion for,

$$e^{-\xi^2} = \sum_{k=0}^{\infty} \frac{(-1)^k \xi^{2k}}{k!}$$

Note that this expansion is around $\xi = 0$. We can integrate the series expansion term-by-term to obtain,

$$erf(x) = \frac{2}{\sqrt{\pi}} \sum_{k=0}^{\infty} \frac{(-1)^k x^{2k+1}}{(2k+1)k!}$$

We can now choose to approximate this function as,

$$erf(x) \approx P_{2n+1}(x) = \frac{2}{\sqrt{\pi}} \sum_{k=0}^{n} \frac{(-1)^k x^{2k+1}}{(2k+1)k!} + R(x)$$

n	$P_{2n+1}(x = 0.5)$	$P_{2n+1}(x = 1.0)$	$P_{2n+1}(x = 2.0)$
2	0.5207	0.865091	2.85856
4	0.5205	0.843449	2.09437
6	0.5205	0.842714	1.33124
8	0.5205	0.842701	1.05793
10	0.5205	0.842701	1.00318
20	0.5205	0.842701	0.995322
Exact	0.5205	0.842701	0.995322

Table 5.1: Convergence of $P_{2n+1}(x)$ to $erf(x)$ at selected values of x

by truncating the infinite series to n terms. The error introduced by truncating such a series is called the *truncation error* and the magnitude of the *residual function*, $R(x)$ represents the magnitude of the truncation error. For x close to zero a few terms of the series (small n) are adequate. The convergence of the series is demonstrated in Table 5.1. It is clear that as we go further away from $x = 0$, more terms are required for $P_{2n+1}(x)$ to represent $erf(x)$ accurately.

The error distribution, defined as $\epsilon(x, n) := |erf(x) - P_{2n+1}(x)|$, is shown in figure 5.1. It is clear from figure 5.1a, that for a fixed number of terms, say $n = 8$, the error increases with increasing values of x. For larger values of x, more terms are required to keep the error small. For $x = 2.0$, more than 10 terms are required to get the error under control.

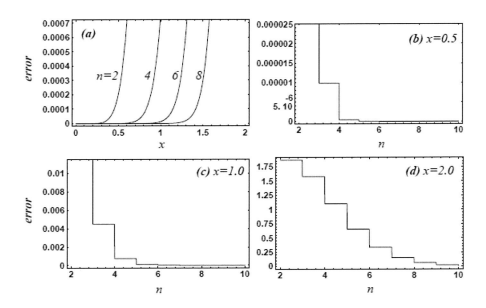

Figure 5.1: Error distribution of $\epsilon(x, n) := |erf(x) - P_{2n+1}(x)|$ for different levels of truncation

5.1.2 Polynomial collocation

In the above example we chose to construct an approximate function to represent $f(x) = erf(x)$ by expanding $f(x)$ in Taylor series around $x = 0$. This required that all the higher order derivative be available at $x = 0$. Also, since the expansion was around $x = 0$, the approximation fails increasingly as x moves away from zero. In another kind of functional approximation we can attempt to get a good representation of a given function $f(x)$ over a range $x \in [a, b]$. We do this by choosing a set of n basis functions, $\{\phi_i(x) | i = 1 \cdots n\}$ that are linearly independent and representing the approximation as,

$$f(x) \approx P_n(x) = \sum_{i=1}^{n} a_i \phi_i(x)$$

Here the basis functions $\phi_i(x)$ are known functions, chosen with care to form a linearly independent set and a_i are unknown constants that are to be determined in such a way that we can make $P_n(x)$ as good an approximation to $f(x)$ as possible - *i.e.*, we can define an error as the difference between the exact function and the approximate representation,

$$e(x; a_i) = |f(x) - P_n(x)|$$

and device a scheme to select a_i such that the error is minimized.

EXAMPLE 5.1 (Polynomial collocation) *So far we have outlined certain general concepts, but left open the choice of a specific basis functions $\phi_i(x)$.*
Let the basis functions be

$$\phi_i(x) = x^{i-1} \qquad i = 1, \cdots n$$

which, incidentally is a poor choice, but one that is easy to understand. Hence the approximate function will be a polynomial of degree $(n-1)$ of the form,

$$P_{n-1}(x) = \sum_{i=1}^{n} a_i x^{i-1}$$

Next, let us introduce the idea of collocation *to evaluate the error at n selected points in the range of interest $x \in [a, b]$. We choose n points $\{x_k | k = 1, \cdots n\}$ because we have introduced n degrees of freedom (unknowns) in a_i. A naive choice would be to space these collocation points equally in the interval $[a, b]$ - i.e.,*

$$x_k = a + (k-1)\frac{(b-a)}{(n-1)} \qquad k = 1, \cdots, n$$

Finally we can require the error at these points to be exactly equal to zero - i.e.,

$$e(x_k; a_i) = f(x_k) - P_{n-1}(x_k) = 0$$

or

$$\sum_{i=1}^{n} a_i x_k^{i-1} = f(x_k) \qquad k = 1, \cdots, n \qquad (5.1)$$

which yields n linear equations in n unknowns a_i. This can be written in matrix form

$$\boldsymbol{P a = f}$$

where the elements of matrix $\boldsymbol{P}$ are given by, $P_{k,i} = x_k^{i-1}$ and the vectors are $\boldsymbol{a} = [a_1, \cdots, a_n]$ and $\boldsymbol{f} = [f(x_1), \cdots, f(x_n)]$. Thus we have reduced the functional approximation problem to one of solving a system of linear algebraic equations and tools of chapter 3 become useful!

Let us be even more specific now and focus on approximating the error function $f(x) = erf(x)$ over the interval $x \in [0.1, 0.5]$. Let us also choose $n = 5$ - i.e., a quartic polynomial. This will allow us to write out the final steps of the approximation problem explicitly. The equally spaced collocation points are,

$$x_k = \{0.1, 0.2, 0.3, 0.4, 0.5\}$$

and the error function values at the collocation points are

$$\boldsymbol{f} = f(x_k) = [0.1125, 0.2227, 0.3286, 0.4284, 0.5205]$$

Thus, equation (5.1) yields the following system *

$$\boldsymbol{P} = \begin{bmatrix} 1 & x_1 & x_1^2 & x_1^3 & x_1^4 \\ 1 & x_2 & x_2^2 & x_2^3 & x_2^4 \\ 1 & x_3 & x_3^2 & x_3^3 & x_3^4 \\ 1 & x_4 & x_4^2 & x_4^3 & x_4^4 \\ 1 & x_5 & x_5^2 & x_5^3 & x_5^4 \end{bmatrix} = \begin{bmatrix} 1.0 & 0.10 & 0.010 & 0.0010 & 0.0001 \\ 1.0 & 0.20 & 0.040 & 0.0080 & 0.0016 \\ 1.0 & 0.30 & 0.090 & 0.0270 & 0.0081 \\ 1.0 & 0.40 & 0.160 & 0.0640 & 0.0256 \\ 1.0 & 0.50 & 0.250 & 0.1250 & 0.0625 \end{bmatrix}$$

Solution of the linear system yields the unknown coefficients as

$$\boldsymbol{a} = \{0.0001, 1.1262, 0.0186, -0.4503, 0.1432\}$$

---

*Also known as the Vandermonde Matrix

Thus the polynomial can be represented as:

$$P_4(x) = \sum_{i=1}^{5} a_i x^{i-1} = a_1 x^0 + a_2 x^1 + a_3 x^2 + a_4 x^3 + a_5 x^4$$

with the values of $\boldsymbol{a}$

$$P_4(x) = 0.0001 + 1.1262x + 0.0186x^2 - 0.4503x^3 + 0.1432x^4$$

A MATLAB function that shows the implementation of the above procedure for a specified degree of polynomial n is given in figure 5.2.

```
function a=erf_apprx(n)
%   Illustration functional (polynomial) approximation
%   fits error function in (0.1, 0.5) to a
%   polynomial of degree n

%define interval
a = 0.1;    b=0.5;

%pick collocation points
x=a + [0:(n-1)] *(b-a)/(n-1);

%Calculate the error function at collocation points
f=erf(x);    %Note that erf is a MATLAB function

%Calculate the matrix
for k=1:n
 P(k,:) = x(k).^[0:n-1];
end

%Print the determinant of P
fprintf(1,'Det. of P for deg. %2i is = %12.5e\n', n,det(P) );

%Determine the unknown coefficients a_i
a=P\f';
```

Figure 5.2: MATLAB implementation illustrating steps of functional approximation

Recall that we had made a comment earlier that the basis function $\phi_i(x) = x^{i-1}$ $i = 1, \cdots n$ is a poor choice. We can understand why this is so, by using the function shown in figure 5.2 for increasing degree of polynomials. The matrix $\boldsymbol{P}$ becomes poorly scaled and nearly singular with increasing degree of polynomial as evidenced by computing the determinant of $\boldsymbol{P}$. For example the determinant of $\boldsymbol{P}$ is 1.60000×10^{-2} for $n = 3$ and it goes down rapidly to 1.21597×10^{-12} for $n = 6$. Selecting certain orthogonal polynomials such as Chebyshev polynomials and using the roots of such polynomials as the collocation points results in well conditioned matrices and improved accuracy.

We can also write the polynomial in such a way that there is no need to solve a system of equation, thus avoiding the potential round-off errors.

5.2   Approximate representation of data

The concepts of polynomial approximation were discussed in section §5.1.2 in the context of constructing approximate representations of complicated functions (such as the error function). We will develop and apply these ideas further in later chapters for solving differential equations. Let us briefly explore the problem of constructing approximate functions for representing a discrete set of m pairs of data points

$$\{(x_k, f_k) \mid k = 1, \cdots, m\}$$

gathered typically from experiments. As an example, let us consider the saturation temperature vs. pressure data taken from steam tables and shown in Table 5.2. Here the functional form that we wish to construct is to represent pressure as a function of temperature, $P(T)$ over the temperature range $T \in [220, 232]$. Figure 5.2 shows a plot of the data.

$T(^oF)$	$P(psia)$
220.0000	17.1860
224.0000	18.5560
228.0000	20.0150
232.0000	21.5670

Table 5.2: Saturation temperature vs. pressure from steam tables

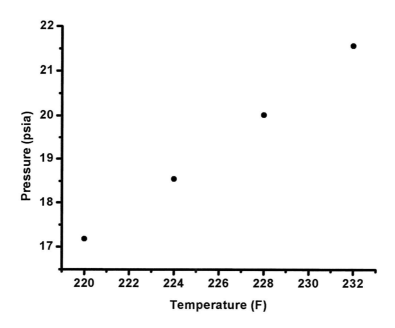

Figure 5.3: Plot of data in table 5.2

A number of choices present themselves.

- We can choose to fit a cubic polynomial, $P_3(T)$ that will pass through each of the four data points over the temperature range $T \in [220, 232]$. This will be considered as a *global polynomial* as it covers the entire range of interest in T.

- Alternately we can choose to construct *piecewise polynomials* of a lower degree with a limited range of applicability. For example, we can take the first three data points and fit

a quadratic polynomial, and the last three points and fit a
different quadratic polynomial.

- As a third alternative, we can choose to fit a global polynomial of degree less than three, that will not pass through
  any of the given data points, but will produce a function that
  minimizes the error over the entire range of $T \in [220, 232]$.

The choice of method will largely depend on the nature of the
data as well as the type of polynomial selected. If the data in
question is known to be accurate, then it will make sense to try
to make the approximating polynomial be able to reproduce the
experimental values accurately. On the otherhand, if the data
is not accurate, there is no point to require the approximating
polynomial to go through the experimental data exactly. Instead
one should focus on minimizing the error over the entire range.
We therefore have the following definitions:

Interpolation: A procedure for estimating a value between
known values of data points. This is carried out by determining a polynomial which gives exact values at each data point and
use the polynomial to find the in-between points. Interpolation
is used when the data points are known to be precise.

Curve fitting: Curve fitting is a procedure by which a mathematical formula (or equation) is used to best fit a given set of
data points. This is used when the data in question is not precise
and the aim of fitting is to smooth-out and minimize the effect
of data uncertainty.

Figure 5.2 shows raw data which has been fitted both by interpolation and curve fitting.

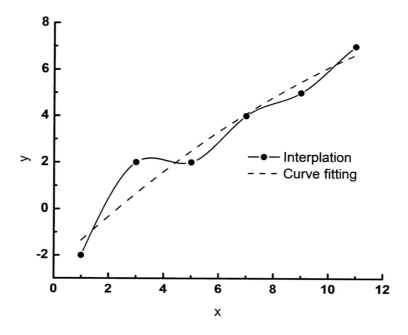

Figure 5.4: Interpolation and curve fitting

The procedures developed in section §5.1.2 are directly applicable to Interpolation and ended with the solution of a linear system. It is also possible to write the polynomial differently so that we do not solve a system of equation, *e.g.*, Lagrange polynomial or Newton polynomial. We shall develop such algorithms in section § 5.7. For now, let us develop the algorithm for curve fitting using the least-squares minimization concept.

5.2.1 Accuracy of the approximation

When a continuous function $f(x) : x \in [a, b]$ or a set of discrete data $(f(x_k) : k = 1 \cdots m)$ is represented by an approximate function $\bar{f}(x)$, it is often desirable to choose $\bar{f}(x)$ such that the error between the approximate function and the real data is as small as possible. The difference between the true value of function and the model prediction can be quantified using the **norm**. In other words, we choose the parameters for for the approximating function such that

$$f(e_1, e_2 \cdots e_m) = ||f_k - \bar{f}(x_k)||_p$$

is minimized. The **norm** as defined in chapter 3 may be used, *e.g.*,

- L_1 norm (the least absolute deviation)

$$||f_k - \bar{f}(x_k)||_1 = \sum_{i=1}^{m} |f_k - \bar{f}(x_k)|$$

- L_2 norm (the least squares or Eucledien norm)

$$||f_k - \bar{f}(x_k)||_2 = \sum_{i=1}^{m} \left(f_k - \bar{f}(x_k)\right)^2$$

- L_∞ norm (the - Chebyshev norm)

$$||f_k - \bar{f}(x_k)||_\infty = \max_{k=1\cdots m} \sum_{i=1}^{m} |f_k - \bar{f}(x_k)|$$

Statistical considerations show that the L_2 norm is the most suitable choice for smoothing the data in the case when additive data errors have a normal distribution because then the influence of errors is minimized.

The L_∞ norm considers only those data points where the maximal error appears. The first systematic analysis of this norm was carried out in the second half of 19th century by Chebyshev (because of this, the L_∞ norm is also called the Chebyshev norm) In practice, this norm is used if the data errors are very small with respect to an approximation error.

For the L_1 norm, all deviations are equally valued regardless of whether they are very small or very large. This criterion is suitable for use if the errors are subjected to outliers.

5.3 Curve fitting

5.3.1 Least squares approximation

Suppose there are m independent experimental observations ($m = 4$ in the above example) and we wish to fit a global polynomial of degree n ($n < m$) we define the error at every observation point as,

$$e_k = (f_k - P_{n-1}(x_k)) \qquad k = 1, \cdots, m$$

The basis functions are still the set, $\{x^{i-1} \mid i = 1, \cdots n\}$ and the polynomial is

$$P_{n-1}(x) = \sum_{i=1}^{n} a_i x^{i-1}$$

Here a_i are the unknowns that we wish to determine. Next we construct an objective function which is the sum of squares of the error at every observation point - viz.

$$S(\boldsymbol{a}) = \frac{\sum_{k=1}^{m} \epsilon_k^2}{m} = \frac{\sum_{k=1}^{m} (f_k - P_{n-1}(x_k))^2}{m} = \frac{\sum_{k=1}^{m} (f_k - \sum_{i=1}^{n} a_i x_k^{i-1})^2}{m}$$

The scalar objective function $S(\boldsymbol{a})$ is a function of n unknowns a_i. From elemetary calculus, the condition for the function $S(\boldsymbol{a})$ to have a minimum is,

$$\frac{\partial S(\boldsymbol{a})}{\partial \boldsymbol{a}} = 0$$

This condition provides n linear equations of the form $\boldsymbol{Pa} = \boldsymbol{b}$ that can be solved to obtain $\boldsymbol{a}$. The expanded form of the equations are,

$$
\begin{bmatrix}
\sum_{k=1}^{m} 1 & \sum_{k=1}^{m} x_k & \sum_{k=1}^{m} x_k^2 & \cdots & \sum_{k=1}^{m} x_k^{n-1} \\
\sum_{k=1}^{m} x_k & \sum_{k=1}^{m} x_k^2 & \sum_{k=1}^{m} x_k^3 & \cdots & \sum_{k=1}^{m} x_k^{n} \\
\sum_{k=1}^{m} x_k^2 & \sum_{k=1}^{m} x_k^3 & \sum_{k=1}^{m} x_k^4 & & \sum_{k=1}^{m} x_k^{n+1} \\
\vdots & \vdots & & \ddots & \vdots \\
\sum_{k=1}^{m} x_k^{n-1} & \sum_{k=1}^{m} x_k^{n} & \sum_{k=1}^{m} x_k^{n+1} & \cdots & \sum_{k=1}^{m} x_k^{2(n-1)}
\end{bmatrix}
\begin{bmatrix}
a_1 \\ a_2 \\ a_3 \\ \vdots \\ a_n
\end{bmatrix}
\tag{5.2}
$$

$$
=
\begin{bmatrix}
\sum_{k=1}^{m} f_k \\
\sum_{k=1}^{m} f_k x_k \\
\sum_{k=1}^{m} f_k x_k^2 \\
\vdots \\
\sum_{k=1}^{m} f_k x_k^{n-1}
\end{bmatrix}
$$

Observe that the equations are not only linear, but the matrix is also symmetric.

EXAMPLE 5.2 (Linear Least squares approximation)

A special well known case of approximation is the linear least squares approximation. In this case, we fit a linear polynomial to a given set of data. for $n = 2$, equation and m points equation 5.2 becomes

$$
\begin{bmatrix}
\sum_{k=1}^{m} 1 & \sum_{k=1}^{m} x_k \\
\sum_{k=1}^{m} x_k & \sum_{k=1}^{m} x_k^2
\end{bmatrix}
\begin{bmatrix}
a_1 \\ a_2
\end{bmatrix}
=
\begin{bmatrix}
\sum_{k=1}^{m} f_k \\
\sum_{k=1}^{m} f_k x_k
\end{bmatrix}
$$

this can be solved by the methods of chapter 3, e.g., using Cramer's rule to obtain the coefficients a_1 and a_2 as:

$$
a_1 = \frac{\begin{vmatrix} \sum_{k=1}^{m} f_k & \sum_{k=1}^{m} x_k \\ \sum_{k=1}^{m} f_k x_k & \sum_{k=1}^{m} x_k^2 \end{vmatrix}}{\begin{vmatrix} m & \sum_{k=1}^{m} x_k \\ \sum_{k=1}^{m} x_k & \sum_{k=1}^{m} x_k^2 \end{vmatrix}}
$$

and

$$a_2 = \frac{\begin{vmatrix} m & \sum_{k=1}^{m} f_k \\ \sum_{k=1}^{m} f_k x_k & \sum_{k=1}^{m} f_k x_k \end{vmatrix}}{\begin{vmatrix} m & \sum_{k=1}^{m} x_k \\ \sum_{k=1}^{m} x_k & \sum_{k=1}^{m} x_k^2 \end{vmatrix}}$$

EXAMPLE 5.3 (Linear regression) *Fit use linear regressin to fit the data in table 5.2.*

In this case $m = 4$, $f_k = P$, $x_k = T$

$$\sum_{k=1}^{4} f_k = 17.1860 + 18.5560 + 20.0150 + 21.5670 = 77.3240$$

$$\sum_{k=1}^{4} x_k = 220.0000 + 224.0000 + 228.0000 + 232.0000 = 904.0000$$

$$\sum_{k=1}^{4} x_k^2 = 204384.0000$$

$$\sum_{k=1}^{4} f_k x_k = 1.7504 \times 10^4$$

thus

$$a_1 = \frac{\begin{vmatrix} 77.3240 & 904.0000 \\ 1.7504 \times 10^4 & 204384.0000 \end{vmatrix}}{\begin{vmatrix} 4 & 904.0000 \\ 904.0000 & 204384.0000 \end{vmatrix}} = -63.1703$$

and

$$a_2 = \frac{\begin{vmatrix} 4 & 77.3240 \\ 1.7504 \times 10^4 & 1.7504 \times 10^4 \end{vmatrix}}{\begin{vmatrix} 4 & 904.0000 \\ 904.0000 & 204384.0000 \end{vmatrix}} = 0.3651$$

Thus the linear polynomial is

$$P_1 = a_1 T^0 + a_2 T^1 = -63.1703 + 0.3651T$$

Note that MATLAB has a function called $\texttt{polyfit(x,y,n)}$ which will accept a set of pairwise data $\{x_k, y_k = f(x_k) \mid k = 1, \cdots, m\}$ and produce a polynomial fit of degree n (which can be different from m) using a least-squares minimization.

Work through the following example using MATLAB to generate a quadratic, least-squares fit for the data shown in Table 5.2. Make sure that you understand what is being done at each stage of the calculation. This example illustrates a cubic fit that passes through each of the four data points, followed by use of the cubic fit to interpolate data at intermediate temperatures of $T = [222, 226, 230]$. In the last part the least squares solution is obtained using the procedure developed in this section. Finally MATLAB's $\texttt{polyfit}$ is used to generate the same least squares solution!

```
>>x=[220,224,228,232]            % Define temperatures
>>f=[17.186,18.556,20.015,21.567] % Define pressures
>>a3=polyfit(x,f,3)              % Fit a cubic.  Coefficients in a3
>>polyval(a3,x)                  % Check cubic passes through pts.
>>xi=[222,226,230]               % Define interpolation points
>>polyval(a3,xi)                 % Evaluate at interpolation pts.
>>%get ready for least square solution!
>>x2=x.^2                        % Evaluate x^2
>>x3=x.^3                        % Evaluate x^3
>>x4=x.^4                        % Evaluate x^4
>>P=[4,sum(x),sum(x2); ...       % Define matrix P over next 3 lines
```

```
>>sum(x), sum(x2), sum(x3); ...
>>sum(x2), sum(x3), sum(x4) ]
>>b=[sum(f), f*x', f*x2']            % Define right hand side
>>a = P\b'                          % ans:  (82.0202,-0.9203,0.0028)
>>c1=polyfit(x,f,1)                 % Let MATLAB do it!  compare c1 & a
>>c2=polyfit(x,f,2)                 % Let MATLAB do it!  compare c2 & a
>>norm(f-polyval(a3,x))             % error in cubic fit 3.3516 × 10⁻¹⁴
>>norm(f-polyval(c2,x))             % error in quadratic fit 8.9443 × 10⁻⁴
>>norm(f-polyval(c1,x))             % error in linear fit 9.1000 × 10⁻²
```

We can also revisit the first example for evaluating the error function by collocation method. Try using the function `polyfit(x,y,n)` for the error function and compare the polynomial coefficients a produced by the two approaches.

```
>>x=[0.1:0.1:0.5]   % Define Collocation Points
>>y=erf(x)          % Calculate the function at Collocation Points
>>a=polyfit(x,y,4)  % Fit 4th degree polynomial.  Coefficients in a
>>polyval(a,x)      % Evaluate the polynomial at collocation pts.
>>erf(x)            % Compare with exact values at the same pts.
```

EXAMPLE 5.4 (Accuracy of regression: regression coefficient)

We can determine the accuracy of the least squares fit by computing the sum of squares of the deviation of the data around the mean.

The mean of a function

$$\bar{f} = \frac{1}{n} \sum_{i=1}^{n} f_k \qquad (5.3)$$

Let us define the sum of squares before the application of regression

$$S_o = \sum_{k=1}^{n} (f_k - \bar{f})^2 \qquad (5.4)$$

and the sum of squares after the application of regression:

$$S = \sum_{i=1}^{n} \left(f_k - \sum_{i=1}^{n} a_i x^{i-1} \right)^2 \qquad (5.5)$$

With a_i obtained by solving equation 5.2.
The correlation coefficient is a normalized quantity defined as:

$$r^2 = \left(\frac{S_o - S}{S_o} \right) \qquad (5.6)$$

If we have a perfect fit, $S=0$ and therefore $r =1$. Otherwise if the fit is useless, $S_0 = S$ and therefore $r =0$.

5.4   General non-linear regression and linearization

In the previous sections, we have used polynomials to represent the functional approximations. In general, any function can be used and the procedure for minimization remains the same.

5.4.1   Linearization

It is sometimes desirable to use linear regression, even if the function to be fitted is not linear. In this case, a procedure to transform the non-linear equation to its linear form may be used.

For example, suppose we want to fit the exponential function $y = a_1 e^{a_2 x}$ to a data set (x_i, y_i), $i = 1 \cdots m$. If we take the natural logarithm of the to-be-fitted function, we obtain a function that is linear in the unknown parameters a_1 and a_2:

$$\ln(y) = \ln(a_1) - a_2 x$$

If we designate a new variable $\tilde{y} = \ln(y)$ and a new independent variable $\tilde{x} = x$, we obtain a new linear function in the transformed variables. We can now fit the new function $\tilde{y} = b + c\tilde{x}$ to the data set $(\tilde{x}_i, \tilde{y}_i), i = 1 \cdots m$ by linear regression. Table 5.3 shows some common non-linear functions and their equivalent transformations.

Table 5.3: Some non-linear relations and their transformed linear forms

Original relation	Transformation and linear relation $\tilde{y} = c\tilde{x} + d$
$y = ax^b$	$\ln y = \ln a + b \ln x$ $\tilde{y} = \ln y; \tilde{x} = \ln x, c = b, d = \ln a$
$y = ae^{bx}$	$\ln y = \ln a + bx$ $\tilde{y} = \ln y; \tilde{x} = x, c = b, d = \ln a$
$y = \frac{ax}{b+x}$	$\frac{1}{y} = \frac{b+x}{ax}$ $\tilde{y} = \frac{1}{y}, \tilde{x} = \frac{1}{x}, c = \frac{b}{a}, d = \frac{1}{a}$
$y = \frac{a}{b+x}$	$\frac{1}{y} = \frac{b+x}{a}$ $\tilde{y} = \frac{1}{y}, \tilde{x} = x, c = \frac{1}{a}, d = \frac{b}{a}$
$y = a_0 x_1^{a1} x_2^{a2} x_3^{a3} \cdots x_m^{am}$	$\ln y = \ln a_0 + a_1 \ln x_1 + \cdots + a_m \ln a_m$ $\tilde{y} = c_0 + c_1 \tilde{x}_1 + c_2 \tilde{x}_2 + \cdots + c_m \tilde{x}_m$ $\tilde{y} = \ln y, c_0 = \ln a_0, c_i = a_i, i = 1, 2, \cdots m$ $\tilde{x}_i = \ln x_i, i = 1, 2, \cdots m$

At the end of the regression process, variables are transformed to their original equivalent.

5.5   Difference operators

In the previous sections we developed polynomial approximation schemes in such a way that they required a solution of a system of linear algebraic equation. For uniformly spaced data, introduction of *difference operators* and difference tables, allows us to solve the same polynomial approximation problem in a more elegant manner without the need for solving a system of algebraic equations. This difference operator approach also lends itself naturally to recursive construction of higher degree polynomials with very little additional computation as well as extension to numerical differentiation and integration of discrete set of data (Chapter 6).

Consider the set of data $\{(x_i, f_i) \mid i = 1, \cdots, m\}$ where the independent variable, x is varied uniformly generating an equally spaced data - *i.e.*,

$$x_{i+1} = x_i + h, \qquad i = 1, \cdots m \quad \text{or} \quad x_i = x_1 + (i-1)h$$

The forward difference operator, as introduced already in section §2.8, is defined by,

Forward difference operator

$$\Delta f_i = f_{i+1} - f_i \tag{5.7}$$

In a similar manner we can define a backward difference, central difference and shift operators as shown below.

Backward difference operator

$$\nabla f_i = f_i - f_{i-1} \tag{5.8}$$

Central difference operator

$$\delta f_i = f_{i+1/2} - f_{i-1/2} \tag{5.9}$$

Shift operator

$$Ef_i = f_{i+1} \qquad (5.10)$$

We can also add the differential operator to the above list.

Differential operator

$$Df(x) = \frac{df(x)}{dx} = f'(x) \qquad (5.11)$$

The difference operators are nothing but rules of calculations, just like a differential operator defines a rule for differentiation. Clearly these rules can be applied repeatedly to obtain higher order differences. For example a second order forward difference with respect to reference point i is,

$$\Delta^2 f_i = \Delta(\Delta f_i) = \Delta(f_{i+1} - f_i) = f_{i+2} - 2f_{i+1} + f_i$$

5.5.1 Operator algebra

Having introduced some new definitions of operators, we can discover some interesting relationships between various operators such as the following.

$$\Delta f_i = f_{i+1} - f_i \quad \text{and} \quad Ef_i = f_{i+1}$$

Combining these two we can write,

$$\Delta f_i = Ef_i - f_i = (E - 1)f_i$$

Since the operand f_i is the same on both sides of the equation, the operators (which define certain rules and hence have certain effects on the operand f_i) have an equivalent effect given by,

$$\Delta = (E - 1) \quad \text{or} \quad \boxed{E = (1 + \Delta)} \qquad (5.12)$$

Equation (5.12) can then be applied on any other operand like f_{i+k}. All of the operators satisfy the distributive, commutative and associative rules of algebra. Also, repeated application of the operation can be represented by,

$$E^\alpha = (1 + \Delta)^\alpha$$

Note that $E^\alpha f(x)$ simply implies that the function f is evaluated after shifting the independent variable by α - *i.e.*,

$$E^\alpha f(x) = f(x + \alpha h)$$

Hence α can be an integer or any real number. Similarly, we have

$$\nabla f_i = f_i - f_{i-1} \quad \text{and} \quad E f_{i-1} = f_i \quad \text{and} \quad f_{i-1} = E^{-1} f_i$$

where we have introduce the inverse of the shift operator E to shift backwards. Combining these we can write,

$$\nabla f_i = f_i - E^{-1} f_i = (1 - E^{-1}) f_i$$

Once again recognizing that the operand f_i is the same on both sides of the equation, the operators are related by,

$$\nabla = (1 - E^{-1}) \quad \text{or} \quad E^{-1} = (1 - \nabla) \quad \text{or} \quad \boxed{E = (1 - \nabla)^{-1}}$$

$$(5.13)$$

Yet another relation between the shift operator E and the differential operator D can be developed by considering the Taylor series expansion of $f(x + h)$,

$$f(x + h) = f(x) + h f'(x) + \frac{h^2}{2!} f''(x) + \cdots$$

which can be written in operator notation as,

$$E f(x) = \left[1 + hD + \frac{h^2 D^2}{2!} + \cdots \right] f(x)$$

The term in square brackets is the exponential function and hence

$$\boxed{E = e^{hD}} \qquad (5.14)$$

While such a game of discovering relationships between various operators can be played indefinitely, let us turn to developing some useful algorithms from these.

5.5.2 Newton forward difference approximation

Our objective is to construct a polynomial representation for the discrete set of data $\{(x_i, f_i) \mid i = 1, \cdots, m\}$ using an alternate approach from that of section §5.1.2.

Assuming that there is a function $f(x)$ representing the given data*, we can express such a function as,

$$f(x) = P_n(x) + R(x)$$

where $P_n(x)$ is the polynomial approximation to $f(x)$ and $R(x)$ is the residual error. Given a set of m data points we know at least one way (section §5.1.2) to can construct a polynomial of degree $(m - 1)$. Now let us use the power of operator algebra to develop an alternate way to construct such a polynomial and in the process, also learn something about the residual function $R(x)$. Applying equation (5.12) repeatedly α time on $f(x)$ we get,

$$E^\alpha f(x) = (1 + \Delta)^\alpha f(x)$$

Now for integer values of α the right hand side is the binomial expansion while for any real number, it yields an infinite series. Using such an expansion the above equation can be written as,

$$f(x + \alpha h) = \left[1 + \alpha\Delta + \frac{\alpha(\alpha - 1)}{2!}\Delta^2 + \frac{\alpha(\alpha - 1)(\alpha - 2)}{3!}\Delta^3 + \cdots \right.$$
$$\left. \frac{\alpha(\alpha - 1)(\alpha - 2)\cdots(\alpha - n + 1)}{n!}\Delta^n + \cdots \right] f(x) \quad (5.15)$$

Up to this point in our development we have merely used tricks of operator algebra. We will now make the direct connection to

---

*Is such an assumption always valid?

the given, discrete set of data $\{(x_i, f_i) \mid i = 1, \cdots, m\}$. Taking x_1 as the reference point, the transformation

$$x = x_1 + \alpha h$$

makes α the new independent variable and for integer values of $\alpha = 0, 1, \cdots (m - 1)$ we retrieve the equally spaced data set $\{x_1, x_2, \cdots x_m\}$ and for non-integer (real) values of α we can reach the other values of $x \in (x_1, x_m)$. Splitting equation (5.15) into two parts,

$$f(x_1 + \alpha h) = \left[1 + \alpha\Delta + \frac{\alpha(\alpha - 1)}{2!}\Delta^2 + \frac{\alpha(\alpha - 1)(\alpha - 2)}{3!}\Delta^3 + \cdots \right.$$
$$\left. \frac{\alpha(\alpha - 1)(\alpha - 2) \cdots (\alpha - m + 2)}{(m - 1)!}\Delta^{m-1} \right] f(x_1) + R(x)$$

we can recognize the terms in the square brackets as a polynomial of degree $(m - 1)$ in the transformed variable α. We still need to determine the numbers $\{\Delta f(x_1), \Delta^2 f(x_1), \cdots, \Delta^{(m-1)} f(x_1)\}$. These can be computed and organized as a forward difference table shown in figure 5.5.

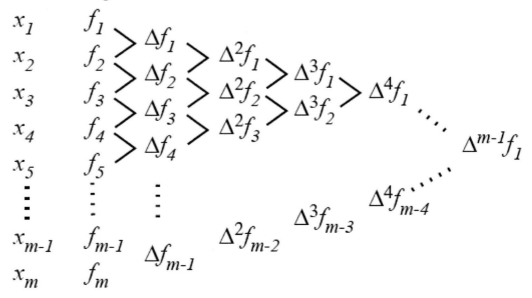

Figure 5.5: Structure of Newton forward difference table for m equally spaced data

Since forward differences are needed for constructing the polynomial, it is called the Newton forward difference polynomial and it is given by,

$$P_{m-1}(x_1 + \alpha h) = \left[1 + \alpha\Delta + \frac{\alpha(\alpha-1)}{2!}\Delta^2 + \frac{\alpha(\alpha-1)(\alpha-2)}{3!}\Delta^3 \right.$$
$$\left. \frac{\alpha(\alpha-1)(\alpha-2)\cdots(\alpha-m+2)}{(m-1)!}\Delta^{m-1} \right] f(x_1) \qquad (5.16)$$

The polynomial in equation (5.16) will pass through the given data set $\{(x_i, f_i) \mid i = 1, \cdots, m\}$ - *i.e.*, for integer values of $\alpha = 0, 1, \cdots (m-1)$ it will return values of $\{f_1, f_2, \cdots f_m\}$. This implies that the residual function $R(x)$ will have roots at the data points $\{x_i \mid i = 1, \cdots, m\}$. For a polynomial of degree $(m-1)$, shown in equation (5.16), the residual at other values of x is typically represented as $R(x) \approx \mathcal{O}(h^m)$ to suggest that the leading term in the truncated part of the series is of order m.

EXAMPLE 5.5 (forward difference table) *A set of five ($m = 5$) equally spaced data points and the forward difference table for the data are shown in figure 5.6.*

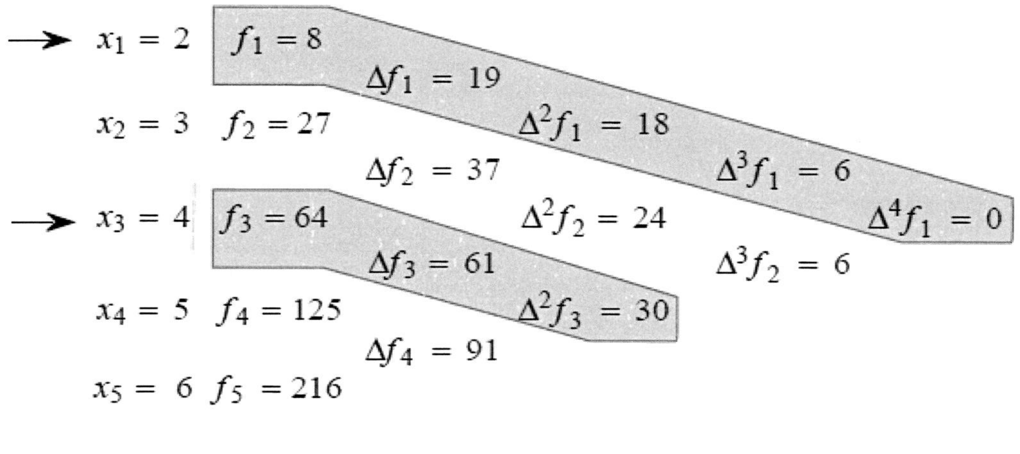

Figure 5.6: Example of a Newton forward difference table

For this example, clearly $h = 1$ and $x = x_1 + \alpha$. We can take the reference point as $x_1 = 2$ and construct the following linear, quadratic and cubic polynomials, respectively. *

$$P_1(2 + \alpha) = [1 + \alpha\Delta] f(x_1) = (8) + \alpha(19) + \mathcal{O}(h^2)$$

$$P_2(2 + \alpha) = (8) + \alpha(19) + \frac{\alpha(\alpha - 1)}{2!}(18) + \mathcal{O}(h^3)$$

$$P_3(2 + \alpha) = (8) + \alpha(19) + \frac{\alpha(\alpha - 1)}{2!}(18) + \frac{\alpha(\alpha - 1)(\alpha - 2)}{3!}(6) + \mathcal{O}(h^4)$$

You can verify easily that $P_1(2 + \alpha)$ passes through $\{x_1, x_2\}$, $P_2(2+\alpha)$ passes through $\{x_1, x_2, x_3\}$ and $P_3(2+\alpha)$ passes through $\{x_1, x_2, x_3, x_4\}$. For finding the interpolated value of $f(x = 3.5)$ for example, first determine the values of α at $x = 3.5$ from the equation $x = x_1 + \alpha h$. It is $\alpha = (3.5 - 2)/1 = 1.5$. Using this value in the cubic polynomial,

$$P_3(2+1.5) = (8)+1.5(19)+\frac{1.5(0.5)}{2!}(18)+\frac{1.5(0.5)(-0.5)}{3!}(6) = 42.875$$

As another example, by taking $x_3 = 4$ as the reference point we can construct the following quadratic polynomial

$$P_2(4 + \alpha) = (64) + \alpha(61) + \frac{\alpha(\alpha - 1)}{2!}(30)$$

which will pass through the data set $\{x_3, x_4, x_5\}$. This illustration should show that once the difference table is constructed, a variety of polynomials of varying degrees can be constructed quite easily.

5.5.3   Newton backward difference approximation

An equivalent class of polynomials using the *backward difference* operator based on equation (5.13) can be developed. Applying equation (5.13) repeatedly α times on $f(x)$ we get,

$$E^\alpha f(x) = (1 - \nabla)^{-\alpha} f(x)$$

---

*Note that $P_4(2 + \alpha) = P_3(2 + \alpha)$ for this case! Why?

which can be expanded as before to yield,

$$f(x + \alpha h) = \left[1 + \alpha\nabla + \frac{\alpha(\alpha + 1)}{2!}\nabla^2 + \frac{\alpha(\alpha + 1)(\alpha + 2)}{3!}\nabla^3 + \cdots \right.$$
$$\left. \frac{\alpha(\alpha + 1)(\alpha + 2)\cdots(\alpha + n - 1)}{n!}\nabla^n + \cdots \right] f(x) \quad (5.13)$$

As with the Newton forward formula, the above equation (5.13) terminates at a finite number of terms for integer values of α and for non-integer values, it will always be an infinite series which must be trancated, thus sustaining a *trunctaion error*.

In making the precise connection to a given discrete data set $\{(x_i, f_i) \mid i = 0, -1 \cdots, -n\}$, typically the largest value of x (say, x_0) is taken as the reference point. The transformation

$$x = x_0 + \alpha h$$

makes α the new independent variable and for negative integer values of $\alpha = -1, \cdots - n$ we retrieve the equally spaced data set $\{x_{-1}, \cdots x_{-n}\}$ and for non-integer (real) values of α we can reach the other values of $x \in (x_{-n}, x_0)$. Splitting equation (5.13) into two parts,

$$f(x_0 + \alpha h) = \left[1 + \alpha\nabla + \frac{\alpha(\alpha + 1)}{2!}\nabla^2 + \frac{\alpha(\alpha + 1)(\alpha + 2)}{3!}\nabla^3 + \cdots \right.$$
$$\left. \frac{\alpha(\alpha + 1)(\alpha + 2)\cdots(\alpha + n - 1)}{n!}\nabla^n + \cdots \right] f(x_0) + R(x)$$

we can recognize the terms in the square brackets as a polynomial of degree n in the transformed variable α. We still need to determine the numbers $\{\nabla f(x_0), \nabla^2 f(x_0), \cdots, \nabla^n f(x_0)\}$. These can be computed and organized as a backward difference table shown in figure 5.7.

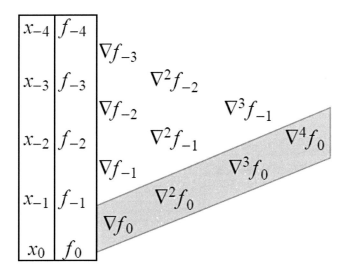

Figure 5.7: Structure of Newton backward difference table for 5 equally spaced data

Since backward differences are needed for constructing the polynomial, it is called the Newton backward difference polynomial and it is given by,

$$P_n(x_0 + \alpha h) = \left[1 + \alpha\nabla + \frac{\alpha(\alpha+1)}{2!}\nabla^2 + \frac{\alpha(\alpha+1)(\alpha+2)}{3!}\nabla^3 + \cdots \right.$$
$$\left. \frac{\alpha(\alpha+1)(\alpha+2)\cdots(\alpha+n-1)}{n!}\nabla^n \right] f(x_0) + \mathcal{O}(h^{n+1}) \qquad (5.11)$$

The polynomial in equation (5.11) will pass through the given data set $\{(x_i, f_i) \mid i = 0, \cdots, -n\}$ - i.e., for integer values of $\alpha = 0, -1, \cdots - n$ it will return values of $\{f_0, f_{-1}, \cdots f_{-n}\}$. At other values of x the residual will be of order $\mathcal{O}(h^{n+1})$.

EXAMPLE 5.6 *A set of five ($n = 4$) equally spaced data points and the backward difference table for the data are shown in figure 5.8.*

$x_{-4} = 2 \quad f_{-4} = 8$

$\nabla f_{-3} = 19$

$x_{-3} = 3 \quad f_{-3} = 27$ $\qquad \nabla^2 f_{-2} = 18$

NBF around x_{-2} $\nabla f_{-2} = 37$ $\qquad \qquad \nabla^3 f_{-1} = 6$

$\longrightarrow x_{-2} = 4 \quad f_{-2} = 64$ $\qquad \nabla^2 f_{-1} = 24$ $\qquad \qquad \nabla^4 f_0 = 0$

NFF around x_{-2} $\nabla f_{-1} = 61$ $\qquad \qquad \nabla^3 f_0 = 6$

$x_{-1} = 5 \quad f_{-1} = 125$ $\qquad \nabla^2 f_0 = 30$

$\nabla f_0 = 91$

$\longrightarrow x_0 = 6 \quad f_0 = 216$

NBF around x_0

Figure 5.8: Example of a Newton backward difference table

This is the same example as used in the previous section! It is clear that $h = 1$ and $x = x_0 + \alpha$. In the previous case we constructed a linear, quadratic and cubic polynomials, with $x_3 = 4$ as the reference point. In the present case let us use the same reference point, but it is labelled as $x_{-2} = 4$. A quadratic backward difference polynomial in α is,

$$P_2(4 + \alpha) = (64) + \alpha(37) + \frac{\alpha(\alpha + 1)}{2!}(18) + \mathcal{O}(h^3)$$

which passes through the points (x_{-2}, f_{-2}), (x_{-3}, f_{-3}) and (x_{-4}, f_{-4}) for $\alpha = 0, -1, -2$, respectively. Recall that the forward difference polynomial around the same point was, *

$$P_2(4 + \alpha) = (64) + \alpha(61) + \frac{\alpha(\alpha - 1)}{2!}(30)$$

which passes through the three forward point for $\alpha = 0, 1, 2$. Although they are based on the same reference point, these are two different polynomials passing through a different set of data points.

As a final example, let us construct a quadratic backward differ-

---

*Calculate the interpolated value of $f(4.5)$ from these two polynomials ence polynomial around $x_0 = 6$. It is, [*]

$$P_2(6 + \alpha) = (216) + \alpha(91) + \frac{\alpha(\alpha + 1)}{2!}(30)$$

5.6   Inverse interpolation

One of the objectives in constructing an interpolating polynomial is to be able to evaluate the function $f(x)$ at values of x other than the ones in the discrete set of given data points (x_i, f_i). The objective of *inverse interpolation* is to determine the independent variable x for a given value of f using a given discrete data set (x_i, f_i). If x_i are equally spaced, we can combined two of the tools (polynomial curve fitting and root finding) to meet this objective, although this must be done with caution.
We illustrate this with the example data shown in figure 5.6. Suppose we wish to find the value of x where $f = 100$. Using the three data points in the neighbourhood of $f = 100$ in figure 5.6 viz. (x_3, x_4, x_5), and using a quadratic polynomial fit, we have,

$$P_2(4 + \alpha) = (64) + \alpha(61) + \frac{\alpha(\alpha - 1)}{2!}(30)$$

A graph of this polynomial approximation $P_2(4 + \alpha)$ and the actual function $f(x) = x^3$ used to generate the data given in figure 5.6 are shown in figure 5.9.

---

[*]Is this polynomial different from the NFF, $P_2(4 + \alpha)$ constructed above?

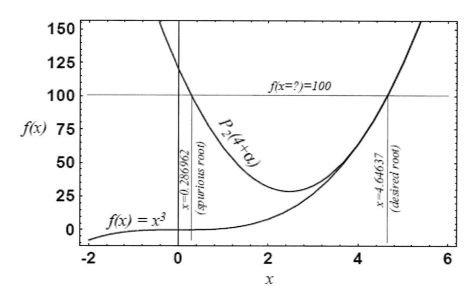

Figure 5.9: Example of a inverse interpolation

It is clear that the polynomial approximation is quite good in the range of $x \in (4,6)$, but becomes a poor approximation for lower values of x. Note, in particular, that if we solve the inverse interpolation problem by setting

$$P_2(4+\alpha)-100 = 0 \qquad \text{or} \qquad (64)+\alpha(61)+\frac{\alpha(\alpha-1)}{2!}(30)-100 = 0$$

we will find two roots. One of them at $\alpha = 0.64637$ or $x = 4.64637$ is the desired root while the other at $\alpha = -3.71304$ or $x = 0.286962$ is a spurious one. This problem can become compounded as we use higher degree polynomial in an effort to improve accuracy.

In order to achieve high accuracy, but stay close to the desired root, we can generate an initial guess from a *linear interpolation*, followed by constructing a *fixed point iteration* scheme on the polynomial approximation of the desired accuracy. Convergence is generally fast as shown in Dahlquist and Björck (1974). Suppose we wish to find x corresponding to $f(x) = d$, the desired function value. We first construct a polynomial of degree $(m-1)$

to represent the tabular data.

$$P_{m-1}(x_1 + \alpha h) = \left[1 + \alpha\Delta + \frac{\alpha(\alpha-1)}{2!}\Delta^2 + \frac{\alpha(\alpha-1)(\alpha-2)}{3!}\Delta^3 + \cdots \right.$$
$$\left. \frac{\alpha(\alpha-1)(\alpha-2)\cdots(\alpha-m+2)}{(m-1)!}\Delta^{m-1}\right] f(x_1)$$

Then we let $f(x_1 + \alpha h) = d$ and rearrange the polynomial in the form

$$\alpha_{i+1} = g(\alpha_i) \qquad i = 0, 1, 2\cdots$$

where $g(\alpha)$ is obtained by rearranging the polynomial,

$$g(\alpha) = \frac{1}{\Delta f_1}\left[d - f_1 - \frac{\alpha(\alpha-1)}{2!}\Delta^2 f_1 - \frac{\alpha(\alpha-1)(\alpha-2)}{3!}\Delta^3 f_1 + \cdots\right]$$

and the initial guess obtained by truncating the polynomial after the linear term,

$$\alpha_0 = \frac{d - f_1}{\Delta f_1}$$

EXAMPLE 5.7 *Continuing with the task of finding x where $f(x) = 100$ for the data shown in figure 5.6, the fixed point iterate is,*

$$\alpha_{i+1} = [100 - 64 - 15\alpha_i(\alpha_i - 1)]/61$$

and the initial guess is

$$\alpha_0 = \frac{d - f_1}{\Delta f_1} = \frac{100 - 64}{61} = 0.5902$$

The first ten iterates, produced from the m-file given below,

```
function a=g(a)
for i=1:10
fprintf(1,'%2i %12.7e\n',i,a);
a=(100 - 64 - 15*a*(a-1))/61;
end
```

are shown in Table 5.4.

---

i	α_i
1	.59016393
2	.64964028
3	.64613306
4	.64638815
5	.64636980
6	.64637112
7	.64637102
8	.64637103
9	.64637103
10	.64637103

Table 5.4: Inverse interpolation

5.7 Lagrange polynomials

So far we have examined ways to construct polynomial approximations using equally spaced data in x. For a data set $\{x_i, f_i | i = 0, \cdots n\}$, that contains unequally spaced data in the independent variable x, we can construct Lagrange interpolation formula as follows.

$$P_n(x) = \sum_{i=0}^{n} f_i L_i(x) \qquad (5.9)$$

where

$$L_i(x) = \prod_{j=0, j \neq i}^{n} \frac{x - x_j}{x_i - x_j}$$

Note that

$$L_i(x_j) = \begin{cases} 0 & j \neq i \\ 1 & j = i \end{cases}$$

and each $L_i(x)$ is a polynomial of degree n. It is also clear from equation (5.7) that $P_n(x_j) = f_j$ - *i.e.*, the polynomial passes through the data points (x_j, f_j).

If we wish to construct a quadratic polynomial passing through $(x_0, f_0), (x_1, f_1), (x_2, f_2)$ for example using equation (5.7), it will be

$$P_2(x) = f_0 \frac{(x - x_1)(x - x_2)}{(x_0 - x1)(x_0 - x_2)} + f_1 \frac{(x - x_0)(x - x_2)}{(x_1 - x_0)(x_1 - x_2)} + f_2 \frac{(x - x_0)(x - x_1)}{(x_2 - x_0)(x_2 - x_1)}$$
$$= 1.00 \frac{(x - 1.2)(x - 1.5)}{(1 - 1.2)(1 - 1.5)} + 1.728 \frac{(x - 1)(x - 1.5)}{(1.2 - 1)(1.2 - 1.5)} + 3.375 \frac{(x - 1)(x - 1.2)}{(1.5 - 1)(1.5 - 1.2)}$$

A MATLAB function that implements that Lagrange interpolation formula shown in equation (5.7) is given in figure 5.10.

```
function f=LagrangeP(xt,ft,x)
% (xt,ft) are the table of unequally spaced values
%  x is where interpolated values are required
%  f the interpolated values are returned

m=length(x);
nx=length(xt);
ny=length(ft);

if (nx ~= ny),
   error(' (xt,ft) do not have the same # values')
end

for k=1:m
 sum = 0;
 for i=1:nx
  delt(i)=1;
  for j=1:nx
   if (j ~= i),
      delt(i) = delt(i)*(x(k)-xt(j))/(xt(i)-xt(j));
   end
  end
  sum = sum + ft(i) * delt(i) ;
 end
 f(k)=sum;
end
```

Figure 5.10: MATLAB implementation of Lagrange interpolation polynomial

This function accepts a table of values $(\boldsymbol{xt}, \boldsymbol{ft})$, constructs the highest degree Lagrange polynomial that is possible and finally evaluates and returns the interpolated values of the function $\boldsymbol{y}$ at specified values of x.

```
>>xt=[1  1.2  1.5 1.6]        % Define xt, unequally spaced
>>ft=[1  1.728  3.375 4.096]  % Define ft, the function values
>>x=[1.0:0.1:1.6]             % x locations for interpolation
>>f=LagrangeP(xt,ft,x)        % interpolated f values.
```

5.8 Newton's divided difference polynomials

An alternate way to construct the polynomial is based on introducing the divided difference and constructing a divided difference table. The polynomial itself is written in the form

$$P_n(x) = \sum_{i=0}^{n} a_i \prod_{j=0}^{i} (x - x_{j-1}) \tag{5.8}$$
$$= a_0 + a_1(x - x_0) + a_2(x - x_0)(x - x_1) + \cdots$$
$$+ a_n(x - x_0) \cdots (x - x_{n-1})$$

The advantage of writing it the form shown in equation (5.8) is that the unknown coefficients a_i can be constructed recursively or found directly from the divided difference table. The first divided difference is defined by the equation,

$$f[x_0, x_1] = \frac{f_1 - f_0}{x_1 - x_0}$$

Similarly the second divided difference is defined as,

$$f[x_0, x_1, x_2] = \frac{f[x_1, x_2] - f[x_0, x_1]}{x_2 - x_0}$$

With these definitions, we return to the task of finding the coefficients a_i in equation (5.8) For example, the first coefficient a_0 is,

$$P_n(x_0) = a_0 = f[x_0] = f_0$$

The second coefficient, a_1, is obtained from,

$$P_n(x_1) = a_0 + a_1(x_1 - x_0) = f_1$$

which can be rearranged as,

$$a_1 = \frac{f_1 - f_0}{x_1 - x_0} = f[x_0, x_1]$$

The third coefficient is obtained from,

$$P_n(x_2) = a_0 + a_1(x_2 - x_0) + a_2(x_2 - x_0)(x_2 - x_1) = f_2$$

The only unknown here is a_2, which after some rearrangement becomes,

$$a_2 = \frac{f[x_1, x_2] - f[x_0, x_1]}{x_2 - x_0} = f[x_0, x_1, x_2]$$

In general the n-th coefficient is the n-th divided difference.

$$a_n = f[x_0, x_1, \cdots, x_n]$$

Example

Consider the example data and the divided difference table shown in figure 5.11.

$x_0 = 1.0 \;\; f_0 = 1.000$			
	$f[x_0, x_1] = 3.6400$		
$x_1 = 1.2 \;\; f_1 = 1.728$		$f[x_0, x_1, x_2] = 3.700$	
	$f[x_1, x_2] = 5.4900$		$f[x_0, x_1, x_2, x_3] = 1.000$
$x_2 = 1.5 \;\; f_2 = 3.375$		$f[x_1, x_2, x_3] = 4.300$	
	$f[x_2, x_3] = 7.2100$		
$x_3 = 1.6 \;\; f_3 = 4.096$			

Figure 5.11: Structure of divided difference table for 4 unequally spaced data

If we wish to construct a quadratic polynomial passing through $(x_0, f_0), (x_1, f_1), (x_2, f_2)$ for example using equation (5.8) and the difference table shown in figure 5.11 will be written as,

$$
\begin{aligned}
P_2(x) &= f_0 + f[x_0, x_1](x - x_0) + f[x_0, x_1, x_2](x - x_0)(x - x_1) \\
&= 1.000 + 3.64(x - 1) + 3.70(x - 1)(x - 1.2)
\end{aligned}
$$

Observe that in order to construct a cubic polynomial by adding the additional data point (x_3, f_3) Lagrange polynomial based on equation (5.7) requires a complete reconstruction of the equation, while that based on equation (5.8) is simply,

$$
\begin{aligned}
P_2(x) &= f_0 + f[x_0, x_1](x - x_0) + f[x_0, x_1, x_2](x - x_0)(x - x_1) + \\
&\quad f[x_0, x_1, x_2, x_3](x - x_0)(x - x_1)(x - x_2) \\
\\
&= 1.000 + 3.64(x - 1) + 3.70(x - 1)(x - 1.2) + \\
&\quad 1(x - 1)(x - 1.2)(x - 1.5)
\end{aligned}
$$

5.9   Piecewise continuous functions - splines

In the methods outlined above, we sought to fit a single function over the entire range of data. This will work well for low order polynomials, whereas high order polynomials may exhibit osculations. Figure 5.12a shows a 9th degree polynomial fit to a data set with ten points. Here we see that although the plynomial passes through all data points exactly, there are large variations in between data points. To overcome the problem of large fluctuations for situations with large $n(n > 4)$ we usually interpolate in a piecewise manner. In this case, each pair of data points is fitted with a low order polynomial. Figure 5.12b shows the same data points fitted with cubic splines. The word "spline" is a legacy term which refers to a strip of metal or wood. In earlier times, curves were designed for planes and ships by mounting strips of metal or wood such that they went through desired points but were free to move.

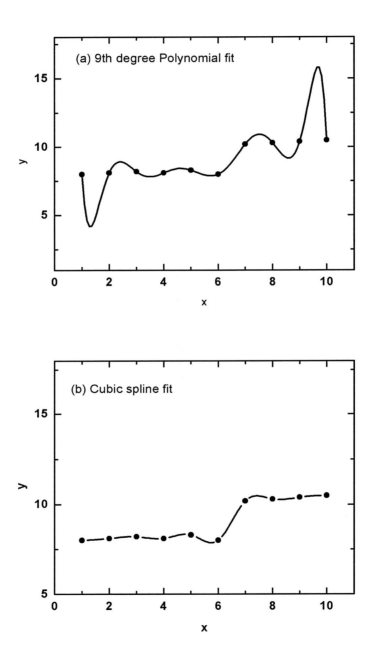

Figure 5.12: Fitting a single polynomial vs. splines

In computational application, we have our set of n points , $i = 1 \cdots n - 1$. through which we want to determine a function which can be used to determine the value of $f(x_k)$ for any x_k.

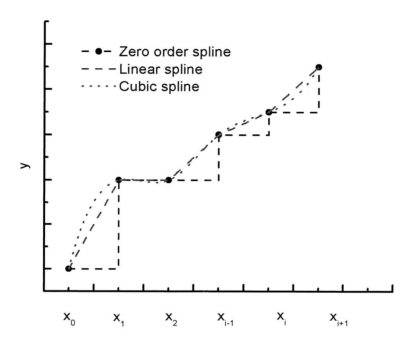

Figure 5.13: Spline interpolation

With zeroth-order splines, what we construct ends up to be a step function. From figure 5.13, it is obvious that this is not the best representation and the function f is discontinuous over the range.

Zero order splines - Constant

$$f_i(x) = f_{i-1} \qquad \text{for } x_{i-1} \leq x \leq x_i$$

First order splines - Linear interpolation: $f_i(x) = a_i + b_i x$

With linear splines, straight lines are drawn between each subsequent point. This is obviously more accurate than zero-order splines, but the derivatives are discontinuous at the junction nodes (aka knots).

$$f_i(x) = f_{i-1} + \left(\frac{f_i - f_{i-1}}{x_i - x_{i-1}} \right) (x - x_{i-1}) \qquad \text{for } x_{i-1} \leq x \leq x_i$$

The logical next step is to use second-order splines. In this case we assume a quadratic function ($f_i(x) = a_i + b_i x + c_i x^2$) in the interval $x_{i-1} \leq x \leq x_i$. Since we have n such intervals, we need to determine $3n$ constants. This requires 3n conditions. The points $i = 1$ to $i = n - 1$ are interior points (knots). The points $i = 0$ and $i = n$ are the end points. The conditions are:

- For knot i:
$$f_i(x_i) = a_i + b_i x_i + c_i x_i^2$$
  and
$$f_{i+1}(x_i) = a_{i+1} + b_{i+1} x_i + c_{i+1} x_i^2 = f_i$$
  these are $2(n - 1)$ conditions.

- For knot i: the derivative approaching from the left must be the same as the one approaching from the right:
$$f_i'(x_i) = f_{i+1}'(x_i)$$
  This implies that
$$b_i + 2c_i x_i = b_{i+1} + 2c_{i+1} x_i$$
  these are $(n - 1)$ conditions.

We still need the remaining $3n - 2(n-1) - (n-1) = 3$ conditions. Two obvious choices are obtained by specifying the start and end points:

$$f_i(x_0) = f_0 \text{ and } f_n(x_n) = f_n$$

We are still left with one final condition. This is often quite arbitrary. *e.g.*, we can assume that the second derivative at one of the extrema is equal to zero, *e.g.*, the last point, n:

$$f_n''(x_n) = 2c_n = 0$$

Thus 3n conditions form a linear system in the 3n unknowns that we can easily solve using the methods of chapter 3.

EXAMPLE 5.8 (✎ Quadratic splines) *The following measurements have been obtained from experiment*

i	0	1	2	3	4
x	5.0	7.0	12.0	15.0	20.0
y	2.0	5.0	8.0	11.0	5.0

Fit a second order spline to the data and determine the value of y at $x = 11.0$.

Solution

Here we note that there are five data points, thus we have 4 intervals for which we can fit 4 quadratics. The equation for any quadratic i

$$f_i(x) = a_i + b_i x_i + c_i x_i^2$$

Each quadratic has 3 parameters, thus we have $3 \times 4 = 12$ unknowns.

The unknown coefficients are $[a_1, b_1, c_2, a_2, b_2, c_2, a_3, b_3, c_3, a_4, b_4, c_4]$

Twelve equations from conditions

For the four quadratics: i=1

$$f_1(x) = a_1 + b_1 x_0 + c_1 x_0^2 = a_1 + 5b_1 + 5^2 c_1 = 2$$

$$f_1(x) = a_1 + b_1x_1 + c_1x_1^2 = a_1 + 7b_1 + 7^2c_1 = 5$$

$i=2$

$$f_2(x) = a_2 + b_2x_1 + c_2x_1^2 = a_2 + 7b_2 + 7^2c_2$$

$$f_2(x) = a_2 + b_2x_2 + c_2x_2^2 = a_2 + 12b_2 + 12^2c_2$$

$i=3$

$$f_i(x) = a_3 + b_3x_2 + c_3x_2^2 = a_3 + 12b_3 + 12^2c_3$$

$$f_i(x) = a_3 + b_3x_3 + c_3x_3^2 = a_3 + 15b_3 + 15^2c_3$$

$i=4$

$$f_i(x) = a_4 + b_4x_3 + c_4x_3^2 = a_4 + 15b_4 + 15^2c_4$$

$$f_i(x) = a_4 + b_4x_4 + c_4x_4^2 = a_4 + 20b_4 + 20^2c_4$$

Continuity of derivatives :

$$b_i + 2c_ix_i = b_{i+1} + 2c_{i+1}x_i$$

quadratic 1 and 2 , at node $i=2$

$$b_1 + 2c_1x_2 = b_2 + 2c_2x_2 \Rightarrow b_1 + 10c_1 - b_2 - 10c_2 = 0$$

quadratic 2 and 3 at node $i=3$

$$b_2 + 2c_2x_3 = b_3 + 2c_3x_3 \Rightarrow b_2 + 24c_2 - b_3 - 24c_3 = 0$$

quadratic 3 and 4 at node $i=4$

$$b_3 + 2c_3x_4 = b_4 + 2c_4x_4 \Rightarrow b_3 + 30c_2 - b_4 - 30c_4 = 0$$

and finally, for the last condition, the second derivative at the end node is zero, or

$$2c_4 = 0 \Rightarrow c_4 = 0$$

We have a system of 12×12 equations (note that we could have kept the number of unknowns as 11 because c_4 is known from the last condition)!. Collecting all the equations in matrix form

$$
\begin{bmatrix}
1 & 5 & 5^2 & 0 & 0 & 0 & 0 & 0 & 0 & 0 & 0 & 0 \\
1 & 7 & 7^2 & 0 & 0 & 0 & 0 & 0 & 0 & 0 & 0 & 0 \\
0 & 0 & 0 & 1 & 7 & 7^2 & 0 & 0 & 0 & 0 & 0 & 0 \\
0 & 0 & 0 & 1 & 12 & 12^2 & 0 & 0 & 0 & 0 & 0 & 0 \\
0 & 0 & 0 & 0 & 0 & 0 & 1 & 12 & 12^2 & 0 & 0 & 0 \\
0 & 0 & 0 & 0 & 0 & 0 & 1 & 15 & 15^2 & 0 & 0 & 0 \\
0 & 0 & 0 & 0 & 0 & 0 & 0 & 0 & 0 & 1 & 15 & 15^2 \\
0 & 0 & 0 & 0 & 0 & 0 & 0 & 0 & 0 & 1 & 20 & 20^2 \\
0 & 1 & 10 & 0 & 0 & -1 & -10 & 0 & 0 & 0 & 0 & 0 \\
0 & 0 & 0 & 0 & 0 & 1 & 24 & 0 & -1 & -24 & 0 & 0 \\
0 & 0 & 0 & 0 & 0 & 0 & 0 & 1 & 30 & 0 & -1 & 0 \\
0 & 0 & 0 & 0 & 0 & 0 & 0 & 0 & 0 & 0 & 0 & 1
\end{bmatrix}
\begin{bmatrix}
a_1 \\ b_1 \\ c_1 \\ a_2 \\ b_2 \\ c_2 \\ a_3 \\ b_3 \\ c_3 \\ a_4 \\ b_4 \\ c_4
\end{bmatrix}
=
\begin{bmatrix}
2 \\ 5 \\ 5 \\ 8 \\ 8 \\ 11 \\ 11 \\ 5 \\ 0 \\ 0 \\ 0 \\ 0
\end{bmatrix}
$$

Solving in MATLAB we obtain

$$
\begin{bmatrix}
a_1 \\ b_1 \\ c_1 \\ a_2 \\ b_2 \\ c_2 \\ a_3 \\ b_3 \\ c_3 \\ a_4 \\ b_4 \\ c_4
\end{bmatrix}
=
\begin{bmatrix}
66.9500 \\
-23.3400 \\
2.0700 \\
31.0400 \\
-6.2400 \\
0.3600 \\
-88.0000 \\
13.6000 \\
-0.4667 \\
17.0000 \\
-0.4000 \\
0.0000
\end{bmatrix}
$$

Thus the four quadratics may be written as

$$f_1(x) = 66.9500 - 23.3400x + 2.0700x^2 \qquad 5.0 \le x \le 7.0$$
$$f_2(x) = 31.0400 - 6.2400x + 0.3600x^2 \qquad 7.0 \le x \le 12.0$$
$$f_3(x) = -88.0000 + 13.6000x - 0.4667x^2 \qquad 12.0 \le x \le 15$$
$$f_4(x) = 17.0000 - 0.4000x \qquad 15.0 \le x \le 20.0$$

The value for $x = 11.0$ is obtained by using $f_2(x)$ viz.

$$f_2(11.0) = 31.0400 - 6.2400(11.0) + 0.3600(11.0)^2 = 5.9600$$

NOTE that the the last interpolant is linear because of the condition imposed at the last node.

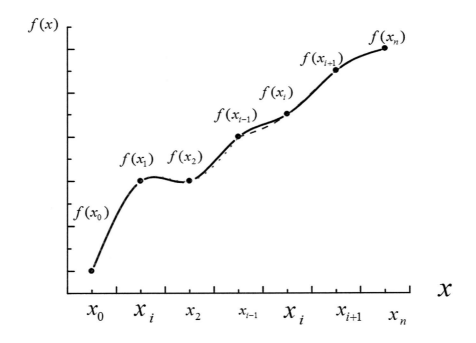

Figure 5.14: Fitting cubic splines

Cubic splines - $f_i(x) = a_i + b_i x + c_i x^2 + d_i x^3$

Cubic (third-order) splines are the most widely used splines. They are a natural extension of second-order splines. Here we assume a cubic function in the interval $x_{i-1} \leq x \leq x_i$, thus making the second derivative continous over the entire length of the curve.

We have 4 coefficients with n subintervals, thus giving 4n conditions. Conditions at the knots (points $i = 1 \cdots n-1$), the function is continuous – gives $2(n-1)$ conditions. The first derivative is also continuous, thus we have $(n-1)$ conditions. The second derivative is also continuous, thus $(n-1)$ conditions. We are left with $4n - 2(n-1) - (n-1) - (n-1) = 4$

For the end points (i=0 and i=n): we demand that the function must go through the end points (2 conditions). Thus we still need two more conditions.

There are a lot of variations for cubic splines, depending on the simplifications used to solving the system of linear equations for the coefficients a_i, b_i, c_i, and d_i. The most popular are the natural cubic splines where the final two conditions usually require that the second derivatives at the endpoints are made equal to zero:

$$f_1''(x_0) = 2c_1 + 6d_1 x_0 = 0 \text{ and } = f_n''(x_n) = 2c_n + 6d_n x_n = 0$$

Note that in deriving the above functions we used the standard polynomial form. We could also have used lagrange polynomials for the splines. We shall explore such possibilities in our problem samples.

5.10   Exercise Problems: I

P5I.1. Micro-turbine power

The power generation P [kW] in a micro-turbine depends, among others, on the diameter D [m] of the pipe which conveys water to the turbine.

D (m)	0.3	0.6	0.9	1.2
$P(kW)$	25	60	120	250

Fit a cubic polynomial to the data and determine the power output for a 1m diameter pipe.

P5I.2. Thermal conductivity of iron

The themal conductivity of iron has been determined as a function of temperature and reported as:

T (K)	300	500	700	1000	1300
$k(W/m.K)$	0.9	0.6	0.4	0.3	0.28

Determine the equation which best represents the thermal conductivity.

P5I.3. Heat transfer coefficent

The convective heat transfer coefficent for the flow over an exposed pipeline has been found to depend on the wind velocity. Determine if a linear fit is good for the correlation

V (m/s)	1	2	4	8	10
$h(W/m^2.K)$	20	60	100	500	1000

P5I.4. Enzyme Kinetics

The data below has been obtained from experiment on the growth of bacteria as a function of oxygen concentration in a biological treatment reactor. It is proposed to model the reactor using substrate inhibition model

$$\mu = \frac{\mu_{max} C}{k_m + k_1 C^2}$$

where C is the substrate concentration (g/L) and μ is the growth rate in hr^{-1}. Transform the equation into linear form and use linear regression to estimate the parameters k_m and k_1 given $\mu_{max} = 2.1$ and the following data:

μ (1/hr)	1.0	2.0	3.0	4.0
$C(g/L)$	0.7	0.9	1.2	1.4

P5I.5. Viscosity correlation

The viscosity of the gas saturated heavy oil is highly dependent of the temperature. A typical correlation gives dependency in an arrhenius type correlation:

$$\mu = Ae^{k/T}$$

where μ is the dynamic viscosity and T the temperature. A and k are fitted parameters. Fit this model for the following data for heavy crude oil

i	1	2	3	4	5
$T(^oF)$	25	50	75	100	125
$\mu(cp)$	5.0×10^6	5×10^3	1.0×10^2	5.0×10^1	1.0×10^1

P5I.6. Heat capacity ratio for natural gas

Heat capacity ratio is an important parameter in the design and performance evaluation of compressors. The heat capacity ratio is defined as the heat capacity at constant pressure divided by heat capacity at constant volume. For a pure compound, the heat capacity ratio (γ) is defined

Table 5.5: Natural gas composition

Component	mol%
Methane	93.74
Ethane	0.52
Propane	0.05
i-butane	0.01
n-butane	0.02
i-pentane	0.01
n-pentane	0.01
Carbon dioxide	1.54
Nitrogen	4.10

as the ratio of molar heat capacity at constant pressure (C_P) to molar heat capacity at constant volume (C_V):

$$\gamma = \frac{C_P}{C_V}$$

For an ideal gas, $C_V = C_P - R$, therefore the above equation can be written as:

$$\gamma = \frac{C_P}{C_P - R}$$

Where R is the universal gas constant and is equal to 8.314 kJ/kmol-C. For a mixture of gases, the specific capacity may be found from a weighted average of the pure component values

$$C_{Pm} = \sum C_{Pi} w_i$$

Given natural gas with composition shown in table 5.5, determine the heat capacity ratio.

P5I.7. Power dissipation in a pulp mixer

The rate of power dissipation from a pulp suspension mixer varies with the agitation speed. The following measurements have been obtained:

N (rpm)	15	40	60	90	110
Power (kW)	5	10	12	15	12

(a) Determine a fourth order Lagrange polynomial which passes through the points.

(b) Use the polynomial obtained in (a) to calculate the power at 100 rpm.

(c) Use linear splines interpolation to find the power at 100 rpm.

(d) Use quadratic splines interpolation to calculate the power at 100 rpm.

(e) Determine a fourth order Newton polynomial which passes through the data points.

(f) Use the polynomial obtained in (e) to calculate the power dissipation at 50 rpm.

P5I.8. Vapour pressure of Carbon dioxide

Table 5.6 represents data of vapour pressure vs temperature for carbon dioxide. In a design problem, the data needs to be correlated using algebraic expressions which can provide the pressure P (kPa) as a function of temperature T (K).

A simple polynomial could be used as an empirical modeling equation in the form:

$$P = a_0 + a_1 T + a_2 T^2 + a_3 T^3 + \cdots + a_n T^n \qquad (1)$$

where $a_0 \cdots a_n$ are coefficients to be determined by regression and n is the degree of the polynomial. Typically, the degree of the polynomial is determined to give the best data representation when using least-squares objective function.

Another useful correlation is the Antoine equation given by

$$\log(P) = A - \frac{B}{T + C} \qquad (2)$$

where P is the pressure in mmHg * and T is the temperature in degree celcius. A, B and C are parameters to be determined by regression.

Extensions to the Antoine can be made by introducing additional parameters to increase the flexibility of the equation and allow the description of the entire vapor pressure curve. For example:

$$\log(P) = A - \frac{B}{T + C} + D \ln T + ET^F \qquad (3)$$

(a) Regress the data with polynomial in the form (1). Determine the degree of the polynomial which best represents the data

(b) Regress the data using non-linear regression on equation (2).

(c) Regress the data using non-linear regression on equation (3).

---

*The coefficients of Antoine's equation are normally given in mmHgeven today where the SI is recommended and pascals are preferred. The usage of the pre-SI units has only historic reasons and originates directly from Antoine's original publication.

Table 5.6: Vapour pressure for CO2

Temperature (K)	Pressure (kPa)
250.00	1783.700
254.00	2024.300
256.00	2147.700
260.00	2417.300
266.00	2872.300
270.00	3201.800
273.15	3480.000
273.15	3486.590
278.15	3970.000
283.15	4500.000
287.91	5059.160
288.15	5080.000
293.15	5730.000
293.34	5753.230
296.79	6231.490
298.15	6440.000

P5I.9. Exponential fit

Write a MATLAB user defined function that determines the best fit of an exponential function of the form

$$y = ae^{-bx}$$

to a given set of data points. Name the function

function [a b] = ExpFit (x,y) where the input arguments x and y are vectors containing the data points, and the output arguments a and b are the values of the fitted parameters

P5I.10. Given the data

N (rpm)	15	40	60	90	110
Power (kW)	5	10	12	15	12

(a) Use the exponential function developed in problem **P5I**.9. to fit the function

$$P = Ae^{kN}$$

(b) Using MATLAB built-in function.

For each part, plot the data points and the fitting function

Part II

Numerical Differentiation and Integration

Having obtained approximate functional representations as outlined in Part I of this chapter, we can proceed to construct algorithms for approximate representations of derivatives and antiderivatives (integration).

5.11   Numerical differentiation

5.11.1   Approximations for first order derivatives

Consider the Newton forward formula given in equation (5.16)

$$f(x) \approx P_{m-1}(x_1 + \alpha h) = \left[1 + \alpha\Delta + \frac{\alpha(\alpha - 1)}{2!}\Delta^2 + \right.$$

$$\left. \frac{\alpha(\alpha - 1)(\alpha - 2)}{3!}\Delta^3 + \cdots + \frac{\alpha(\alpha - 1)\cdots(\alpha - m + 2)}{(m - 1)!}\Delta^{m-1} \right] f(x_1)$$

that passes through the given data set $\{(x_i, f_i) \mid i = 1, \cdots, m\}$. Note that the independent variable x has been transformed into α using $x = x_1 + \alpha h$, hence $dx/d\alpha = h$. Now, the first derivative is obtained as,

$$f'(x) = \frac{df}{dx} \approx \frac{dP_{m-1}}{dx} = \frac{dP_{m-1}}{d\alpha}\frac{d\alpha}{dx} = \frac{1}{h}\left[\Delta + \frac{\alpha + (\alpha - 1)}{2}\Delta^2 + \right.$$

$$\left. \frac{\{\alpha(\alpha - 1) + (\alpha - 1)(\alpha - 2) + \alpha(\alpha - 2)\}}{6}\Delta^3 + \cdots \right] f(x_1)$$

Equation (5.-10) forms the basis of deriving a class of approximations for first derivatives from a tabular set of data. Note that the equation (5.-10) is still a function in α and hence it can be used to evaluate the derivative at any value of $x = x_1 + \alpha h$. Also, the series can be truncated after any number of terms. Thus, a whole class of successively more accurate representations for the first derivative can be constructed from equation (5.-10) by truncating the series at higher order terms. For example evaluating the derivative at the reference point x_1, (*i.e.*, $\alpha = 0$) equation (5.-10) reduces to,

$$f'(x_1) = \frac{1}{h}\left[\Delta - \frac{1}{2}\Delta^2 + \frac{1}{3}\Delta^3 - \frac{1}{4}\Delta^4 \cdots \pm \frac{1}{m-1}\Delta^{m-1}\right] f(x_1) + \mathcal{O}(h^{m-1})$$

This equation can also be obtained directly using equation (5.14) as,

$$E = e^{hD} \quad \text{or} \quad hD = \ln E = \ln(1 + \Delta)$$

Expanding the logarithmic term we obtain,

$$hD = \Delta - \frac{\Delta^2}{2} + \frac{\Delta^3}{3} - \frac{\Delta^4}{4} + \cdots$$

Operating both sides with $f(x_1)$ (*i.e.*, using x_1 as the reference point), we get,

$$Df(x_1) = f'(x_1) = \frac{1}{h}\left[\Delta - \frac{\Delta^2}{2} + \frac{\Delta^3}{3} - \frac{\Delta^4}{4} + \cdots\right] f(x_1)$$

$$(5.-12)$$

Now, truncating the series after the first term ($m = 2$),

$$f'(x_1) = \frac{1}{h}\left[\Delta f(x_1)\right] + \mathcal{O}(h)$$

$$= \frac{1}{h}\left[f_2 - f_1\right] + \mathcal{O}(h)$$

which is a 2-point, first order accurate, forward difference approximation for first derivative at x_1. Truncating the series after the first two terms $(m = 3)$,

$$
\begin{aligned}
f'(x_1) &= \frac{1}{h}\left[\Delta f(x_1) - \frac{1}{2}\Delta^2 f(x_1)\right] + \mathcal{O}(h^2) \\
&= \frac{1}{h}\left[(f_2 - f_1) - \frac{1}{2}(f_1 - 2f_2 + f_3)\right] + \mathcal{O}(h^2) \\
&= \frac{1}{2h}[-3f_1 + 4f_2 - f_3] + \mathcal{O}(h^2)
\end{aligned}
$$

which is the 3-point, second order accurate, forward difference approximation for the first derivative at x_1. Clearly both are approximate representations of the first derivative at x_1, but the second one is more accurate since the truncation error is of the order h^2.

Note that while, equation (5.11.1) is evaluated at the reference point on both sides of the equation, the earlier equation (5.-10) is a polynomial that is constructed around the reference point x_1, but can be evaluated at any other point by choosing appropriate α values. For example, consider the first derivative at $x = x_2$ or $\alpha = 1$. Two term truncation of equation (5.-10) yields,

$$
f'(x_2) = \frac{1}{h}\left[\Delta + \frac{1}{2}\Delta^2\right] f(x_1) + \mathcal{O}(h^2)
$$

or

$$
f'(x_2) = \frac{1}{2h}[f_3 - f_1] + \mathcal{O}(h^2)
$$

which is a 3-point, second order accurate, central difference approximation for the first derivative at x_2.

Going through a similar exercise as above with the Newton backward difference formula (5.11), truncating the series at various levels and using diffrent reference points, one can easily develop a whole class of approximations for first order derivatives. Some of the useful ones are summarized in Table 5.7.

Derivative at x_i	Difference approximation	truncation error
	Forward differences	
$f'(x_i)$	$(f_{i+1} - f_i)/h$	$\mathcal{O}(h)$
$f'(x_i)$	$(-3f_i + 4f_{i+1} - f_{i+2})/2h$	$\mathcal{O}(h^2)$
$f''(x_i)$	$(f_{i+2} - 2f_{i+1} + f_i)/h^2$	$\mathcal{O}(h)$
	Backward differences	
$f'(x_i)$	$(f_i - f_{i-1})/h$	$\mathcal{O}(h)$
$f'(x_i)$	$(+3f_i - 4f_{i-1} + f_{i-2})/2h$	$\mathcal{O}(h^2)$
$f''(x_i)$	$(f_i - 2f_{i-1} + f_{i-2})/h^2$	$\mathcal{O}(h)$
	Centered differences	
$f'(x_i)$	$(f_{i+1} - f_{i-1})/2h$	$\mathcal{O}(h^2)$
$f''(x_i)$	$(f_{i+1} - 2f_i + f_{i-1})/h^2$	$\mathcal{O}(h^2)$

Table 5.7: Summary of difference approximations for derivatives

5.11.2   Approximations for second order derivatives

The second derivative of the polynomial approximation is obtained by taking the derivative of equation (5.-10) one more time - viz.

$$f''(x) \approx \frac{d}{d\alpha}\left[\frac{dP_{m-1}}{d\alpha}\frac{d\alpha}{dx}\right]\frac{d\alpha}{dx} = \frac{1}{h^2}\left[\Delta^2 + \right.$$

$$\frac{\{\alpha + (\alpha-1) + (\alpha-1) + (\alpha-2) + \alpha + (\alpha-2)\}}{6}\Delta^3$$

$$\left. + \cdots\right]f(x_1) + \mathcal{O}(h^{m-2}) \tag{5.-18}$$

Evaluating at $\alpha = 0$ (*i.e.*, $x = x_1$), we obtain,

$$f''(x_1) = \frac{1}{h^2}\left[\Delta^2 - \Delta^3 + \frac{11}{12}\Delta^4 - -\frac{5}{6}\Delta^5 + \frac{137}{180}\Delta^6\cdots\right]f(x_1) \tag{5.-17}$$

This equation can also be obtained directly using equation (5.14) as,

$$(hD)^2 = (\ln E)^2 = (\ln(1+\Delta))^2$$

Expanding the logarithmic term we obtain,

$$(hD)^2 = \left[\Delta - \frac{\Delta^2}{2} + \frac{\Delta^3}{3} - \frac{\Delta^4}{4} + \frac{\Delta^5}{5}\cdots\right]^2$$

$$= \left[\Delta^2 - \Delta^3 + \frac{11}{12}\Delta^4 - \frac{5}{6}\Delta^5 + \frac{137}{180}\Delta^6 - \frac{7}{10}\Delta^7 + \frac{363}{560}\Delta^8\cdots\right]$$

Operating both sides on $f(x_1)$ (*i.e.*, using x_1 as the reference point), we get,

$$D^2 f(x_1) = f''(x_1) = \frac{1}{h^2}\left[\Delta^2 - \Delta^3 + \frac{11}{12}\Delta^4 - \cdots\right]f(x_1)$$

Truncating after one term,

$$f''(x_1) = \frac{1}{h^2}\left[\Delta^2 f(x_1)\right] = \frac{1}{h^2}(f_1 - 2f_2 + f_3) + \mathcal{O}(h)$$

Truncating after two terms,

$$f''(x_1) = \frac{1}{h^2}\left[\Delta^2 f(x_1) - \Delta^3 f(x_1)\right]$$

$$= \frac{1}{h^2}(2f_1 - 5f_2 + 4f_3 - f_4) + \mathcal{O}(h^2)$$

Evaluating equation(5.-18) at x_2 (or $\alpha = 1$), we get,

$$f''(x_2) = \frac{1}{h^2}\left[\Delta^2 - 0\cdot\frac{\delta^3}{6}\right]f(x_1) + \mathcal{O}(h^2)$$

Note that the third order term turns out to be zero and hence this formula turns out to be more accurate. This is a 3-point, second order accurate central difference approximation for the second derivative given as,

$$f''(x_2) = \frac{1}{h^2}\left[\Delta^2 f(x_1)\right] = \frac{1}{h^2}(f_1 - 2f_2 + f_3) + \mathcal{O}(h^2)$$

5.11.3   Taylor series approach

One can derive finite difference approximations from Taylor series expansion also. Consider the following expansions around x_i.

$$f(x_i + h) = f(x_i) + hf'(x_i) + \frac{h^2}{2}f''(x_i) + \frac{h^3}{3!}f'''(x_i) + \cdots$$

$$f(x_i - h) = f(x_i) - hf'(x_i) + \frac{h^2}{2}f''(x_i) - \frac{h^3}{3!}f'''(x_i) + \cdots$$

Subtracting the second from the first equation, and extracting $f'(x_i)$, we get,

$$f'(x_i) = \frac{f(x_i + h) - f(x_i - h)}{2h} - \frac{h^2}{6}f''(x_i) + \cdots$$

or,

$$f'(x_i) = \frac{f_{i+1} - f_{i-1}}{2h} + \mathcal{O}(h^2)$$

which is a central difference formula for the first derivative that we derived in the last section §5.11. Adding the two Taylor series expansions above, we get,

$$f_{i+1} + f_{i-1} = 2f_i + h^2 f''(x_i) + \frac{h^4}{12}f''''(x_i) + \cdots$$

or,

$$f''(x_i) = \frac{1}{h^2}\left[f_{i+1} + f_{i-1} - 2f_i\right] + \mathcal{O}(h^2)$$

which is a central difference formula for the second derivative that we derived in the last section §5.11.

5.12   Numerical integration

The ability to evaluate definite integrals numerically is useful either (i) when the function is complicated and hence is not easy to integrate analytically or (ii) the data is given in equally spaced, tabular from. In either case the starting point is to use the functional approximation methods seen in earlier sections followed by the integration of the approximate function. By doing this formally, with the Newton forward polynomials, we can develop a class of integration formulas. Consider the integral,

$$\int_a^b f(x)dx \qquad (5.\text{-}21)$$

Since the function can be represented by a polynomial of degree n as,

$$f(x) = P_n(x_0 + \alpha h) + \mathcal{O}(h^{n+1})$$

with an error of order h^{n+1}, we can use this approximation to carry out the integration. We first divide the interval $x \in [a, b]$ into n subdivisions as shown in the sketch below; hence there will be

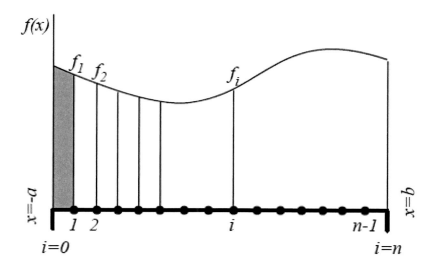

$(n + 1)$ data points labelled as $\{x_0, x_1, \cdots x_n\}$ and we have

$$h = (b - a)/n, \qquad x = x_0 + \alpha h \qquad dx = h d\alpha$$

As an illustration let us take a first degree polynomial between x_0 and x_1. We have

$$\int_{x_0}^{x_1} f(x)dx \approx \int_0^1 P_1(x_0 + \alpha h)hd\alpha + \int_0^1 \mathcal{O}(h^2)hd\alpha$$

or,

$$\int_{x_0}^{x_1} f(x)dx \approx \int_0^1 [1 + \alpha\Delta] \ f_0 \ h \ d\alpha + \mathcal{O}(h^3)$$

which upon, completing the integration becomes,

$$\int_{x_0}^{x_1} f(x)dx \approx \frac{h}{2}[f_0 + f_1] + \underbrace{\mathcal{O}(h^3)}_{local \ error} \qquad (5.\text{-}21)$$

This formula is the well known trapezoidal rule for numerical integration. The geometrical interpretation is that it represents the shaded area under the curve. Note that while numerical differentiation, as developed in equation (5.-10), lowers the order of the truncation error by one due to the term $d\alpha/dx = 1/h$ numerical integration increases the order of the truncation error by one due to the term $dx = hd\alpha$. In the above formula the truncation error is of order $\mathcal{O}(h^3)$. It is called the *local truncation error* since it is the error in integrating over *one* interval $x \in (x_0, x_1)$. To obtain the complete integral over the interval $x \in [a, b]$ we apply equation (5.12) repeatedly over each of the subdivisions as,

$$\int_a^b f(x)dx = \sum_{i=1}^n \int_{x_{i-1}}^{x_i} f(x)dx = \sum_{i=1}^n \frac{h}{2}[f_{i-1} + f_i] + \underbrace{\sum_{i=1}^n \mathcal{O}(h^3)}_{global \ error}$$

Recalling that $n = (b - a)/h$ the global or accumulated error becomes of order $\mathcal{O}(h^2)$. Thus the trapezoidal rule has a *local truncation error* of order $\mathcal{O}(h^3)$ and a *global truncation error* of order $\mathcal{O}(h^2)$ and the equation is,

$$\boxed{\int_a^b f(x)dx = \frac{h}{2}\sum_{i=1}^n [f_{i-1} + f_i] + \underbrace{\mathcal{O}(h^2)}_{global\ error}}$$ (5.-21)

By taking an quadratic functional approximation and integrating over the range of $x \in [x_0, x_2]$ we obtain the Simpson's 1/3 rule.

$$\int_{x_0}^{x_2} f(x)\ dx \approx \int_0^2 P_2(x_0 + \alpha h)\ h\ d\alpha + \int_0^2 \mathcal{O}(h^3)hd\alpha$$

or,

$$\int_{x_0}^{x_2} f(x)\ dx \approx \int_0^2 \left[1 + \alpha\Delta + \frac{\alpha(\alpha-1)}{2}\Delta^2\right] f_0\ h\ d\alpha + \mathcal{O}(h^4)$$

which upon, completing the integration becomes,

$$\int_{x_0}^{x_2} f(x)\ dx \approx \frac{h}{3}[f_0 + 4f_1 + f_2] + \underbrace{\mathcal{O}(h^4)}_{local\ error}$$ (5.-21)

Note that the next neglected term in the polynomial $P_2(x_0 + \alpha h)$ that corresponds to order $\mathcal{O}(h^3)$ term viz.

$$\int_0^2 \frac{\alpha(\alpha-1)(\alpha-2))}{3!}\Delta^3 f_0\ h\ d\alpha$$

turns out to be exactly zero, thus making the *local truncation error* in the Simpson's 1/3 rule to be actually of order $\mathcal{O}(h^5)$ Repeated application of the Simpson's rule results in,

$$\boxed{\int_a^b f(x)dx = \frac{h}{3}[f_0 + 4f_1 + 2f_2 + 4f_3 + 2f_4 + \cdots + f_n] + \underbrace{\mathcal{O}(h^4)}_{global\ error}}$$

(5.-21)

Note that in applying Simpson's rule repeatedly over the interval $x \in [a, b]$, we must have an even number of intervals (n even) or equivalently an odd number of points. In order to accomodate both even and odd number, the Simpson's 3/8 rule has been developed. In this case, we use a cubic function to approximate the function and the result is:

$$\int_{x_0}^{x_3} f(x) \; dx \approx \frac{3h}{8} \left[f_0 + 3f_1 + 3f_2 + f_3 \right] + \underbrace{\mathcal{O}(h^4)}_{local \; error} \qquad (5.\text{-}21)$$

Repeated application of the Simpson's 3/8 rule results in,

$$\int_a^b f(x)dx = \frac{h}{3} \left[f_0 + 3f_1 + 3f_2 + 2f_3 + 3f_4 + \cdots + f_n \right] + \underbrace{\mathcal{O}(h^4)}_{global \; error}$$

$$(5.\text{-}21)$$

The two equations can be combined to solve for any combination of odd and even intervals.

EXAMPLE 5.9 (- Numerical integration) *Evaluate   the integral*

$$\int_0^2 e^x \; dx$$

- *Analytically.*

- *Numerically by single application of the trapezoidal rule.*

- *Composite trapezoidal rule with 2 intervals and 4 intervals.*

- *A single application of Simpsn's 1/3 rule.*

- *Application of simpson's rules with 5 intervals.*

a) Analytically

$$f(x) = e^x$$

$$I = \int_0^2 e^x \, dx = [e^x]_0^2 = e^2 - e^0 = 7.3891 - 1.0000$$

$$= 6.3891$$

b) A single application of the trapezoidal rule
1 interval $a = 0, b = 2, h = (b-a)/n = 2$

$$\int_a^b f(x)dx = \frac{h}{2}[f_0 + f_1]$$

$$\int_0^2 f(x)dx = \frac{2}{2}[1.0000 + 7.3891] = 8.3891$$

c) Composite trapezoidal rule - 2 intervals

$h = \frac{2-0}{2} = 1$ Intervals: 0, 1; 1, 2
$\int_0^2 f(x)dx = \frac{2}{2}[1.0000 + 2.7183] + \frac{2}{2}[2.7183 + 7.3891] = 6.9128$

c) Composite trapezoidal rule - 4 intervals

Intervals: 0, 0.5; 0.5, 1.0; 1.0, 1.5; 1.5, 2.0
$\int_0^2 f(x)dx = \frac{0.5}{2}[1.0000+1.6487]+\frac{0.5}{2}[1.6487+2.7183]+\frac{0.5}{2}[2.7183+$
$4.4817] + \frac{0.5}{2}[4.4817 + 7.3891] = 6.5216$

d) A single application of the Simpson's 1/3 rule

Two intervals n= 2, $h = \frac{b-a}{n} = 1$, $x_0 = 0, x_1 = 1, x_2$

$$I = \int_{x_0}^{x_2} f(x)dx \approx \frac{h}{3}[f_0 + 4f_1 + f_2]$$

$$I = \frac{1}{3}[1.0000 + 4(2.7183) + 7.3891] = 6.4208$$

e) For five intervals, we need to combine Simpson's 1/3 and 3/8 rules.

Five intervals n= 5, $h = \frac{b-a}{n} = \frac{2-0}{5} = 2/5$,
$x_0 = 0, x_1 = 2/5, x_2 = 6/5, x_3 = 8/5, x_4 = 2$

Use the first three points with Simpson 1/3 and the last four points with Simpsons 3/8

$$I = \frac{h}{3}[f_0 + 4f_1 + f_2]$$
$$+ \frac{3h}{8}[f_2 + 3f_3 + 3f_4 + f_5]$$

Setting the function values at each point we obtain

$$I = \frac{0.4}{3}[1.0000 + 4(1.4918) + 2.2255]$$
$$+ \frac{3 \times 0.4}{8}[2.2255 + 3(3.3201) + 3(4.9530) + 7.3891]$$
$$= 6.3908$$

Both the Simpsons methods have the same order of approximation. However, the 1/3 rule uses less function evaluations.

5.12.1 Richardson Extrapolation

An idea similar to that used in section §2.8.3 to accelerate convergence is the notion of extrapolation to improve accuracy of numerical integration. The basic idea is to estimate the *truncation error* by evaluating the integral on two different grid sizes, h_1 and h_2.

When applied to numerical integration with the trapezoidal rule, we obtain a very powerful interration rule called *Romberg Intergartion*

Let us apply this idea on the trapezoidal rule which has a *global truncation error* of $\mathcal{O}(h^2)$. Let the exact integral be represented as,

$$I = I(h_1) + E(h_1)$$

where $I(h_1)$ is the approximate estimate of the integral using grid size of h_1 and $E(h_1)$ is the error. Similarly we have,

$$I = I(h_2) + E(h_2)$$

But, for trapezoidal rule we have $E(h_i) \propto h_i^2$. Hence

$$\frac{E(h_1)}{E(h_2)} = \frac{h_1^2}{h_2^2}$$

We can combine these equations as,

$$I = I(h_1) + E(h_1) = I(h_2) + E(h_2)$$

or,

$$I(h_1) + E(h_2)\frac{h_1^2}{h_2^2} = I(h_2) + E(h_2)$$

which can be solved to obtain $E(h_2)$ as,

$$E(h_2) = \frac{I(h_1) - I(h_2)}{[1 - (h_1/h_2)^2]}$$

Hence a better estimate for the integral is,

$$I = I(h_2) + \frac{1}{[(h_1/h_2)^2 - 1]}[I(h_2) - I(h_1)]$$

If $h_2 = h_1/2$ then we have,

$$I = I(h_2) + \frac{1}{[2^2 - 1]}[I(h_2) - I(h_1)]$$

Since we have estimated and eliminated the truncation error of order $\mathcal{O}(h^2)$ term, the above equation will have an error of order

$\mathcal{O}(h^4)$ which is the next leading term in the Taylor series expansion. By repeated application of the above approach to estimate and eliminate successively higher order terms, we can arrive at the following general formula for Romberg extrapolation.

$$I_{j,k} = \frac{4^{k-1}I_{j+1,k-1} - I_{j,k-1}}{4^{k-1} - 1}$$

(5.-33)

Example of Romberg integration

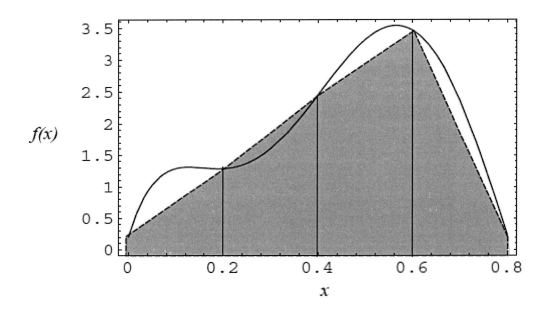

| | | $O(h^2)$ | $O(h^4)$ | $O(h^6)$ |
		$(k=1)$	$(k=2)$	$(k=3)$
$j=1$	$h=0.8$	0.1728	1.3674667	1.64053334
$j=2$	$h=0.4$	1.0688	1.6234667	1.64053334
$j=3$	$h=0.2$	1.4848	1.6394667	
$j=4$	$h=0.1$	1.6008		

Figure 5.15: Illustration of Romberg extrapolation

Consider the following integral,

$$\int_0^{0.8} (0.2 + 25x - 200x^2 + 675x^3 - 900x^4 + 400x^5) \, dx = 1.64053334$$

$$(5.\text{-}33)$$

which has the exact value as shown. A sketch of the function $f(x)$ and the Romberg extrapolation results are shown in figure 5.15. It is clear from this example that by combining three rather poor estimates of the integral on grids of $h = 0.8, 0.4$ and 0.2, a result accurate to eight significant digits has been obtained! For example, $I_{2,2}$ is obtained by using $j = 2$ and $k = 2$ which results in,

$$I_{2,2} = \frac{4 \times I_{3,1} - I_{2,1}}{4 - 1} = \frac{4 \times 1.4848 - 1.0688}{3} = 1.6234667$$

Similarly, $I_{1,3}$ is obtained by using $j = 1$ and $k = 3$ which results in,

$$I_{1,3} = \frac{4^2 \times I_{2,2} - I_{1,2}}{4^2 - 1} = \frac{4^2 \times 1.6234667 - 1.3674667}{15} = 1.64053334$$

EXAMPLE 5.10 (MATLAB example) *MATLAB provides a m-file to evaluate definite integrals using adaptive, recursive Simpson's quadrature. You must of course, define the function through a m-file which should accept a vector of input arguments and return the corresponding function values. A m-file that implements equation (5.15) is shown in figure 5.16. After creating such a file work through the following example during an interactive session.*

```
function f=int_ex(x)
%defines a 5th degree polynomial

m=length(x);
for i=1:m
 f(i) = 0.2 + 25*x(i)  - 200*x(i)^2 + ...
       675*x(i)^3 - 900*x(i)^4 + 400*x(i)^5;
end
```

Figure 5.16: MATLAB implementation of quadrature evaluation

```
>>quad('int_ex',0,0.8,1e-5)        % evaluate integral over (0,0.8)
>>quad('int_ex',0,0.8,1e-5,1)      % Display results graphically
>>quad('int_ex',0,0.8,1e-8)        % Note the warning messges!
```

5.12.2   Gaussian quadratures

Whereas the above methods (known as Newton-Cotes methods) require the data to be evenly spaced (value of h to be the same for all intervals), Gaussian quadrature method does not. The most popular Gaussian quadrature method is called the Gauss-Legendre method which we will discuss in this section.
In Gaussian rules the points and weights are selected to integrate exactly polynomials of degree $m \le 2n - 1$ where n is the number of points chosen.

$$f(\xi) = a_1 + a_2 + \cdots + a_{2n}\xi^{2n-1}$$

The points usually end up being irrational numbers.

Gauss Legendre

It is convenient to define the integration in a reference space from -1 to +1 for this integration method, and the real space is mapped onto the reference space using the appropriate coordinate transformation. We define the general Gaussian form:

$$\int_{-1}^{1} f(\xi)d\xi = w_1 f_1(\xi_1) + w_2 f_2(\xi_2) + \cdots w_n f_n(\xi_n) = \sum_{i=1}^{n} w_i f(\xi_i)$$

As noted, the w_i and ξ_i (there are n of each) are selected to integrate exactly the polynomial given above. Substitute the equation:

$$f(\xi) = a_1 + a_2\xi + \cdots + a_{2n}\xi^{2n-1}$$

into the integral 5.12.2 we obtain:

$$I = \int_{-1}^{1} f(\xi)d\xi = a_1 \int_{-1}^{1} d\xi + a_2 \int_{-1}^{1} \xi d\xi + \cdots + a_{2n} \int_{-1}^{1} \xi^{2n-1}d\xi$$

The integration yields the expression:

$$\begin{aligned}
I = {} & a_1(w_1 + w_2 + \cdots + w_n) \\
& + a_2(w_1\xi_1 + w_2\xi_2 + \cdots + w_n\xi_n) \cdots \\
& + a_{2n}(w_1\xi_1^{2n-1} + w_2\xi_2^{2n-1} + \cdots + w_n\xi_n^{2n-1})
\end{aligned}$$

For the integral to be valid, the following equalities must hold:

$$\int_{-1}^{1} \xi^\alpha d\xi = \frac{2}{\alpha+1} = \sum_{i=1}^{n} w_i\xi_i^\alpha = \qquad \alpha = 0, 2, 4, 6, \cdots 2n - 2$$

$$\int_{-1}^{1} \xi^\alpha d\xi = 0 = \sum_{i=1}^{n} w_i\xi_i^\alpha = \qquad \alpha = 1, 3, 5, \cdots 2n - 1$$

Thus generate a system of n equations to solve. *e.g.*, for n = 2:

$$I = \int_{-1}^{1} f(\xi)d\xi = w_1 f(\xi_1) + w_2 f(\xi_2)$$

The generated equations are:

$$2 = w_1 + w_2$$
$$0 = w_1\xi_1 + w_2\xi_2$$
$$\frac{2}{3} = w_1\xi_1^2 + w_2\xi_2^2$$
$$0 = w_1\xi_1^3 + w_2\xi_2^3$$

The solution is:

$$w_1 = w_2 = 1 \qquad xi_1 = -\xi_2 = \frac{1}{\sqrt{3}}$$

for n= 3 it can be similarly shown that:

$$w_1 = \frac{8}{9} \quad w_2 = w_3 = \frac{5}{9}$$

$$\xi_1 = 0 \quad \xi_2 = -\xi_3 = \sqrt{\frac{3}{5}}$$

and likewise for n = 4:

$$w_1 = w_2 = \frac{1}{2} + \frac{1}{6\sqrt{6/5}} \qquad \xi_1 = -\xi_2 = \sqrt{\frac{3 - 2\sqrt{6/5}}{7}}$$

$$w_3 = w_4 = \frac{1}{2} - \frac{1}{6\sqrt{6/5}} \qquad \xi_3 = -\xi_4 = \sqrt{\frac{3 + 2\sqrt{6/5}}{7}}$$

These values are defined over the range that spans from -1 to +1.

EXAMPLE 5.11 (Evaluate the integral $\int_{-1}^{1} x^2 dx$) *Lets il-lustrate the concept behind quadrature methods by finding the integral of the function $f(x) = x^2$, which has an obvious solution*

Analytical

$$\int_{-1}^{1} x^2 dx = \left[\frac{3}{2}\right]_{-1}^{1} = \frac{1}{3} - \left(-\frac{1}{3}\right) = \frac{2}{3}$$

Gauss Method

$$\int_{-1}^{1} x^2 dx = w1f(\xi_1) + w_2 f(\xi_2)$$

$$= 1\left(\frac{-1}{\sqrt{3}}\right)^2 + 1\left(\frac{1}{\sqrt{3}}\right)^2 \qquad = \frac{1}{3} + \frac{1}{3} = \frac{2}{3}$$

The answers are obviously identical !! For n =2, we should expect exact integral for $f(x) = 1$, $f(x) = x$, $f(x) = x^2$ and $f(x) = x^3$

EXAMPLE 5.12 (Evaluate the integral $\int_{-1}^{1} \cos x \, dx$)

Using 2-point and 3-point Gauss quadrature

2-point Gauss quadrature:
From table 5.8 for $n = 2$: $w_1 = 1.000000000$, $w_2 = 1.000000000$ and $\xi_1 = -0.577350269$, $\xi_2 = 0.577350269$
Therefore

$$\int_{-1}^{1} \cos x \, dx = w_1 f(\xi_1) + w_2 f(\xi_2)$$

$$= (1)\cos(-0.577350269) + (1)\cos(0.577350269)$$
$$= 1.67582366$$

3-point Gauss quadrature:
From table 5.8 for $n = 3$: $w_1 = 0.555555556$, $w_2 = 0.888888889$, $w_3 = 0.555555556$; $\xi_1 = -0.774596669$, $\xi_2 = 0$ and $\xi_3 = 0.774596669$

Therefore

$$\int_{-1}^{1} \cos x dx = w_1 f(\xi_1) + w_2 f(\xi_2) + w_3 f(\xi_3)$$

$$= 0.555555556 \cos(-0.774596669) + 0.888888889 \cos(0)$$
$$+ 0.555555556 \cos(0.774596669)$$
$$= 1.68285982$$

Analytical:
$\int_{-1}^{1} \cos x dx = [\sin x]_{-1}^{1} = \sin(1) - \sin(-1) = 1.67582366$

Comparing the two answers with the exact (analytical) solution we observe that the 3-point Gauss quadrature is more accurate than the two point (viz. 4.2% error for 2 pont and 0.0005% for 3-point !!)

Knowing that the coefficients are given in the interval [a,b] we can use these points to transform the integral $\int_a^b f(x)dx$ to $\int_{-1}^1 f(\xi)d\xi$ by performing variable transformation

Changing the variable

$$x = \frac{1}{2}(\xi(b - a)) + a + b$$

$$dx = \frac{1}{2}(b - a)d\xi$$

Thus the integration becomes

$$\int_a^b f(x)dx = \int_{-1}^1 f(\xi)d\xi = \int_{-1}^1 f\left(\frac{(b - a)\xi + a + b}{2}\right)\left(\frac{b - a}{2}\right)d\xi$$

or

$$\boxed{\int_a^b f(x)dx = \sum_{i=1}^n w_i f(\xi_i)}$$

Table 1 gives gauss points for different values of n. The rational numbers are given in decimal form.

Table 5.8: Weighting factors and Gauss points used in Gauss Quadrature formulas

Points	Weighing factors	Gauss points
2	$w_1 = 1.000000000$	$\xi_1 = -0.577350269$
	$w_2 = 1.000000000$	$\xi_2 = 0.577350269$
3	$w_1 = 0.555555556$	$\xi_1 = -0.774596669$
	$w_2 = 0.888888889$	$\xi_2 = 0.000000000$
	$w_3 = 0.555555556$	$\xi_3 = 0.774596669$
4	$w_1 = 0.347854845$	$\xi_1 = -0.861136312$
	$w_2 = 0.652145155$	$\xi_2 = -0.339981044$
	$w_3 = 0.652145155$	$\xi_3 = 0.339981044$
	$w_4 = 0.347854845$	$\xi_4 = 0.861136312$
5	$w_1 = 0.236926885$	$\xi_1 = -0.906179846$
	$w_2 = 0.478628670$	$\xi_2 = -0.538469310$
	$w_3 = 0.568888889$	$\xi_3 = 0.000000000$
	$w_4 = 0.478628670$	$\xi_4 = 0.538469310$
	$w_5 = 0.236926885$	$\xi_5 = 0.906179846$
6	$w_1 = 0.171324492$	$\xi_1 = -0.932469514$
	$w_2 = 0.360761573$	$\xi_2 = -0.661209386$
	$w_3 = 0.467913935$	$\xi_3 = -0.238619186$
	$w_4 = 0.467913935$	$\xi_4 = 0.238619186$
	$w_5 = 0.360761573$	$\xi_5 = 0.661209386$
	$w_6 = 0.171324492$	$\xi_6 = 0.932469514$

5.12.3   Multiple integrals

In Engineering, we frequently encounter problems requiring the calculation of surface integrals as well as volume integrals. Simply stated, surface integral involves integration of a function of two variables (2-dimensional) whereas volume integral involves functions with three variables (3-dimensional), *i.e.*, $f(x, y)$ and $f(x, y, z)$ respectively.

For example,

$$S = \iint_A f dA = \iint_A f(x, y) dx dy$$

represents the area on the x-y plane under the surface of integration. It is also called double integral because we are integrating over two variables. To evaluate such an integral, we evaluate the two integrals along their directions. With the limits in the two variables we can write

$$\int_a^b \int_c^d f(x, y) dx dy = \int_c^d \left(\int_a^b f(x, y) dx \right) dy = \int_a^b \left(\int_c^d f(x, y) dy \right) dx$$

Which implies that we keep one of the variables constant and integrate in the other dimension using the one dimensinal methods outlined earlier. The order of integration is not important

EXAMPLE 5.13 *The temperature distribution over a flat plate is given by has been measured at various location and the results are shown in the figure 5.17. Determine the average plate temperature with dimensions and values as shown.*

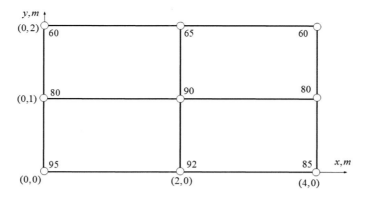

Figure 5.17: Temperature measurements on a plate

Solution

The average temperature is given by

$$T_{ave} = \frac{1}{A} \int_0^2 \int_0^3 T(x, y) dx dy$$

Lets carry out the integration along the x-direction using the Trapezoidal rule

$$\text{Row 1} \quad \frac{(2-0)}{2}(95+92) + \frac{(4-2)}{2}(92+85) = 364$$

$$\text{Row 2} \quad \frac{(2-0)}{2}(80+90) + \frac{(4-2)}{2}(90+80) = 340$$

$$\text{Row 3} \quad \frac{(2-0)}{2}(60+65) + \frac{(4-2)}{2}(65+60) = 250$$

And the y-direction sum

$$\text{column} \quad \frac{(1-0)}{2}(350+250) + \frac{(2-1)}{2}(364+340) = 652$$

The average temperature is therefore

$$T_{ave} = \frac{652}{4 \times 2} = 81.5$$

We could have started our intergation along the columns (y-direction) followed by integration along the x-direction and the results would be the same!

By the same token, triple integral is defined as

$$V = \iiint_V dV = \iiint_V dxdydz$$

Thus for example, the mass of a substance with given density is defined as

$$m = \iiint_V \rho dV = \iiint_V \rho dxdydz$$

Again, as with the double integral, we have a number of options in evaluating the integral within the different limits over which each dimension varies. For example, we can work our way from the inner integral, to the middle integral and finally to the outer integral respectively.

5.13   Unequally spaced data

The difference equations will only work for uniformly spaced data. Also, the Richardson method needs the data to be evenly spread in order to produce succesively halved intervals. One way to handle un-even data is to fit a polynomial through the data and then differentiate the polynomial and evaluate the derivatives.

EXAMPLE 5.14 (Uneven data) *Given   the   points $(x_0, y_0), (x_1, y_1)$ and (x_2, y_2), fit a polynomial through the points and find the first derivative*
Using Lagrange polynomial:

$$f(x) = f(x_0)\frac{(x - x_1)(x - x_2)}{(x_0 - x_1)(x_0 - x_2)} + f(x_1)\frac{(x - x_0)(x - x_2)}{(x_1 - x_0)(x_1 - x_2)}$$

$$+ f(x_2)\frac{(x - x_0)(x - x_1)}{(x_2 - x_0)(x_0 - x_1)}$$

We can now take the derivative

$$f'(x) = f(x_0)\frac{(2x - x_1 - x_2)}{(x_0 - x_1)(x_0 - x_2)} + f(x_1)\frac{(2x - x_0 - x_2)}{(x_1 - x_0)(x_1 - x_2)}$$

$$+ f(x_2)\frac{(2x - x_0 - x_1)}{(x_2 - x_0)(x_0 - x_1)}$$

5.14 Summary

In the first part of this chapter we have introduced different methods for functional approximation. For discrete data points, interpolation techniques are utilized when the data in question is known to be precise. In this case, the interpolating function is made to go through all data points exactly. Different types of polynomials can be used. Collocation methods require the solution of a system of equations. Such methods are therefore prone to errors due to round off effects.

The lagrange and Newton polynomials are well suited for interpolating functions. They both do not require the solution of system of equations and can therefore be developed easily from given data points. The newton polynomial is derived though difference tables and the polynomial coefficients can be easily expanded to include more data points without reculculating the existing coefficients. It is also well suited for equally spaced data. Operator techniques are highly amenable for developing difference equations and polynomials.

When a given set of data from measurements is not precise, it is more convenient to develop polynomials which satisfy the known data in the least squares sense only. Different type of polynomials as well as non-linear functions can easily be fitted to a given data through minimization of an objective function. Lastly, through clever manipulation of non-linear functions, their linear forms may be obtained. In this case, linear regression may be used for both linear and non-linear equations.

In the second part of this chapter, we have explored numerical techniques for differentiation and integration. For discrete data points, an approximating polynomial can be used to fit the data and then applied for the integration or differentiation process. This works for both equally spaced and un-equally spaced data.

With differentiation, we have derived difference formulae for different orders of derivatives. The lagrange as well as the Newton polynomial can be used. The Newton polynomial works well for equally spaced data points

On integration, we have developed methods ranging from the simple trapezoidal rules to complex Gaussian quadratures. The trapezoidal method, coupled with Richardson extraplation technique is capable of high order approximations with minimal computational expenses. Simpson's methods are also useful, giving higher accuracy than trapezoidal rule. Both the 1/3 rule and 3/8 rules may have to be used when the number of data points is odd.

The Gaussian quadrature methods improve the determination of integrals to high order accurary with arbitrary data points. Finally, we have shown that integration methods can easily be extended to multiple variables.

5.15 Exercise Problems

P5II.1. Exercise on MATLAB - Numerical integration and differentiation

Consider the function

$$f(x) = sinh(2 - x^3)e^{2x}$$

(a) Write an *m-file* that will take a set of x values and return the corresponding set of function values.

(b) Then use it with the $MATLAB$ function *quad* to evaluate the integral of the function

$$\int_{-1}^{1} f(x)\ dx$$

with a tolerance of 1.0×10^{-5}.

(c) Plot the function in the range $x \in \{-1, 1\}$

(d) Next generate a set of values for x as $x = [0.2,\ 0.3,\ 0.4,\ 0.5,\ 0.6]$ and evaluate the $f(x)$ for the same function as above.

(e) Finally, using these function values, calculate the *first* and *third* differences with the help of the $MATLAB$ function $diff$.

P5II.2. Uneven data It is desired to determine the diffusion flux $j = -D\frac{dC}{dx}$ at the surface of a reservoir (x $=0$). Concentration measurements have been taken at un-equal spacing along the reservoir domain. The diffusion coeffieicnt is given as $D = 1 \times 10^{-4} m^2/s$.

$x(mm)$	0	1.1	4.2
C (mol/m^3)	15.5	12.3	6.1

P5II.3. Mass transfer coefficient

It is desired to calculate the mass transfer coefficient at the surface of a slab. The following measurements are available

z	0	0.4	0.8	1.2	1.6
P_A	0.1000	0.0800	0.0701	0.0621	0.0510

z	2.0	2.4	2.8	3.2
P_A	0.0411	0.0321	0.0222	0.0201

Here, z is the distance from the slab surface and P_A is the partial pressure of the gas involved. If the pressure gradient at the surface of the slab is given by

$$DP = \left.\frac{P_A}{dz}\right|_{z=0}$$

Determine the pressure gradient by

(a) Fit a cubic polynomial using Newton's divided difference method and evaluate the polynomial at $z = 0$ to determine the gradient.

(b) Fit a cubic polynomial using MATLAB *polyfit* function and use MATLAB functions *polyder* and *polyval* to determine the gradient at $z = 0$.

(c) Calculate the derivative at $z = 0$ using second order accurate finite differences.

P5II.4. Numerical integration

Evaluate the integral

$$\int_0^6 10e^{-2x})dx$$

(a) Analytically.

(b) Numerically by single application of the trapezoidal rule.

(c) Composite trapezoidal rule with 2 intervals and 4 intervals.

(d) A single application of the Simpson's 1/3 rule.

(e) A single application of simpsn's 3/8 rule.

(f) Application of simpson's rule with 5 intervals.

P5II.5. Consider the following integral,

$$\int_0^{0.8} (0.2 + 25x - 200x^2 + 675x^3 - 900x^4 + 400x^5) \, dx$$

with exact integral $I = 1.64053334$.

(a) Use forward and backward difference approximations of $\mathcal{O}(h)$ and centered difference approximation of $\mathcal{O}(h^2)$ to approximate the above derivative.

(b) Use Richardson extrapolation to improve the accuracy of the centered difference approximation obtained above.

P5II.6. Evaluate the following integral,

$$\int_0^{0.8} (0.2 + 25x - 200x^2 + 675x^3 - 900x^4 + 400x^5) \, dx$$

(a) Using Romberg integration with a stopping criterion of $\epsilon_S = 0.5\%$.

(b) Using 3 point gauss quadrature.

P5II.7. Evaluate the following integral,

$$y = \int_{-1}^{1} x^2 \, dx$$

(a) Analytically.

(b) Using 2 point gauss quadrature.

P5II.8. Evaluate the following integral,

$$y = \int_{-1}^{1} \cos x \, dx$$

(a) Analytically.

(b) Using 2 point gauss quadrature.

(c) Using 3 point gauss quadrature.

P5II.9. Compressor work can be determined using the following formula

$$W = \int_{v_0}^{v_1} p dv$$

$v(L)$	0.5	0.55	0.6	0.65	0.70
P, kPa	1348	1250	1160	1110	1005

$v(L)$	0.75	0.80	0.85	0.9	0.95	1.0
P, kPa	995	970	950	910	890	880

Determine the work done using:

(a) Use simpsons's rule.

(b) Use Gauss Quadrature with n = 3.

P5II.10. The length of a connecting path is given by the following equation

$$L(f) = \int_{a}^{b} \sqrt{1 + (f'(x))^2} dx$$

If the following measurements have been obtained

x	0.0000	0.3000	0.5000	1.0000
y	5.0000	6.513	8.214	10.00

(a) Use Newton's divided difference method to obtain a cubic interpolating polynomial between the points and find the value of $y = f(x)$ at $x = 0.40$.

(b) Using the polynomial found in part (a) and the trapezoidal method, determine the length of the path betwen 0 and 1.0 using a step size of 0.25.

(c) Recalculate the integral using two point Gauss quadrature method.

P5II.11. Buried pipes are frequently used to transport petroleum products in cold climates.   The temperature of the ground at various buried depths, assuming a semi-infinite solid is given by

$$\frac{T(x,t) - T_S}{T_i - T_S} = erf(\beta) = \frac{2}{\sqrt{\pi}} \int_0^{\beta} e^{-\xi^2} d\xi$$

where

$\beta = \dfrac{x}{2\sqrt{\alpha t}}$

$\alpha =$ thermal diffusivity of soil $= 2.52 \times 10^{-5} m^2/s$

$T(x,t) =$ Temperature at depth x and time t

$T_S =$ Surface temperature

$T_i =$ initial ground temperature

If the soil temperature at the start of winter is $15°C$ and the ground surface temperature is $-18°C$

(a) Determine the temperature of a pipe at a buried depth of 1.2 m after 21 days

(b) Write a MATLAB script to generate a plot of Temperature variation with time at a depth of 0.8 m for 30 days.

CHAPTER 6 _____

ORDINARY DIFFERENTIAL EQUATIONS - INITIAL VALUE PROBLEMS (IVP)

In this chapter we develop algorithms for solving systems of linear and nonlinear ordinary differential equations of the *initial value type*. Such models arise in describing *lumped parameter, dynamic* models. Entire books (Lapidus & Seinfeld,1971; Lambert 1973) are devoted to the development of algorithms for such problems. We will develop only elementary concepts of *single* and *multistep* methods, *implicit* and *explicit* methods, and introduce concepts of numerical stability and *stiffness*.

6.1   Model equations and initial conditions

Ordinary differential equations of the initial type are represented typically as a system of *first order* equations of the form,

$$\frac{d\boldsymbol{y}}{dt} = \boldsymbol{f}(\boldsymbol{y}, t) \tag{6.1}$$

$$\boldsymbol{y}(t = t_0) = \boldsymbol{y}_0 \tag{6.2}$$

where $\boldsymbol{y}(t)$ is a vector containing elements $\boldsymbol{y} = \{y_1(t), y_2(t), \cdots, y_n(t)\}$ and our objective is to construct an approximate representation of the function $\boldsymbol{y}(t)$ over some interval of interest $t \in [t_0, t_f]$ that satisfy the initial conditions, given by another vector $\boldsymbol{y}_0 = \{y_{1,0}, y_{2,0}, \cdots, y_{n,0}\}$. If the functions $\boldsymbol{f}(\boldsymbol{y}, t)$ depend on t explicitly, then the equations are called *non-autonomous*; otherwise they are called an *autonomous* system of equations.

6.1.1   Higher order differential equations

A higher order differential equation (say of order n) can be converted into an equivalent system of (n) first order equations. Consider the equation,

$$a_n \frac{d^n \theta}{dt^n} + a_{n-1} \frac{d^{n-1}\theta}{dt^{n-1}} + \cdots a_1 \frac{d\theta}{dt} + a_0 \theta = b \qquad (6.3)$$

subject to a set of n initial conditions at t_0 of the form,

$$
\begin{aligned}
\left.\frac{d^{n-1}\theta}{dt^{n-1}}\right|_{t_0} &= c_{n-1} \\
\left.\frac{d^{n-2}\theta}{dt^{n-2}}\right|_{t_0} &= c_{n-2} \\
\vdots &= \vdots \\
\left.\frac{d\theta}{dt}\right|_{t_0} &= c_1 \\
\left.\theta\right|_{t_0} &= c_0
\end{aligned}
\qquad (6.4)
$$

Since all of these conditions are given at t_0, this remains an *initial value problem*. Equation (6.3) can be recast into a system of n first order equations of the form (6.1) as follows. Let us define θ and all of its $(n-1)$ successive higher derivatives as

$$y_1(t) = \theta(t), \quad y_2(t) = \frac{d\theta}{dt}, \quad y_3(t) = \frac{d^2\theta}{dt^2}, \quad \cdots \quad y_n(t) = \frac{d^{n-1}\theta}{dt^{n-1}}$$

Then we have,

$$\frac{dy_1}{dt} = y_2, \qquad y_1(t_0) = c_0$$

$$\frac{dy_2}{dt} = y_3, \qquad y_2(t_0) = c_1$$

$$\vdots = \vdots \qquad\qquad\qquad\qquad (6.5)$$

$$\frac{dy_{n-1}}{dt} = y_n, \qquad y_{n-1}(t_0) = c_{n-2}$$

$$\frac{dy_n}{dt} = \frac{1}{a_n}[b - a_0 y_1 - a_1 y_2 - \cdots - a_{n-1} y_n],, \qquad y_n(t_0) = c_{n-1}$$

where the last equation has been obtained from the n-th order equation (6.3). Also shown in equations (6.5), are the transformed initial conditions from equation (6.4) in terms of the new variable set $\boldsymbol{y}$.

Note that the coefficients $\{a_0, a_1, \cdots a_n, b\}$ in equation (6.3) can in general be nonlinear functions of θ and its derivatives. This nonlinearity will reflect in equations (6.5), since the coefficients $\{a_0, a_1, \cdots a_n, b\}$ will be functions of the transformed variables $\{y_1, y_2 \cdots y_n\}$.

6.2 Taylor Series Methods

6.2.1 Explicit Euler scheme

Consider the differential equation,

$$\frac{dy}{dt} = f(y), \qquad y(t_0) = y_0 \qquad\qquad (6.6)$$

Our task is to construct a sequence $\{y_n | n = 0, 1, \cdots\}$ that represents an approximate solution to $y(t)$ at a discrete set of points $\{t_n | n = 0, 1, \cdots\}$. We can achieve this by constructing a Taylor series expansion for $y(t)$ around t_n with a step size of h as,

$$y(t_n + h) = y(t_n) + y'(t_n)h + y''(t_n)\frac{h^2}{2} + \cdots$$

Truncating after the linear term and recognizing that $y'(t_n) = f(y_n)$, we have the Euler scheme for generating the solution sequence,

$$y_{n+1} = y_n + hf(y_n) + \underbrace{\mathcal{O}(h^2)}_{local\ error} \qquad n = 0, 1, \cdots \qquad (6.7)$$

which is *single-step, explicit* scheme with a local truncation error of order $\mathcal{O}(h^2)$. It is called a *single-step* method because it requires only the value at y_n to predict the value at next step y_{n+1}. It is *explicit* because the right hand side terms $[y_n + hf(y_n)]$ can be computed explicitly using known value of y_n.

EXAMPLE 6.1 (Explicit Euler) *Solve the following differential equation*

$$\frac{dy}{dt} = y \qquad y(0) = 1 \qquad 0 \le t \le 1.5$$

For a step size of h = 0.5.
Explicit Euler

$$y_{k+1} = y_k + hf(t_k, y_k)$$

First we carry out a few steps by hand calculations From the given conditions $y_0 = 1, t_0 = 0$
$y_1 = y_0 + hf(t_0, y_0) = 1 + 0.5(1) = 1.5$
$y_2 = y_1 + hf(t_1, y_1) = 1.5 + 0.5(1.5) = 2.25$
$y_3 = y_2 + hf(t_2, y_2) = 2.25 + 0.5(2.25) = 3.375$
Next we explore calculations using MATLAB script which implements the above algorithm
Figure 6.1 shows different results depending on the step size taken.

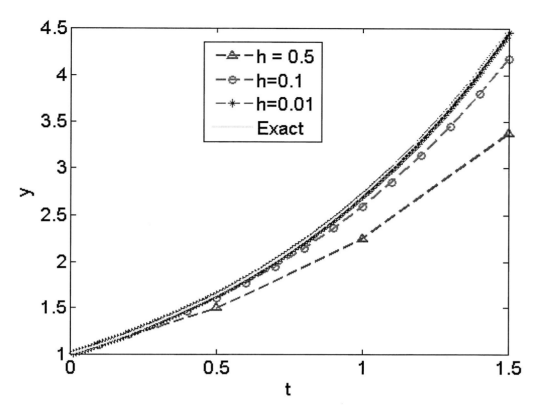

Figure 6.1: Solution of y' = y using Explicit Euler with different step sizes

The implementation of the Euler scheme is simple. First, we need to evaluate the function at an initial point. Then add up the value of the function at the point with the previous value. If we look colsely at the Euler scheme, we see that we can rewrite it as

$$y_{k+1} = y_k + hf(t_k, y_k) \Rightarrow \frac{y_{k+1} - y_k}{h} = f(t_k, y_k)$$

$$f(t_k, y_k) = \frac{y_{k+1} - y_k}{h}$$

which is the forward difference approximation of the slope at point t_k. The bigger the step size h, the further away is the solution from the true value. Whence we have discovered one of the biggest weakness of the Explicit Euler method. The step sizes taken needs *to be small, otherwise the solution will separate further away from the true value. There is another weakness of the method, with regard to making small changes to the initial value. We shall explore the issues of stability in §6.2.5.*

6.2.2   Midpoint method - A modification of Eulers method

The midpoint method is a modification of Eulers explicit method. In this case, the slope used for calculating is the estimate of the slope at the middle of the interval. The estimate is obtained as follows. Eulers method is used to calculate the slope at the middle of the interval, , *i.e.*, $x_m = x_i + 1/2h$

$$y_m = y_i + \frac{h}{2} f(x, y)$$

and the slope at the middle of the interval is estimated using

$$\frac{dy}{dx}\bigg|_{x=x_m} = f(x_m, y_m)$$

The middle slope is then used to calculate the new estimate *i.e.*,

$$y_{i+1} = y_i + f(x_m, y_m)h \tag{6.8}$$

Figure 6.2 shows the graphical depiction of the midpoint method.

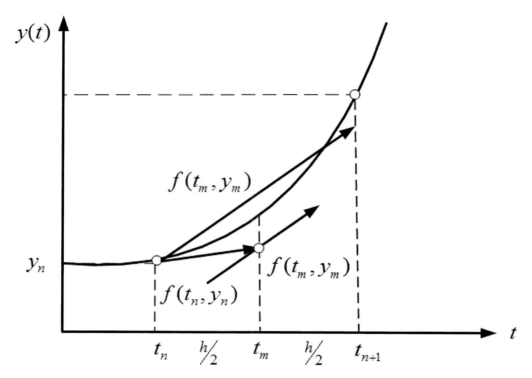

Figure 6.2: The midpoint method - slope manipulation

6.2.3 Implicit Euler scheme - Backward Euler

Alternate derivation using interpolation polynomials

Rewriting the differential equation (6.6) as,

$$\int_{y_n}^{y_{n+1}} dy = \int_{t_n}^{t_{n+1}} f(y)dt \qquad (6.9)$$

and using Newton forward and backward interpolating polynomials to approximate the function $f(y)$ we can recover, not only the Euler scheme, but develop a mechanism for obtaining a whole class of *implicit* and *multistep* methods. First let us use the m-th degree Newton forward polynomial from equation (5.16), viz.

$$f(y) \approx P_m(t_n + \alpha h) = \left[1 + \alpha \Delta + \frac{\alpha(\alpha - 1)}{2!} \Delta^2 + \cdots \right.$$
$$\left. \frac{\alpha(\alpha - 1)(\alpha - 2) \cdots (\alpha - m + 1)}{(m)!} \Delta^m \right] f_n + \mathcal{O}(h^{m+1})$$

where t_n has been used as the reference point, f_n means $f(y_n)$ and h is the step size. Since $t = t_n + \alpha h$ we have $dt = h d\alpha$. Using a one term expansion in equation (6.9), (i.e., $m = 0$) results in,

$$
\begin{aligned}
y_{n+1} - y_n &= \int_{t_n}^{t_{n+1}} P_0(t_n + \alpha h) dt + \underbrace{\int_{t_n}^{t_{n+1}} \mathcal{O}(h) dt}_{local\ truncation\ error} \\
&= \int_0^1 P_0(t_n + \alpha h)\ h d\alpha + \int_0^1 \mathcal{O}(h) h d\alpha \\
&= \int_0^1 f_n\ h d\alpha + \mathcal{O}(h^2) \\
&= f_n\ h + \mathcal{O}(h^2)
\end{aligned}
$$

which is the same equation as (6.7). This approach, however, lends itself naturally to further development of higher order methods. For example a two-term expansion (*i.e.*, $m = 1$) results in,

$$y_{n+1} - y_n = \int_{t_n}^{t_{n+1}} P_1(t_n + \alpha h)dt + \underbrace{\int_{t_n}^{t_{n+1}} \mathcal{O}(h^2)dt}_{local\ truncation\ error}$$

$$= \int_0^1 P_1(t_n + \alpha h)\ hd\alpha + \int_0^1 \mathcal{O}(h^2)hd\alpha$$

$$= \int_0^1 [f_n + \alpha \Delta f_n]\ hd\alpha + \mathcal{O}(h^3)$$

$$= h\left[\alpha\ f_n + \Delta f_n \frac{\alpha^2}{2}\right]_0^1 + \mathcal{O}(h^3)$$

$$= h\left[f_n + (f_{n+1} - f_n)\frac{1}{2}\right] + \mathcal{O}(h^3).$$

Hence we have the final form of the modified Euler scheme as,

$$\boxed{y_{n+1} = y_n + \frac{h}{2}[f_n + f_{n+1}] + \underbrace{\mathcal{O}(h^3)}_{local\ error} \qquad n = 0, 1, \cdots}$$

$$(6.10)$$

Both the Euler method given in equation (6.7) and the modified Euler scheme given by equation (6.10) are *single-step* methods since only y_n is required to predict y_{n+1}. The modified Euler method is an *implicit* scheme since we need to compute f_{n+1} which depends on y_{n+1}. Note that implicit schemes requires the solution of a nonlinear algebraic equation at every time step. Thus to calculate y_{n+1} from equation (6.10) we need to use an *iterative method* that involves providing an initial guess for y_{n+1} and using equation (6.10) as a fixed point iteration scheme until y_{n+1} converges to desired accuracy. At a first glance, this might appear to be a disadvantage of the *implicit* schemes. However, implicit schemes have the ability to anticipate sharp changes in the solution between y_n and y_{n+1} and hence are suitable (in fact required) for solving the so called *stiff differential equations*. This initial guess could be provided by the Euler method (viz. equation (6.7)).

6.2.4   Modified Euler - Heun's Method

When an explicit scheme is combined with an implicit scheme in this manner, we have the so called *predictor-corrector* scheme. The Euler and modified Euler predictor-corrector pair is,

$$\boxed{y^P_{n+1} = y_n + hf(y_n)} \qquad \text{and} \qquad \boxed{y^C_{n+1} = y_n + \frac{h}{2}\left[f(y_n) + f(y^P_{n+1})\right]}$$

$$(6.11)$$

where the superscript P represents the predicted value from an explicit scheme and C represents the corrected value from an implicit scheme. Figure 6.3 shows the scheme for the slope prediction.

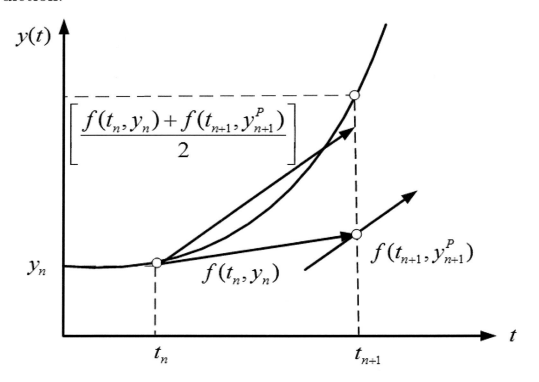

Figure 6.3: Heun's method

It should be clear that extending the Newton forward polynomial to a three-term expansion will not be fruitful, since that would involve not only f_{n+1}, but also f_{n+2}. We can, however, use Newton backward polynomials to develop higher order methods as will be done in section §6.4. But, let us explore first the reason for and the circumstances under which *implicit* schemes are useful.

6.2.5 Stability limits

Let us consider a model, linear equation,

$$\frac{dy}{dt} = \lambda \, y, \qquad y(t = 0) = 1$$

which has the analytical solution,

$$y(t) = e^{\lambda t}$$

For $\lambda < 0$ the exact solution decreases monotonically to zero as $t \to \infty$. Let us examine the sequence $\{y_n | n = 0, 1, \cdots\}$ generated by the explicit, Euler scheme and the implicit, modified Euler scheme. Note that in this model problem the function $f(y) = \lambda y$. The Euler equation is,

$$y_{n+1} = y_n + hf(y_n) = y_n + h\lambda y_n = [1 + h\lambda]y_n$$

Thus the sequence is,

$$\begin{aligned}
y_1 &= [1 + h\lambda]y_0 \\
y_2 &= [1 + h\lambda]y_1 = [1 + h\lambda]^2 y_0 \\
y_3 &= [1 + h\lambda]y_2 = [1 + h\lambda]^3 y_0 \\
\vdots &= \vdots
\end{aligned}$$

leading to the general solution,

$$y_n = [1 + h\lambda]^n y_0$$

When the step size h is chosen to be too large (more specifically $|h\lambda| > 2$ in this case), the sequence will diverge, while the exact solution remains bounded. This phenomenon is called *numerical instability* caused by the discretization. Explicit methods in general have such a stability bound on the step size h.

Stability of the modified Euler (Heun's) method

Consider the modified Euler's (Heun's method)

$$y_{n+1} = y_n + \frac{h}{2}\left[f_n + f_{n+1}\right] = y_n + \frac{h}{2}\left[\lambda y_n + \lambda y_{n+1}\right]$$

Note that y_{n+1} appears on both sides. Solving for y_{n+1} we get,

$$y_{n+1} = \left[\frac{1 + h\lambda/2}{1 - h\lambda/2}\right] y_n$$

Thus the sequence is,

$$y_1 = \left[\frac{1 + h\lambda/2}{1 - h\lambda/2}\right] y_0$$

$$y_2 = \left[\frac{1 + h\lambda/2}{1 - h\lambda/2}\right] y_1 = \left[\frac{1 + h\lambda/2}{1 - h\lambda/2}\right]^2 y_0$$

$$y_3 = \left[\frac{1 + h\lambda/2}{1 - h\lambda/2}\right] y_2 = \left[\frac{1 + h\lambda/2}{1 - h\lambda/2}\right]^3 y_0$$

$$\vdots = \vdots$$

leading to the general solution,

$$y_n = \left[\frac{1 + h\lambda/2}{1 - h\lambda/2}\right]^n y_0$$

It is clear that for $\lambda < 0$, the ratio $\left[\frac{1+h\lambda/2}{1-h\lambda/2}\right] < 1$ for any choice of step size h. Thus the *implicit* scheme is *absolutely stable*. Hence, for explicit schemes, the choice of h is governed by both *stability* and *truncation error* considerations while for *implicit* schemes only *truncation error* considerations dictate the choice of step size, h.

6.2.6 Stiff differential equations

The physical interpretation for λ in the above model problem is that it represents the *characteristic time scale* of the problem. For a second order equation (or equivalently a system of two first-order equations), there will be two such time scales λ_1 and λ_2. If the time scales are widely separated in magnitude then we have a stiff system of differential equations. Consider the spring and dash pot model shown in figure 6.4.

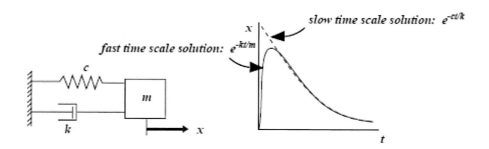

Figure 6.4: Spring and dash pot model

The displacement x is modelled by the force balance equation,

$$m\frac{d^2x}{dt^2} + k\frac{dx}{dt} + cx = 0$$

where c is the spring constant, k is the damping factor, m is the mass and x is the displacement. Let us assume that it is subject to the initial conditions $x(t = 0) = 0$ and $x'(t = 0) = constant$. We can write the characteristic equation as,

$$\frac{m}{k}\lambda^2 + \lambda + \frac{c}{k} = 0$$

and hence the two roots are given by,

$$\lambda = \frac{-1 \pm \sqrt{1 - 4mc/k^2}}{(2m/k)}$$

In the limit of $m \to 0$ we can approximate these as,

$$\lambda_1 = -\frac{k}{m} \qquad \text{and} \qquad \lambda_2 = -\frac{c}{k}$$

where L'Hopitals rule is used to obtain the second root. Clearly as $m \to 0$, we have $\lambda_1 >> \lambda_2$ and this limit corresponds to the stiff behavior of the solution. In general the *stiffness ratio* is defined as the ratio of the largest to the smallest eigenvalues. In this example the stiffness ratio is (k^2/mc) and it becomes large as m is made small. The solution satisfying the first initial condition is,

$$x(t) = A_1[\underbrace{e^{-kt/m}}_{fast} - \underbrace{e^{ct/k}}_{slow}]$$

where the fast and slow response terms are as shown. The sketch in figure 6.4 also shows the fast and slow response solutions. Note that if $m = 0$, the order of the differential equation drops by one and λ_1 is the only time scale for the problem. This kind of phenomena also occurs in a number of chemical reaction systems, where some of the reactions can occur on a rapid time scale while others take place on a longer time scale. The ozone decomposition model discussed in section §1.4.2 is another example of stiff differential equations.

It should now be clear that stiffness phenomena corresponds to large eigenvalues and fast response regions where the solution changes rapidly. In a system of n first order equations there will be n characteristic roots or eigenvalues. If λ_{max} is the largest eigenvalue, then explicit schemes will typically have a numerical stability limit of the form $|h\lambda_{max}| < constant$. Hence explicit schemes require that extremely small step size h be used in regions where the system responds very rapidly; otherwise the integration sequence will diverge. Implicit schemes that are absolutely stable have no such restrictions. The integration sequence using implicit schemes will remain bounded. The choice of step size is determined only by the desired accuracy of the solution. Stability analysis for a variety of explicit and implicit methods are discussed in greater detail by Lapidus and Seinfeld (1971).

6.3 Runge-Kutta Methods

While Taylor series methods increase the order accuracy by increasing the number of retained terms in the Taylor series, Runge-Kutta methods achieve the same goal in a single step, but at the expense of requiring many function evaluations per step. Being single-step schemes, they are self-starters. They are also classified as *explicit, semi-implicit* and *implicit* schemes. Implicit schemes require solution of a set on non-linear algebraic equations at every time step, but they are suitable for *stiff differential equations.*

6.3.1 Explicit schemes

Explicit schemes have the general form,

$$y_{n+1} = y_n + h \sum_{i=1}^{v} w_i \, k_i \qquad (6.12)$$

$$k_i = f\left(t_n + c_i, \; y_n + h \sum_{j=1}^{i-1} a_{ij} \, k_j\right), \qquad c_1 = 0, \qquad i = 1, 2, \cdots v$$

In these equations, $\{c_i, w_i, a_{ij}\}$ are all parameters. The development of a specific scheme entails determining the best possible values for these constants by matching the expansion of this formula with a Taylor series expansion. Often these parameter values are given in tabular form as,

$$
\begin{array}{c|cccc}
0 & & & & \\
c_2 & a_{21} & & & \\
c_3 & a_{31} & a_{32} & & \\
c_4 & a_{41} & a_{42} & a_{43} & \\
\hline
 & w_1 & w_2 & w_3 & w_4
\end{array}
$$

or

$$
\begin{array}{c|c}
\boldsymbol{c} & \boldsymbol{A} \\
\hline
 & \boldsymbol{w}
\end{array}
$$

For explicit methods, $\boldsymbol{A}$ is a lower triangular matrix.

6.3.2   Euler formula revisited

Let us consider $v = 1$ in equation (6.12) and write the equations explicitly as,

$$
\begin{aligned}
y_{n+1} &= y_n + w_1\, k_1 \\
k_1 &= h\, f(t_n, y_n)
\end{aligned}
\tag{6.13}
$$

or

$$
y_{n+1} = y_n + w_1\, h\, f(t_n, y_n)
$$

The procedure to determine w_1 is to match the above equaiton with the Taylor series expansion,

$$
y_{n+1} = y_n + hy'_n + \frac{h^2}{2}y''_n + \frac{h^3}{3!}y'''_n + \cdots
\tag{6.14}
$$

The first term on the right hand side is the same in both equations. Recognizing that $y' = f$ the second term will also match if we make $w_1 = 1$ and this results in recovering the Euler scheme developed in equation (6.7). We cannot match with any higher order terms and hence the local truncation error is of order $\mathcal{O}(h^2)$.

6.3.3 A two-stage $(v = 2)$ Runge-Kutta scheme

Let us consider $v = 2$ in equation (6.12) and write the equations explicitly as,

$$
\begin{aligned}
y_{n+1} &= y_n + w_1 \, k_1 + w_2 \, k_2 \\
k_1 &= h \, f(t_n, y_n) \\
k_2 &= h \, f(t_n + c_2 h, y_n + a_{21} h k_1)
\end{aligned}
\tag{6.15}
$$

This scheme has four unknown paramters $\{w_1, w_2, c_2, a_{21}\}$ which must be determined by matching the Taylor series expansion of equation (6.15) with the equation (6.14). Expanding equation (6.15) we get,

$$
y_{n+1} = y_n + w_1 \, h \, f(t_n, y_n) + w_2 \, h \, f(t_n + c_2 h, y_n + a_{21} k_1)
$$

or,

$$
y_{n+1} = y_n + w_1 \, h \, f_n + w_2 \, h \, \left[f + \frac{\partial f}{\partial t}(c_2 h) + \frac{\partial f}{\partial y} a_{21}(hf) \right]_n + \cdots
\tag{6.16}
$$

Substituting for y' and its higher derivatives in terms of f in equation (6.14) and expanding, we get,

$$
y_{n+1} = y_n + h f_n + \frac{h^2}{2} \frac{df}{dt} + \mathcal{O}(h^3)
$$

or

$$
y_{n+1} = y_n + h f_n + \frac{h^2}{2} \left[\frac{\partial f}{\partial t} + \frac{\partial f}{\partial y} \frac{\partial y}{\partial t} \right] + \mathcal{O}(h^3)
\tag{6.17}
$$

Now comparing the f_n terms between equations (6.16) and (6.17) we require that

$$
w_1 + w_2 = 1
$$

for the two equations to match. Next comparing $\frac{\partial f}{\partial t}$ terms, we require,

$$
w_2 c_2 = 1/2
$$

Finally comparing $\frac{\partial f}{\partial y}\frac{\partial y}{\partial t}$ we require,

$$w_2 a_{21} = 1/2$$

Thus, we have matched all terms of order $\mathcal{O}(h^2)$ leaving a truncation error or order $\mathcal{O}(h^3)$. In that process we have developed 3 constraint equations on the four unknonws $\{w_1, w_2, c_2, a_{21}\}$ appearing in the 2-stage Runge-Kutta scheme (6.15). Any choice of values for $\{w_1, w_2, c_2, a_{21}\}$ that satisfies the above three constraints will result in a 3-rd order, 2-stage Runge-Kutta scheme. Since there are four variables and only three equations, we have one extra degree of freedom. Hence the solution is not unique. Two sets of results are:

$$w_1 = 2/3, \quad w_2 = 1/3, \quad c_2 = 3/2, \quad a_{21} = 3/2$$

and

$$w_1 = 1/2, \quad w_2 = 1/2, \quad c_2 = 1, \quad a_{21} = 1$$

The later is the equivalent of the predictor-corrector pair using Euler and modified Euler schemes developed in equations (6.11). In summary this scheme is a 2-stage RK method since it requires two function evaluations per step. It is explicit and has a local truncation error of $\mathcal{O}(h^3)$.

Using the first set of parameter values in equation (6.15), we have,

$$
\begin{aligned}
y_{n+1} &= y_n + \frac{2}{3}hk_1 + \frac{2}{3}hk_2 \\
k_1 &= f(t_n, y_n) \\
k_2 &= f(t_n + \frac{3}{2}h, y_n + \frac{3}{2}hk_1)
\end{aligned}
$$

or in tabular form,

0		
3/2	3/2	
	2/3	2/3

6.3.4 A fourth order Runge-Kutta scheme

Higher order Runge-Kutta methods can be developed by carrying out the matching process with the Taylor series expansion to higher order terms. An explicit fourth-order form that matches with the Taylor series to h^4 terms (and hence has a truncation error of $\mathcal{O}(h^5)$ is,

$$
\begin{array}{c|cccc}
0 & & & & \\
1/2 & 1/2 & & & \\
1/2 & 0 & 1/2 & & \\
1 & 0 & 0 & 1 & \\
\hline
& 1/6 & 2/6 & 2/6 & 1/6
\end{array}
$$

Which in expanded form,

$$
\begin{aligned}
y_{n+1} &= y_n + \frac{h}{6}\left[k_1 + 2k_2 + 2k_3 + k_4\right] \qquad (6.18) \\
k_1 &= f(t_n, y_n) \\
k_2 &= f(t_n + \frac{h}{2}, y_n + \frac{h}{2}k_1) \\
k_3 &= f(t_n + \frac{h}{2}, y_n + \frac{h}{2}k_2) \\
k_4 &= f(t_n + h, y_n + hk_3)
\end{aligned}
$$

Figure 6.5 shows a schematic depiction of RK4 slopes. The $k's$ may therefore be considered as slopes of the function at different points which are used to obtain an improved slope for the prediction method.

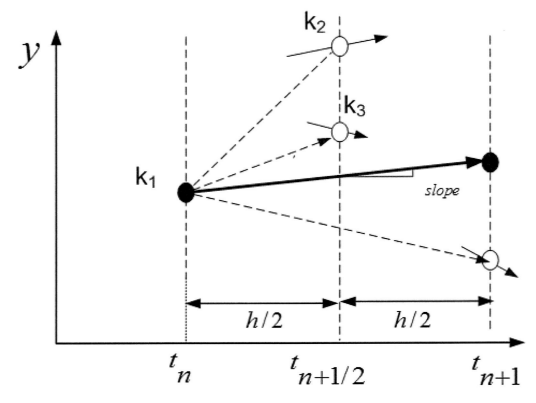

Figure 6.5: Graphical depiction of RK4 slopes

As with all explicit schemes, it is good for non-stiff differential equations.

Embedded forms

The embedded forms of Runge-Kutta algorithms provide a pair of schemes that use a common set of function evaluations to predict two estimates of the solution at y_{n+1}. Typically a lower order scheme is embedded within a higher order scheme. The motivation for developing such schemes is to have a convenient estimate of the local truncation error at every time step, which can then be used to develop a step size control stragegy. A popular scheme, called RK45, is given below.

k_1	0					
k_2	$\frac{1}{4}$	$\frac{1}{4}$				
k_3	$\frac{3}{8}$	$\frac{3}{32}$	$\frac{9}{32}$			
k_4	$\frac{12}{13}$	$\frac{1932}{2197}$	$-\frac{7200}{2197}$	$\frac{7296}{2197}$		
k_5	1	$\frac{439}{216}$	-8	$\frac{3680}{513}$	$\frac{-845}{410}$	
		$\frac{25}{216}$	0	$\frac{1408}{2565}$	$\frac{2197}{4104}$	$-\frac{1}{5}$	$\leftarrow y_{n+1}^{(4)}$
k_6	$\frac{1}{2}$	$-\frac{8}{27}$	2	$-\frac{3544}{2565}$	$\frac{1859}{4104}$	$-\frac{11}{40}$	
		$\frac{16}{135}$	0	$\frac{6656}{12825}$	$\frac{28561}{56430}$	$-\frac{9}{50}$	$\frac{2}{55}$	$\leftarrow y_{n+1}^{(5)}$

MATLAB has an implimentation of this scheme both as a built-in function called `rk45.m` and a m-file called `ode45.m`.

EXAMPLE 6.2 (Classical Runge-Kutta Method RK4)

Here we repeat example 6.1 using RK4 method

$$\frac{dy}{dt} = y \qquad y(0) = 1 \qquad 0 \leq t \leq 1.5$$

Let us demonstrate 1 step with h = 1.0 and then carry out the calculations using MATLAB.

Runge Kutta

$$y_{k+1} = y_k + \frac{h}{6}(k_1 + 2k_2 + 2k_3 + k_4)$$

$$k_1 = f(t_k, y_k), k_2 = f(t_k + h/2, y_k + h/2K_1)$$
$$k_3 = f(t_k + h/2, y_k + h/2K_2), k_4 = f(t_k + h, y_k + hK_3)$$

First we carry out a few steps by hand calculations From the given conditions $y_0 = 1, t_0 = 0$

at t_0, $f(t_0, y_0) = y_0 = 1$
$k_1 = f(t_0, y_0) = 1; k_2 = f(t = 0.5, 1.0 + 1/2 * 1 * 1) = 1.5$
$k_3 = f(t = 0.5, 1.0 + 1/2 * 1 * 1.5) = 1.75$

$k_4 = f(t = 1, 1.0 + 1 * 1.75) = 2.75$
$y_2 = y_1 + \frac{1}{6}(1 + 2(1.5) + 2(1.75) + 2.75) = 2.7083$
Lets do the rest using MATLAB

Next we explore calculations using MATLAB script which implements the above algorithm as shown in figure 6.7. Notice how fast the scheme has converged, as well as the smaller errors even when large steps are taken.

Figure 6.7 shows different results depending on the step size choosen

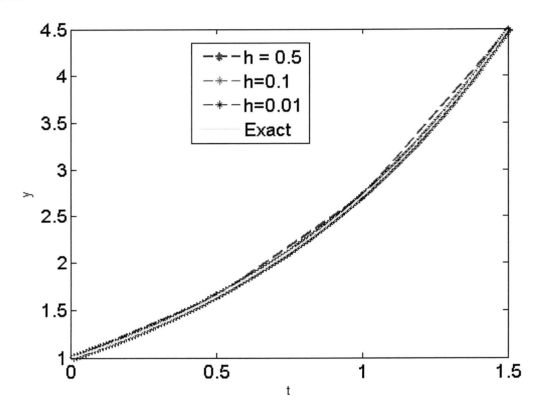

Figure 6.6: Solution of y' = y using RK4 with different step sizes

```
function [tSol,ySol] = RK4(Deqs,txspan,y0,h)
%
% Purpose: This function implements the classical fourth order
% RK (Runge-Kutta) method for systems of first order ODEs
% Syntax:  [tSol,ySol] = RK4(Deqs,txspan,y0,h)
%
% Input:   Deqs   = Name of the m-file with the solved de's.
% txspan   = Vector containing span of the independent variable
% y0       = Initial value vector; y0 must be a row vector
% h        = Stepsize for advancing the independent variables
%
% Output: tSol = Vector of independent variables t(j) =t0+ j*h
% ySol = Matrix of dependent variables values
%
    t=txspan(1);
    tStop = txspan(2);
    y = y0;
    tSol = zeros(2,1);  % create variable to hold t's
    ySol = zeros(2,length(y));  % create variable to hold y's
    tSol(1)    = t;          % set the initial t value
    ySol(1,:) = y;        % set the corresponding y value(s)
    i = 1;
  while t < tStop
     i = i + 1;
     h =  min(h,tStop - t);
     K1 = feval(Deqs,t,y); %    slope at the start point
        K2 = feval(Deqs,t + h/2,y + h*K1/2); % slope at the
           midpoint
        K3 = feval(Deqs,t + h/2,y + h*K2/2); % slope at the
           midpoint
        K4 = feval(Deqs,t+h,y + h*K3); % slope at the
           endpoint
     % advance the solution
        y = y + h*(K1 + 2*K2 + 2*K3 + K4)/6;
      % increment the step
      t = t + h;
     % Store the current solution.
     tSol(i)    = t;
     ySol(i,:) = y;
  end
```

Figure 6.7: MATLAB implementation of the classical RK4 method

6.3.5   Semi-implicit & implicit schemes

In the general form given in equation (6.12), we fixed $c_1 = 0$ and
$\mathbf{A}$ to be lower triangular. These constraints on the paramters
ensure that each of the k_i could be computed explicitly without
the need for iterative solution. Let us now relax these constraints
and write the general form as,

$$y_{n+1} \;=\; y_n + h \sum_{i=1}^{v} w_i \, k_i \tag{6.19}$$

$$k_i \;=\; f\left(t_n + c_i, \; y_n + h \sum_{j=1}^{v} a_{ij} \, k_j\right), \qquad i = 1, 2, \cdots v$$

Thus, for a two-stage process ($v = 2$), we will have,

$$\begin{aligned}
y_{n+1} &= y_n + w_1 \, k_1 + w_2 \, k_2 \\
k_1 &= h \, f(t_n + c_1 h, y_n + a_{11} k_1 + a_{12} k_2) \\
k_2 &= h \, f(t_n + c_2 h, y_n + a_{21} k_1 + a_{22} k_2)
\end{aligned} \tag{6.20}$$

or in compact tabular form,

$$\begin{array}{c|cc}
c_1 & a_{11} & a_{12} \\
c_2 & a_{21} & a_{22} \\
\hline
 & w_1 & w_2
\end{array}$$

Note that in order to compute k_1 and k_2 in the above form, we
need to solve two sets of nonlinear algebraic equations simulata-
neously. On the positive side of such schemes, fully implicit nature of the algorithm results in numerically stable schemes making them suitable for *stiff differential equations*. Also, a two-stage
scheme ($v = 2$) has eight parameters, and hence we can match
these equations with the Taylor series expansion to higher order
terms. Hence more accurate formulas can be constructed. An
example of a fully implicit, 2-stage, 4-th order accurate scheme
is the Gauss form given by,

$$
\begin{array}{c|cc}
(3-\sqrt{3})/6 & 1/4 & (3-2\sqrt{3})/12 \\
(3+\sqrt{3})/6 & (3-2\sqrt{3})/12 & 1/4 \\
\hline
 & 1/2 & 1/2
\end{array}
$$

For an extensive catalogue of such schemes see Lapidus and Seinfeld (1971).

6.3.6 Semi-Implicit forms of Rosenbrock

While the fully-implicit forms of the last section §6.3.5, have desirable stability properties, they are computationally demanding since a system of non-linear algebraic equations must be solved iteratively at every time step. In an effort to reduce the computational demand while retaining the stability characteristics, Rosenbrock (1963) proposed a special form of the algorithm. These are suitable for autonomous system of equations of the form,

$$
\frac{d\boldsymbol{y}}{dt} = \boldsymbol{f}(\boldsymbol{y}) \qquad \boldsymbol{y}(t = t_0) = \boldsymbol{y}_0
$$

A 2-stage, 3-rd order scheme is shown below.

$$
\begin{aligned}
\boldsymbol{y}_{n+1} &= \boldsymbol{y}_n + w_1\,\boldsymbol{k}_1 + w_2\,\boldsymbol{k}_2 & (6.21) \\
\boldsymbol{k}_1 &= h\left[\boldsymbol{I} - ha_1\boldsymbol{J}(\boldsymbol{y}_n)\right]^{-1}\boldsymbol{f}(\boldsymbol{y}_n) \\
\boldsymbol{k}_2 &= h\left[\boldsymbol{I} - ha_2\boldsymbol{J}(\boldsymbol{y}_n + c_1\boldsymbol{k}_1)\right]^{-1}\boldsymbol{f}(\boldsymbol{y}_n + b_1\boldsymbol{k}_1)
\end{aligned}
$$

The parameters are,

$$
a_1 = 1 + \sqrt{6}/6, \qquad a_2 = 1 - \sqrt{6}/6
$$

$$
w_1 = -0.41315432, \qquad w_2 = 1.41315432
$$

$$
b_1 = c_1 = \frac{-6 - \sqrt{6} + \sqrt{58 + 20\sqrt{6}}}{6 + 2\sqrt{6}}
$$

Here $\boldsymbol{J} = \frac{\partial \boldsymbol{f}}{\partial \boldsymbol{y}}$ is the Jacobian, which must be evaluated at every time step. Note that the main advantage in using equation (6.21) is that $\boldsymbol{k}_1, \boldsymbol{k}_2$ could be computed without the need for iteration, although it requires two matrix inverse computations per step.

6.4   Multistep methods

6.4.1   Explicit schemes

Consider approximating the function $f(y)$ in equation (6.9) by the following m-th degree Newton backward polynomial from equation (5.11)),

$$f(y) \approx P_m(t_n + \alpha h) = \left[1 + \alpha \nabla + \frac{\alpha(\alpha + 1)}{2!} \nabla^2 + \cdots \right.$$

$$\left. \frac{\alpha(\alpha + 1)(\alpha + 2) \cdots (\alpha + m - 1)}{m!} \nabla^m \right] f_n + \mathcal{O}(h^{m+1})$$

Here, t_n has been used as the reference point. Since this polynomial involves only points at earlier times such as $\{f_n, f_{n-1}, f_{n-2} \cdots \}$, we can develop a class of *explicit* schemes of high orders. These are called Adams-Bashforth schemes. Consider a three-term expansion (*i.e.*, $m = 2$). Equation (6.9) becomes,

$$
\begin{aligned}
y_{n+1} - y_n &= \int_{t_n}^{t_{n+1}} P_2(t_n + \alpha h) dt + \underbrace{\int_{t_n}^{t_{n+1}} \mathcal{O}(h^3) dt}_{local\ truncation\ error} \\
&= \int_0^1 P_2(t_n + \alpha h)\, h d\alpha + \int_0^1 \mathcal{O}(h^3) h d\alpha \\
&= \int_0^1 \left[f_n + \alpha \nabla f_n + \frac{\alpha(\alpha + 1)}{2!} \nabla^2 f_n \right] h d\alpha + \mathcal{O}(h^4) \\
&= h \left[\alpha\, f_n + \frac{\alpha^2}{2} \nabla f_n + \frac{1}{2!} \left\{ \frac{\alpha^3}{3} + \frac{\alpha^2}{2} \right\} \nabla^2 f_n \right]_0^1 + \mathcal{O}(h^4) \\
&= h \left[f_n + \frac{1}{2}(f_n - f_{n-1}) + \frac{5}{12}(f_n - 2 f_{n-1} + f_{n-2}) \right] + \mathcal{O}(h^4).
\end{aligned}
$$

which can be rearranged into the form, large

$$y_{n+1} = y_n + \frac{h}{12}\left[23\ f_n - 16\ f_{n-1} + 5\ f_{n-2}\right] + \underbrace{\mathcal{O}(h^4)}_{local\ error}$$

$$(6.22)$$

$n = 2, 3, 4, \cdots$

The following points should be observed on the above equation.

- This is a *multistep scheme* since it requires (y_n, y_{n-1}, y_{n-2}) to predict y_{n+1}.

- Hence it is not a self-starter! Typically, in a well posed initial value problem, we know only y_0. Hence y_1 and y_2 must be generated from other single-step methods before we can switch to the above multistep scheme.

- It is an *explicit* method as y_{n+1} does not appear on the right hand side.

- As a consequence it cannot anticipate sharp changes in $y(t)$ - *i.e.*, not suitable for *stiff differential equations*.

- Makes good use of previous calculations to give low truncation error.

- requires only one function evaluation per step.

The next higher order scheme can be developed from a four-term expansion (*i.e.*, $m = 3$) . This is called 5-th order Adams-

Bashforth scheme. viz.

$$y_{n+1} - y_n = \int_{t_n}^{t_{n+1}} P_3(t_n + \alpha h)dt + \underbrace{\int_{t_n}^{t_{n+1}} \mathcal{O}(h^4)dt}_{local\ truncation\ error}$$

$$= \int_0^1 P_3(t_n + \alpha h)\ hd\alpha + \int_0^1 \mathcal{O}(h^4)hd\alpha$$

$$= \int_0^1 \left[f_n + \alpha\nabla f_n + \frac{\alpha(\alpha+1)}{2!}\nabla^2 f_n + \frac{\alpha(\alpha+1)(\alpha+2)}{3!}\nabla^3 f_n \right]\ hd\alpha + \mathcal{O}(h^5)$$

$$= h\left[f_n + \frac{1}{2}\ \nabla f_n + \frac{5}{12}\nabla^2 f_n + \frac{3}{8}\nabla^3 f_n \right] + \mathcal{O}(h^5)$$

which can be rearranged into the form,

$$\boxed{y_{n+1} = y_n + \frac{h}{24}\left[55\ f_n - 59\ f_{n-1} + 37\ f_{n-2} - 9f_{n-3} \right] + \underbrace{\mathcal{O}(h^5)}_{local\ error}}$$

$$(6.23)$$

6.4.2   Implicit schemes

In order to construct implicit schemes we need to construct backward polynomial approximations with t_{n+1} as the reference point. viz.

$$f(y) \approx P_m(t_{n+1} + \alpha h) = \left[1 + \alpha\nabla + \frac{\alpha(\alpha+1)}{2!}\nabla^2 + \cdots \right.$$

$$\left. \frac{\alpha(\alpha+1)(\alpha+2)\cdots(\alpha+m-1)}{m!}\nabla^m \right] f_{n+1} + \mathcal{O}(h^{m+1})$$

In this manner f_{n+1} is introduced on the right hand side. This class of implicit schemes are called Adams-Moulton schemes. We are still integrating one step from t_n to t_{n+1}. Since $t = t_{n+1} + \alpha h$ and the limits of integration in α become $(-1, 0)$. A four-term expansion results in,

$$y_{n+1} - y_n = \int_{t_n}^{t_{n+1}} P_3(t_{n+1} + \alpha h)dt + \underbrace{\int_{t_n}^{t_{n+1}} \mathcal{O}(h^4)dt}_{local\ truncation\ error}$$

$$= \int_{-1}^{0} P_3(t_n + \alpha h)\ hd\alpha + \int_{-1}^{0} \mathcal{O}(h^4)hd\alpha$$

$$= \int_{-1}^{0} \left[f_{n+1} + \alpha \nabla f_{n+1} + \frac{\alpha(\alpha + 1)}{2!} \nabla^2 f_{n+1} \right]$$

$$+ \left[\frac{\alpha(\alpha + 1)(\alpha + 2)}{3!} \nabla^3 f_{n+1} \right]\ hd\alpha + \mathcal{O}(h^5)$$

$$= h \left[f_{n+1} - \frac{1}{2}\nabla f_{n+1} - \frac{1}{12}\nabla^2 f_{n+1} - \frac{1}{24}\nabla^3 f_{n+1} \right] + \mathcal{O}(h^5)$$

which can be expanded and rearranged into the form,

$$\boxed{y_{n+1} = y_n + \frac{h}{24} \left[9\ f_{n+1} + 19\ f_n - 5\ f_{n-1} + f_{n-2} \right] + \underbrace{\mathcal{O}(h^5)}_{local\ error}}$$

(6.24)

$n = 2, 4, \cdots$

The pair of explicit-implicit schemes given by (6.23,6.24) respectively can be used as a *predictor-corrector* pair.

6.4.3 Automatic stepsize control

Some of the start up and step size control issues are illustrated in figure 6.8 for the 5-th order Adams schemes developed in the last section.

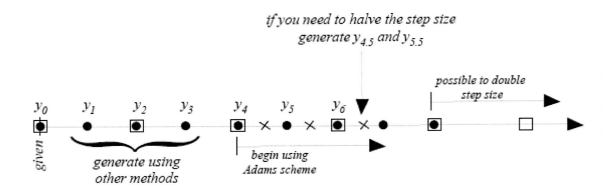

Figure 6.8: Stepsize control strategies for multistep methods

Note that only y_0 is given and hence (y_1, y_2, y_3) must be generated using some other single step methods with a step size of h before the 5-th order Adams scheme given by equations (6.23,6.24) can be used. In doing so, it is important to realize that any error introduced in these three steps are likely to be propagated during the transient phase of the simulation. Hence if lower order schemes are used to generate (y_1, y_2, y_3), then smaller step sizes must be used. The difference between the predicted and corrected values could be used as a measure of the truncation error. If this error is below an acceptable tolerance, then we can choose to double the next step size. But this can begin only after y_6 has been computed, because we need four previous values at equal intervals of $(2h)$ - *i.e.*, (y_0, y_2, y_4, y_6). If at any time during the intergration process, the difference between the predicted and corrected values is above the tolerance, then we must halve the step size and repeat the calculation for that step. In so doing, we need to generate intermediate values at intervals of $(h/2)$. For example if the result for y_7 does not meet the tolerance, then we repeat the calculation from y_6 with a step size of $h/2$. We need to generate intermediate values at $y_{4.5}$ and $y_{5.5}$. This can be done using the Newton backward interpolation polynomials; but the truncation errors in the interpolating polynomials should be of the same order and the Adams scheme. Specifically the interpolation rules are:

$$y_{n-\frac{1}{2}} = \frac{1}{128}[35y_n + 140y_{n-1} - 70y_{n-2} + 28y_{n-3} - 5y_{n-4}]$$

$$y_{n-\frac{3}{2}} = \frac{1}{64}[-y_n + 24y_{n-1} + 54y_{n-2} - 16y_{n-3} + 3y_{n-4}]$$

EXAMPLE 6.3 *MATLAB has several built-in functions for solving initial value problems. Hence the m-files that define the problem must have a special structure. In this section we illustrate how to use these functions to solve the ozone decomposition model. Recall that the equations are,*

$$\frac{dy_1}{dt} = f_1(y_1, y_2) = -y_1 - y_1y_2 + \epsilon\kappa y_2$$

$$\frac{dy_2}{dt} = f_2(y_1, y_2) = (y_1 - y_1y_2 - \epsilon\kappa y_2)/\epsilon$$

The initial compositions are $y(t = 0) = [1.0, 0.0]$. The parameters are $\epsilon = 1/98$ and $\kappa = 3.0$. The equations are clearly nonlinear. The m-file named ozone.m *is shown in figure 6.9. This function should be written in such a way that it should return the derivatives $y'(t)$ in the variable* ydot. *The function receives the initial conditions as shown in the figure 6.9.*

```
function [ydot]=ozone(t,y0)
k=3.0;epsilon=1/98;

    ydot(1)  =  -y(1)  -  y(2)*y(1)  +  k*epsilon*y(2);
    ydot(2)  =  (y(1)-y(1)*y(2)-epsilon*k*y(2))/epsilon;
    ydot=ydot'; % equations in column vector
return
```

Figure 6.9: MATLAB implementation of ozone decomposition model

To use the matlab built in functions and integrate the ozone model to a final time of 3.0 do the following during an interactive MATLAB session.

```
>>tspan=[0 3];                    % Define time timespan
>>y0=[1 0];                       % initial conditions
>>type ozone                      % test that ozone.m exists
>>[t,y]=ode23s('ozone',tspan,y0)  % Integrate using ode23s
>>[t,y]=ode45('ozone',tspan, y0)  % Integrate using ode45
```

The independent variable **t** and the solution **y** at the same time values are returned in the corresponding variables. These results are shown graphically in figure 6.10.

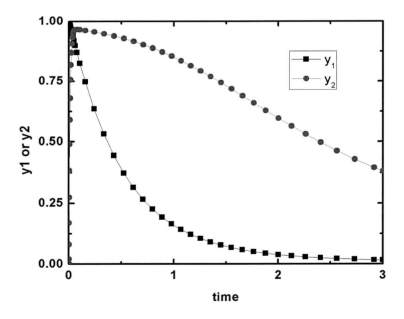

Figure 6.10: Results of ozone decomposition model shows a stiff system behavior

Observe that $y_2(t)$ increases rapidly from an initial condition of zero and hence the system is very stiff during the early times.

6.5 Summary

In this chapter we have explored different methods for solving initial value problems for first order differential equations. Higher order differential equations can be converted to a system of first order equations. Implicit and explicit have been explored, with implicit methods being shown to be unconditionally stable, whereas expicit method suffer from stability limitations.

Single step and multi-step methods have been presented and their accuracy and numerical stability analysed. The choice of a particular method is dictated by the problem at hand, the accuracy desired as well as the preference of the user.

Taylor series methods can achieve high accuracy by increasing the number of retained terms. Runge Kutta methods achieve the same accuracy of Taylor series methods in a single step at the expense of requiring more functional evaluations. The explicit Euler's method is the simplest method to implement but suffers from low accuracy (1st order) and conditional stability. The classical fourth order Runge-Kutta method (RK4) is the best general purpose single-point method with fourth order accuracy. Stiff methods are best solved using the Adam's method or MATLAB's ode23s method.

6.6 Exercise Problems

P6.1. Euler's method

Given the initial value problem

$$\frac{dy}{dt} = 1 + \frac{y}{t} \qquad 1 \le t \le 4 \qquad y(1) = 1$$

If the analytical solution is $y(t) = t(1 + \ln t)$,

(a) solve the problem with a step size of h = 0.5 and determine the absolute error at each iteration.

(b) By taking succesively smaller steps, show that the global error associated with the explicit Euler's method is $\mathcal{O}(h)$

P6.2. Euler's method and RK4

Given the initial value problem

$$\frac{dy}{dt} = \frac{y^2 + 1}{t} \qquad 1 \le t \le 4 \qquad y(1) = 0$$

(a) Solve the problem with with explicit Euler's method and a step size of h = 1 and determine the absolute error at each iteration.

(b) Solve the problem with the classical RK4 method and a step size of h = 2

P6.3. van der Pol equation

The classical van der Pol equation is written as

$$\frac{d^2x}{dt^2} + 4(x^2 - 1) + x = 0$$

(a) convert the equation to a system of two 1st order ode's

(b) solve the equations using the classical RK4 method with initial values $x(0) = 1$ and $x'(0) = 0$ and a step size of h = 0.01

(c) Plot the results over the range $0 \le t \le 20$

P6.4. Given the two equations

$$\frac{dx}{dt} = y$$

$$\frac{dy}{dt} = -x - 2y$$

and the initial conditions $x(0) = 1$ and $y(0) = -1$

(a) carry out 4 steps of the explicit Euler method with a step size of h $= 0.25$

(b) carry out 4 steps of the Heun's method with a step size of h $= 0.25$

P6.5. Backward Euler method

Use backward Euler's method to solve the following problem

$$\frac{dy}{dt} = ty^3 - y \qquad 0 \le t \le 1 \qquad y(0) = 0$$

Carry out 3 iterations. Use Newton's method for the non-linear algebraic equations

P6.6. Use backward Euler's method to solve the following problem

$$\frac{dy}{dt} = t^2 - y^2 \qquad 0 \le t \le 1 \qquad y(0) = 0$$

Carry out 3 iterations. Use Newton's method for the non-linear algebraic equations

P6.7. Repeat problem P6.5 with modified Euler's method.

P6.8. Repeat problem P6.6 with modified Euler's method.

P6.9. Higher order equations

Convert the following higher order equations into a system of first order equations

(a) $\frac{d^3x}{dt^3} + 5\frac{d^2x}{dt^2} + \frac{dx}{dt} = 0$

(b) $\frac{d^2x}{dt^2} + 2\frac{dx}{dt} + x^2 = 0$

(c) $\frac{d^2x}{dt^2} + sin(x) = 1$

(d) $\frac{d^3x}{dt^3} + 2x\frac{d^2x}{dt^2} + x = 0$

P6.10. Second order ode

Consider the differential equation

$$10x^2\frac{d^2c}{dx^2} + 2x\frac{dc}{dx} + c = 0 \qquad\qquad (6.25)$$

together with the following conditions.

$$c(x = 0) = 1 \qquad\qquad (6.26)$$

$$\left.\frac{dc}{dx}\right|_{x=0} = -1 \qquad\qquad (6.27)$$

a) Does this model represent an *initial value problem* or a *boundary value problem*?

b) Is the system *linear* or *non-linear*?

c) Convert the equations into a system of two *first order* equations.

d) Is the resulting system *autonomous* or *non-autonomous*?

e) If it is *non-autonomous* convert it into a system of autonomous equations.

f) Recommend a numerical scheme for solving the model equations.

P6.11. **1D Diffusion in a tube** A chemical compound diffuses and reacts when passing through a 4-cm tube. The governing equation for one-dimensional diffusion and reaction is given by

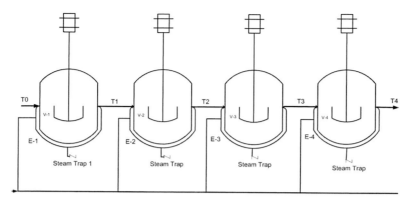

Figure 6.11: Heat exchange tank cascade

$$D\frac{\partial^2 C}{\partial x^2} - kC = 0 \qquad C(x = 0) = 0.1, \frac{\partial C}{\partial x}\Big|_{x=0} = -0.08$$

Determine the concentration distribution along the tube

(a) Using explicit Euler method with $\Delta x = 1$.

(b) Using implicit Euler method with $\Delta x = 2$.

(c) Using modified Euler (Heuns) method with $\Delta x = 2$.

(d) Using the classical RK4 method with $\Delta x = 2$.

P6.12. **Heat transfer in a cstr cascade**

Four perfectly stirred tanks arranged in series as shown in the figure below are use to heat a haydrocarbon mixture before it is fed to a stripper column. The initial amount of hydrocarbon in each tank is 500 kg at 300K. Each tank is equipped with heating jacket though which saturated steam at 500 K is condensing. The feed rate at the first tank is 50 kg/min at 300K.

The heat transfer (q kW) for a given tank is

$$q = UA\Delta T$$

where U is the heat transfer coefficient(W/m^2K), A is the heat transfer area for the coil (m^2), and ΔT is the temperature difference between the condensing steam and the tank temperature (perfectly mixed).

(a) Perform energy balance for the four tanks to obtain the equation for the rate of channge of temperature in each tank with time.

(b) Solve the four simultaneous differential equation to determine the steady state temperature in each tank.

(c) Calculate the time necessary for each tank to reach steady state.

P6.13. **Lumped parameter model - Transient heating in stirred tank reactor** The steady state behaviour of a tank system is described by the following differential equations

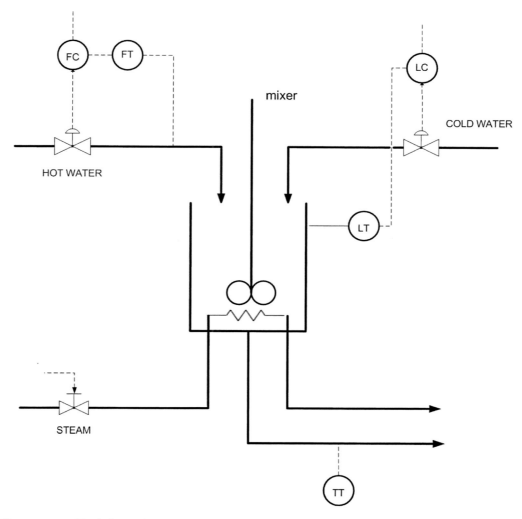

Figure 6.12: Tank heated system with flow and temperature control

$$\frac{dh}{dt} = F_i + k\sqrt{h} = 0 \qquad (6.28)$$

$$\frac{dT}{dt} = \frac{F_i}{Ah}(T_i - T) + \frac{Q}{\rho C_P} = 0 \qquad (6.29)$$

where h is the liquid height, Q the steam heating rate, T is the temperature and F the stream feed rate.

(a) identify the dependent variables (state variables), independent variable (input) and parameters in this system.

(b) If the Temperature T_i is decreased by 15% from its steady state value $\bar{T}_i$, the liquid height will stay the same but the temperature will decease with time. Determine how the temperature varies with time by solving equation 6.29 using initial condition $T(0) = \bar{T}$.

(c) If the feed rate F_i is decreased by 15% from its steady state value, $\bar{F}_i$, determine how the tank temperature and height will change with time. Solved the coupled non-linear equations(6.28 and 6.29). Use initial condition as $T(0) = \bar{T}, h(0) = \bar{h}$.

CHAPTER 7

ORDINARY DIFFERENTIAL EQUATIONS : BOUNDARY VALUE PROBLEMS (BVP)

In the present chapter we develop algorithms for solving systems of (linear or nonlinear) ordinary differential equations of the boundary value type. Such equations arise in describing distributed, steady state models in one spatial dimension. The di.erential equations are transformed into systems of (linear and nonlinear) algebraic equations through a discretization process. In doing so, we use the tools and concepts developed in Chapter 5. In particular we will develop (i) finite difference methods using the difference approximations given in Table 5.4, and (ii) shooting methods based on methods for initial value problems seen in chapter 6.

Consider the model for heat transfer through a fin developed in section §1.5.1. We will consider three specific variations on this model equation (1.22) and the associated boundary conditions. First let us scale the problem by introducing the following dimensionless temperature and distance variables,

$$\theta = \frac{T - T_\infty}{T_0 - T_\infty} \qquad \xi = \frac{x}{L}$$

311

Using these definitions, equation (1.22) can be rewritten as,

$$\frac{d}{d\xi}\left[kA\frac{d\theta}{d\xi}\right] - hPL^2\theta = 0 \tag{7.1}$$

$$\theta(\xi = 0) = 1 \qquad \theta(\xi = 1) = 0$$

where the objective is to find the continuous function $\theta(\xi)$ over the domain of interest, viz. $\xi \in [0,1]$ for a prescribed set of parameters k, A, h, P, L. All of these parameters can be constants, or some of them might be dependent on the position ξ (*e.g.*, $A(\xi)$) or on the unknown temperature itself (*e.g.*, $k(\xi)$). We examine each case next.

For constant area, A and thermal conductivity, k, equation (7.1) results in a second order *linear differential equation* with constant coefficients for which an analytical solution is possible. But we focus only on developing methodologies for obtaining a numerical solutions.

$$\frac{d^2\theta}{d\xi^2} - hPL^2\theta = 0 \tag{7.2}$$

$$\theta(\xi = 0) = 1 \qquad \theta(\xi = 1) = 0$$

When the values of the dimensionless temperature, θ on the boundary are specified, the boundary condition is called the Dirichlet boundary conditions. In a variation of the above model, if we let the area be a variable $A(\xi)$ (*i.e.*, tapered fin), but keep the thermal conductivity, k, constant, we obtain a variable coefficient, linear boundary value problem, still of second order.

$$A(\xi)\frac{d^2\theta}{d\xi^2} + \frac{dA(\xi)}{d\xi}\frac{d\theta}{d\xi} - hPL^2k\theta = 0 \tag{7.3}$$

$$\theta(\xi = 0) = 1 \qquad \left.\frac{d\theta}{d\xi}\right|_{\xi=1} = 0$$

In the above model, we have also introduced a variation on the boundary condition at $\xi = 1$. Such boundary conditions, where the derivatives are specified, are called *Newman boundary conditions*. The temperature value at $\xi = 1$ is an unknown and must be found as part of the solution procedure. In yet another variation, consider the case where the thermal conductivity is a function of temperature, viz. $k(\theta) = \alpha + \beta\theta^2$ where α and β are experimentally determined constants. Let the area, A be a constant. The equation is nonlinear and must be solved numerically.

$$A(\xi)\frac{d^2\theta}{d\xi^2} + \frac{dA(\xi)}{d\xi}\frac{d\theta}{d\xi} - hPL^2 k\theta = 0 \qquad (7.4)$$

$$\theta(\xi = 0) = 1 \qquad \left.\frac{d\theta}{d\xi}\right|_{\xi=1} = 0$$

At this opportunity a third variation on the boundary condition, called the mixed or Robin boundary condition has been used. Once again, the temperature value at x = L is an unknown and must be found as part of the solution procedure. All of these problems can be represented symbolically as,

$$\mathcal{D}\theta = f \qquad \text{on } \Omega$$

$$\mathcal{B}\theta = g \qquad \text{on } \partial\Omega$$

where $\mathcal{D}$ and $\mathcal{B}$ are differential operators, Ω is the domain of interest and $\partial\Omega$ represents its boundary. Our task is to obtain an *approximate solution*, θ to the above problem. The approximation consists in constructing a discrete version of the differential equations which results in a system algebraic equations. If the differential equations are linear (as in equations (7.2,7.3)), then the resulting discrete, algebraic equations will also be linear of the type $A\bar{\theta} = b$ and methods of Chapter 3 can be used to obtain the final approximate solution. If the differential equations are nonlinear (as in equation (7.4)) then the resulting discrete, algebraic equations will also be nonlinear of the type $\mathcal{F}(\theta) = 0$ and methods of Chapter 4 can be used to obtain the final approximate solution.

In the following sections we develop various schemes for constructing approximate solutions.

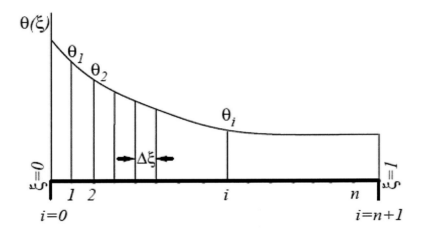

Figure 7.1: One dimensional finite difference grid of equally spaced data points

7.1 Finite difference method

7.1.1 Linear problem with constant coefficients

Let us consider equation (7.2) which is a linear problem subject to Dirichlet boundary conditions. In solving equation (7.2) by the finite difference method, we divide the domain $\Omega = \xi \in [0, 1]$ into $(n + 1)$ equally spaced subdivisions as shown in figure 7.1. The distance between the two grid points is denoted by $\Delta\xi$. The grid spacing $\Delta\xi$ and the value of the independent variable ξ at the nodal point i are given by,

$$\frac{1 - 0}{n + 1} \qquad \xi_i = i\Delta\xi \qquad i = 0, 1, \cdots (n + 1)$$

Next, instead of attempting to find a solution $\theta(\xi)$ as a continuous function of ξ that satisfies the differential equation (7.2) exactly at every ξ, we content ourselves with finding an approximate solution at the selected nodal points shown in the figure - *i.e.*, $\theta(\xi) = \bar{\theta}_i | i = 1, 2, \cdots n$, where n is the number of *interior* grid points. Note that for the *Dirichlet* type of boundary conditions θ_0 and θ_{n+1} are known. Hence, it remains to determine only n unknowns at the interior points. We obtain n equations by evaluating the differential equation (7.2) at the interior nodal points. In doing this we replace all the derivatives by the corresponding finite difference approximation from Table 5.4. Clearly, we have several choices; but it is important to match the truncation error in every term to be of the same order. We illustrate this process using *central difference approximations*.

Using the central difference approximation for the second derivative in equation (7.2), we obtain,

$$\left[\frac{\bar{\theta}_{i-1} - 2\bar{\theta}_i + \bar{\theta}_{i+1}}{(\Delta\xi)^2} + \mathcal{O}(\Delta\xi)^2 \right] - \frac{hPL^2}{kA}\bar{\theta}_i = 0 \qquad i = 1, 2, \cdots n$$

The term in the square brackets is the central difference approximation for the second derivative and $\mathcal{O}(\Delta\xi)^2$ is included merely to remind us of the order of the truncation error. We now have a system of n linear algebraic equations. Let us write these out explicitly for $n = 4$.

$$\bar{\theta}_0 - 2\bar{\theta}_1 + \bar{\theta}_2 - \alpha\bar{\theta}_1 = 0$$

$$\bar{\theta}_1 - 2\bar{\theta}_2 + \bar{\theta}_3 - \alpha\bar{\theta}_2 = 0$$

$$\bar{\theta}_2 - 2\bar{\theta}_3 + \bar{\theta}_4 - \alpha\bar{\theta}_3 = 0$$

$$\bar{\theta}_3 - 2\bar{\theta}_4 + \bar{\theta}_5 - \alpha\bar{\theta}_4 = 0$$

where $\alpha = \frac{hPL^2}{kA}(\Delta\xi)^2$, $\bar{\theta}_0$ in the first equation and $\bar{\theta}_5$ in the last equation are known from the *Dirichlet* boundary conditions. The above equations can be expressed in matrix notation as, $\mathcal{T}\bar{\theta} = b$,

$$
\begin{bmatrix}
-(2+\alpha) & 1 & 0 & 0 \\
1 & -(2+\alpha) & 1 & 0 \\
0 & 1 & -(2+\alpha) & 1 \\
0 & 0 & 1 & -(2+\alpha)
\end{bmatrix}
\begin{bmatrix}
\bar{\theta}_1 \\
\bar{\theta}_2 \\
\bar{\theta}_3 \\
\bar{\theta}_4
\end{bmatrix}
=
\begin{bmatrix}
-\bar{\theta}_0 \\
0 \\
0 \\
-\bar{\theta}_5
\end{bmatrix}
\tag{7.5}
$$

Note that the boundary values $\bar{\theta}_0$ and $\bar{\theta}_5$ appear as forcing terms on the right hand side. Equation (7.5) is the *discrete* version of equation (7.2). Once the structure is apparent, we can increase n to reduce $(\Delta\xi)$ and hence reduce the truncation error. In the limit of $(\Delta\xi) \to 0$ the solution to equations (7.5) will approach that of equation (7.2). The matrix size will increase with decreasing $(\Delta\xi)$ and increasing n. The matrix $\mathcal{T}$ is tridiagonal and hence the Thomas algorithm developed in section §3.4.4 can be used to get the solution.

7.1.2 Linear problem with variable coeffcients

Next we consider equation (7.3) which is also a linear problem subject to Dirichlet condition at $\xi = 0$ and Neuman boundary condition at $\xi = 1$. It also has variable coeffcients, $A(\xi)$ and $A'(\xi)$ - *i.e.*, A is a known function of ξ. The discretization procedure remains the same as seen in the previous section §7.2.1, with the exception that $\bar{\theta}_{n+1}$ is now included in the unknown set

$$\bar{\theta} = [\bar{\theta}_1, \bar{\theta}_2, \cdots, \bar{\theta}_{n+1}]$$

But we have the Neuman boundary condition as an extra condition that will provide the additional equation. Using the central difference approximations for both the second and first derivatives in equation (7.3), we obtain,

$$A(\xi_i)\left[\frac{\bar{\theta}_{i-1} - 2\bar{\theta}_i + \bar{\theta}_{i+1}}{(\Delta\xi)^2}\right] + A'(\xi_i)\left[\frac{\bar{\theta}_{i-1} - \bar{\theta}_{i+1}}{2(\Delta\xi)}\right] - \frac{hPL^2}{k}\bar{\theta}_i = 0$$

$$i = 1, 2, \cdots n + 1$$

Once again the truncation error term has been retained at this stage, only to emphasize that it should preferably be of the same order for every derivative that has been replaced by a difference approximation; otherwise the e.ective error is of the same order as the term with the lowest order truncation error. Multiplying throughout by $(\Delta\xi)^2$ and collecting like terms together, we get,

$$\left[A(\xi_i) - A'(\xi_i)\frac{(\Delta\xi)}{2}\right]\bar{\theta}_{i-1} + \left[-2A(\xi_i) - \frac{hPL^2(\Delta\xi)^2}{k}\right]\bar{\theta}_i +$$

$$\left[A(\xi_i) - A'(\xi_i)\frac{(\Delta\xi)}{2}\right]\bar{\theta}_{i+1} = 0 \qquad i = 1, 2, \cdots n + 1$$

Letting

$$a_i = \left[A(\xi_i) - A'(\xi_i)\frac{(\Delta\xi)}{2}\right]$$

$$d_i = \left[-2A(\xi_i) - \frac{hPL^2(\Delta\xi)^2}{k}\right]$$

$$c_i = \left[A(\xi_i) - A'(\xi_i)\frac{(\Delta\xi)}{2}\right]$$

we can rewrite the equation as,

$$a_i\bar{\theta}_{i-1} + d_i\bar{\theta}_i + c_i\bar{\theta}_{i+1} \qquad i = 1, 2, \cdots n + 1$$

Observe that the coefficients (a_i, d_i, c_i) in the above equations are known. However, unlike in equation (7.5), they vary with the grid point location i. Also, for i =1, $\bar{\theta}_0$ on the left boundary is known through the Dirichlet boundary condition. The last equation for $i = n + 1$ needs special attention since it contains the unknown $\bar{\theta}_{n+2}$ which lies outside the domain of interest. So far we have not used the Neuman boundary condition at the right boundary $\xi_{n+2} = \bar{\theta}_n$. Using the central difference approximation for the first derivative to discretize the Neuman boundary condition we get,

$$\frac{d\theta}{d\xi}\Big|_{\xi_{n+1}=1} = \left[\frac{\bar{\theta}_{n+2} - \bar{\theta}_n}{2\Delta\xi}\right] = 0$$

which implies $\bar{\theta}_{n+2} = \bar{\theta}_n$. This can be used to eliminate $\bar{\theta}_{n+2}$ from the last equation, which becomes,

$$(a_i + c_i)\bar{\theta}_n + d_i\bar{\theta}_{n+1} = 0 \qquad i = n + 1$$

Thus we obtain a tridiagonal system of linear equation of the form T .= b. For n =4, as an example, we get the follwoing five equations.

$$\begin{bmatrix} d_1 & c_1 & 0 & 0 & 0 \\ a_2 & d_2 & c_2 & 0 & 0 \\ 0 & a_3 & d_3 & c_3 & 0 \\ 0 & 0 & a_4 & d_4 & c_4 \\ 0 & 0 & 0 & a_5 & d_5 \end{bmatrix} \begin{bmatrix} \bar{\theta}_1 \\ \bar{\theta}_2 \\ \bar{\theta}_3 \\ \bar{\theta}_4 \\ \bar{\theta}_5 \end{bmatrix} = \begin{bmatrix} -a_1\bar{\theta}_0 \\ 0 \\ 0 \\ 0 \\ 0 \end{bmatrix} \qquad (7.6)$$

Equation (7.6) is the discrete version of equation (7.3). Once the structure is apparent, we can increase n to reduce $(\Delta\xi)$ and hence reduce the truncation error. In the limit of $\Delta\xi \to 0$ the solution to equations (7.6) will approach that of equation (7.3). The matrix size will increase with decreasing $\Delta\xi$ and increasing n. The matrix $\mathcal{T}$ is tridiagonal and hence the Thomas algorithm developed in section §3.4.4 can be used to get the solution.

7.1.3 Nonlinear problem

Conceptually there is no difference in discretizing a linear or a non-linear differential equation. The process of constructing a grid and replacing the di.erential equations with the difference equations at each grid point is the same. The main difference lies in the choice of solution technique available for solving the nonlinear algebraic equations. Let us consider the nonlinear model represented by equation (7.4). In this case we have a Robin condition at $\Delta\xi = 1$ and hence $\bar{\theta}_{n+1}$ is unknown. Thus the unknowns on the discrete grid consist of

$$\bar{\theta} = [\bar{\theta}_1, \bar{\theta}_2, \cdots, \bar{\theta}_{n+1}]$$

and we need n +1 equations. Discretizing equation (7.4) at a typical grid point i, we obtain the following (n +1) nonlinear algebraic equations.

$$f_i(\bar{\theta}) = k(\bar{\theta}_i) \left[\frac{\bar{\theta}_{i-1} - 2\bar{\theta}_i + \bar{\theta}_{i+1}}{(\Delta\xi)^2} \right] + k'(\bar{\theta}_i) \left[\frac{\bar{\theta}_{i-1} - \bar{\theta}_{i+1}}{2(\Delta\xi)} \right]^2$$
$$-\frac{hPL^2}{A}\bar{\theta}_i = 0 \qquad i = 1, 2 \cdots n + 1$$

In this set of equations i =1 and i =(n+1) require special consideration to incorporate the boundary conditions. Thus, making use of the left boundary condition, $\bar{\theta}_0 = 1$, $f_1(\bar{\theta})$ becomes,

$$f_1(\bar{\theta}_1, \bar{\theta}_2) = k(\bar{\theta}_1) \left[\frac{1 - 2\bar{\theta}_1 + \bar{\theta}_2}{(\Delta\xi)^2} \right] + k'(\bar{\theta}_1) \left[\frac{\bar{\theta}_2 - 1}{2(\Delta\xi)} \right]^2 - \frac{hPL^2}{A}\bar{\theta}_1 = 0$$

At the right boundary, we discretize the Robin boundary condition as,
.

$$k(\bar{\theta}_{n+1}) \left[\frac{\bar{\theta}_{n+2} - \bar{\theta}_n}{2(\Delta\xi)} \right] + h\bar{\theta}_{n+1} = 0$$

which can be rearranged as,

$$\bar{\theta}_{n+2} = \left[\bar{\theta}_n - \left(\frac{2(\Delta\xi)h}{k(\bar{\theta}_{n+1})}\right)\bar{\theta}_{n+1}\right] + [\bar{\theta}_n - \beta\bar{\theta}_{n+1}]$$

This can be used in the equation $f_{n+1}(\bar{\theta})$ to eliminate $\bar{\theta}_{n+2}$.

$$f_n(\bar{\theta}_n, \bar{\theta}_{n+1}) = k(\bar{\theta}_{n+1})\left[\frac{\bar{\theta}_n - 2\bar{\theta}_{n+1} - \beta\bar{\theta}_{n+1}}{(\Delta\xi)^2}\right] +$$

$$k'(\bar{\theta}_{n+1})\left[\frac{\bar{\theta}_n - \beta\bar{\theta}_{n+1} - \bar{\theta}_n}{2(\Delta\xi)}\right]^2 - \frac{hPL^2}{A}\bar{\theta}_{n+1} = 0$$

The above equations $f_1 = 0, f_2 = 0, \cdots f_{n+1} = 0$ can be represented symbolically as a system of $(n+1)$ nonlinear equations of the form, $\mathcal{F}(\bar{\theta}) = 0$. These can be solved most effectively by the Newton method for the unknowns $\bar{\theta} = \bar{\theta}_1, \bar{\theta}_2, \cdots, \bar{\theta}_{n+1}$.

$$\bar{\theta}^{p+1} = \bar{\theta}^p - \boldsymbol{J}^{-1}f(\bar{\theta}^p) \qquad 0, 1, \cdots$$

The Jacobian matrix, $\{\boldsymbol{J} = \frac{\partial\mathcal{F}}{\partial\theta}\}$ has the following tridiagonal structure.

$$\boldsymbol{J} = \begin{bmatrix} \frac{\partial f_1}{\partial\theta_1} & \frac{\partial f_1}{\partial\theta_2} & 0 & 0 \\ \frac{\partial f_2}{\partial\theta_1} & \frac{\partial f_2}{\partial\theta_2} & \frac{\partial f_2}{\partial\theta_3} & 0 \\ 0 & \frac{\partial f_3}{\partial\theta_2} & \frac{\partial f_3}{\partial\theta_3} & \frac{\partial f_3}{\partial\theta_4} \\ 0 & 0 & \frac{\partial f_4}{\partial\theta_3} & \frac{\partial f_4}{\partial\theta_4} \end{bmatrix}$$

7.2 Shooting method

Recall the model for dimensionless temperature distribution in aa fin of constant cross section

$$\frac{d^2\theta}{d\xi^2} - hPL^2\theta = 0 \qquad (7.7)$$

$$\theta(\xi = 0) = 1 \qquad \theta(\xi = 1) = 0$$

Suppose we can guess the boundary conditions required at one end of the domain ($\xi = 0$ or $\xi = 1$). We can then solve this problem by using the initial value methods discussed in initial value problem (Chapter 6). If our guessed value gives the correct value at the end of the domain, we have arrived, otherwise we have to guess again, and again until convergence.

7.2.1 Linear Systems

For a system of linear ODEs, the shooting method does not need iteration. As an example consider a system of two linear ODEs:

$$\begin{aligned}
\frac{dy_1}{dx} &= g_1(x) + y_1 g_2(x) + y_2 g_3(x) \\
\frac{dy_2}{dx} &= g_4(x) + y_1 g_5(x) + y_2 g_6(x)
\end{aligned} \qquad (7.8)$$

with boundary conditions $y_1(a) = y_{1a}$ and $y_2(b) = y_{2b}$ First numerically solve the system in equation 7.8 as an initial value problem with $y_1(a) = y_{1a}$, $y_2(a) = 0$. Call this solution $y_1^{(1)}(x)$, $y_2^{(1)}(x)$. Then solve the homogeneous system

$$\begin{aligned}
\frac{dy_1}{dx} &= y_1 g_2(x) + y_2 g_3(x) \\
\frac{dy_2}{dx} &= y_1 g_5(x) + y_2 g_6(x)
\end{aligned} \qquad (7.9)$$

as an initial value problem with $y_1(a) = 0$, $y_2(a) = 1$. Call this solution $y_1^{(2)}(x)$, $y_2^{(2)}(x)$.

Now $y_1^{(1)}(x) + cy_1^{(2)}(x)$ and $y_2^{(1)}(x) + cy_2^{(2)}(x)$ is also a solution to equation 7.8 and it satisties the condition $y_1(a) = y_{1a}$ for all values of the constant c. Linear interpolation can be used to determine the correct initial condition.

EXAMPLE 7.1 *Consider the following second order boundary value ODE*

$$\frac{d^2 y}{dt^2} = 4t \qquad 0 < t < 1$$

With boundary conditions $y(0) = 0, \quad y(1) = 1$
Transform the second order ODE into a system of two first order ODE's
Define two new variables u_1 *and* u_2

$$u_1 = y \tag{7.10}$$

$$u_2 = \frac{du_1}{dt} = \frac{dy}{dt} = y'$$

Now our two equations are obtained by taking the derivative of the new variables, i.e.,

$$u_1' = y' = u_2 \tag{7.11}$$

$$u_2' = \frac{d^2 u_1}{dt^2} = \frac{d^2 y}{dt^2} = y'' = 4t \tag{7.12}$$

in vector form

$$U' = \begin{bmatrix} u_1' \\ u_2' \end{bmatrix} = \begin{bmatrix} u_2 \\ 4t \end{bmatrix}$$

The vector containing the two variables is

$$U = \begin{bmatrix} u_1 \\ u_2 \end{bmatrix}$$

The rhs function

$$F = \begin{bmatrix} u_2 \\ 4t \end{bmatrix}$$

The problem can now be solved, in vectorial form, taking account that both variables have to be solved at the same time.

e.g.,
Using the Euler formula

$$U^{(k+1)} = U^{(k)} + hF(t_k, U^{(k)})$$

or the classical Runge-Kutta method (RK4)

$$U^{(k+1)} = U^{(k)} + hF(K_1 + 2K_2 + 2K_3 + K_4)$$

Lets demonstrate the solution using the RK4 method
From the boundary conditions, we know $u_1(0) = y(0) = 0$ and $u_1(1) = y(1) = 1$. However, we do not know the value of $y'(0) = u_2(0)$ which is required to solve as initial value problem. So we will make guesses to determine which value of $y'(0) = u_2(0)$ coincides the given boundary $y(1) = 1$
First try, let $u_2(0) = 1$ with a step size of $h = 0.5$
First iteration: from $t_0 = 0$ to $t_1 = t_0 + h = 0.5$

$$U^{(1)} = U^{(0)} + hF(K_1 + 2K_2 + 2K_3 + K_4)$$

$$U^{(1)} = U^{(0)} + hF(K_1 + 2K_2 + 2K_3 + K_4)$$

$$K_1 = F(t_k, U_k), K_2 = F\left(t_k + \frac{h}{2}, U_k + \frac{h}{2}K_1\right),$$

$$K_3 = F\left(t_k + \frac{h}{2}, U_k + \frac{h}{2}K_2\right), K_4 = F(t_k + h, K_3)$$

$$U^{(1)} = \begin{bmatrix} 0 \\ 1 \end{bmatrix} + \left(\begin{bmatrix} 1 \\ 0 \end{bmatrix} + 2\begin{bmatrix} 1 \\ 1 \end{bmatrix} + 2\begin{bmatrix} 1.250 \\ 1.000 \end{bmatrix} + \begin{bmatrix} 1.500 \\ 2.000 \end{bmatrix}\right)$$

$$U^{(1)} = \begin{bmatrix} 0.583 \\ 1.500 \end{bmatrix} \qquad \textit{after 1 step}$$

For the second step, $t_2 = t_1 + h = 0.5 + 0.5 = 1.0$

$$U^{(2)} = \begin{bmatrix} 0.583 \\ 0.500 \end{bmatrix} + \frac{0.5}{4} \left(\begin{bmatrix} 1.50 \\ 2.00 \end{bmatrix} + 2 \begin{bmatrix} 2 \\ 3 \end{bmatrix} + 2 \begin{bmatrix} 2.25 \\ 3.00 \end{bmatrix} + \begin{bmatrix} 3 \\ 4 \end{bmatrix} \right)$$

$$U^{(1)} = \begin{bmatrix} 1.667 \\ 3.000 \end{bmatrix} \qquad \textit{after 2 steps}$$

So we have missed the target of $u_1(1) = 1.667 \neq 1$. Lets try again with a different initial value, say, $u_2(0) = -1$
First iteration: from $t_0 = 0$ to $t_1 = t_0 + h = 0.5$

$$U^{(1)} = \begin{bmatrix} 0 \\ -1 \end{bmatrix} + \left(\begin{bmatrix} -1 \\ 0 \end{bmatrix} + 2 \begin{bmatrix} -1 \\ 1 \end{bmatrix} + 2 \begin{bmatrix} -0.750 \\ 1.000 \end{bmatrix} + \begin{bmatrix} = -0.500 \\ 2.000 \end{bmatrix} \right)$$

$$U^{(1)} = \begin{bmatrix} -0.4167 \\ -0.5000 \end{bmatrix} \qquad \textit{after 1 step}$$

For the second step, $t_2 = t_1 + h = 0.5 + 0.5 = 1.0$

$$U^{(2)} = \begin{bmatrix} -0.4167 \\ -0.5000 \end{bmatrix} + \frac{0.5}{4} \left(\begin{bmatrix} -0.5000 \\ 2.000 \end{bmatrix} + 2 \begin{bmatrix} 0 \\ 3 \end{bmatrix} + 2 \begin{bmatrix} 0.25 \\ 3.00 \end{bmatrix} + \begin{bmatrix} 1 \\ 4 \end{bmatrix} \right)$$

$$U^{(2)} = \begin{bmatrix} u_1^{(2)} \\ u_2^{(2)} \end{bmatrix} = \begin{bmatrix} -0.333 \\ 1.000 \end{bmatrix} \qquad \textit{after 2 steps}$$

We have missed the target again because $u_1(1) = -0.333 \neq 1$. However, since the equations are linear, we do not need to make further guesses, rather, we use linear interpolation to obtain the better try.

$$try = try1 + \frac{(try2 - try1)}{(sol2 - sol1)}(true - sol1)$$

$$try = 1 + \frac{(-1-1)}{(-0.3333 - 1.6667)}(1 - 1.6667) = 0.3333$$

Thus the initial value of $u_2(0.3333)$ will give the correct result as shown in the figure 7.2 below:

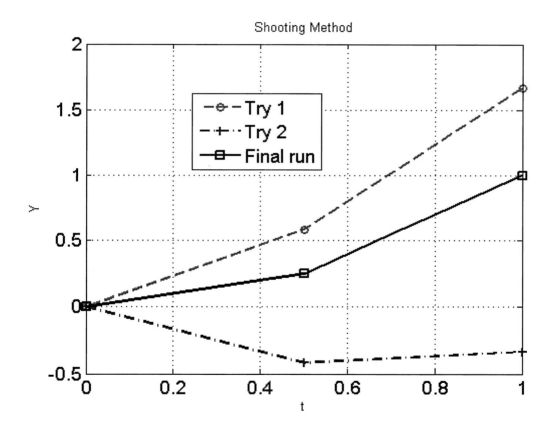

Figure 7.2: Solution by shooting method

Non-Linear problems

For non-linear problems, the procedure above does not work because we cannot simply combine solutions. Instead, the typical procedure for non-linear boundary problems is as follows.

Consider again a second order ODE :

$$\frac{d^2\theta}{d\xi^2} = f\left(\frac{d\theta}{d\xi}, \theta, \xi\right) \tag{7.13}$$

with the boundary conditions $\theta(a) = \theta_a$, $\frac{d\theta}{d\xi}(b) = \theta_b'$.
We will write this as a system of two first-order ODE's by introducing new variables

$$y_1 = \theta$$
$$y_2 = \frac{d\theta}{d\xi}$$

Therefore we can write the two first order differential equations as

$$\frac{dy_1}{d\xi} = y_2 \tag{7.14}$$
$$\frac{dy_2}{d\xi} = f\left(\frac{d\theta}{d\xi}, \theta, \xi\right) = f(y_2, y_1, \xi)$$

with the boundary conditions $y_2(a) = y_a$, $y_1(b) = y_b'$.

Let us make this an initial value problem by assuming some initial value for y_1 : $y_1^{(0)}(a)$. We now solve the initial value problem and get the solution $y_1^{(0)}(\xi)$ which includes $y_1^{(0)}(b)$. However, $y_1^{(0)}(b) \neq y_b'$

At this point we should realize that we can largely use the arsenal of methods for solving non-linear algebraic equations (Chapter 2) to get to the right initial value for y_1. We can use bracketed methods such as the bisection method or the false position method if we have two initial conditions, say $y_1^{(upper)}(a)$ and $y_1^{(lower)}(a)$ with $y_1^{(upper)}(b) > y_b'$ and $y_1^{(lower)}(b) < y_b'$.

If we apply the bisection method, we would consider a new initial condition to be

$$y_1^{(mid)}(b) = \frac{y_1^{(upper)}(b) + y_1^{(lower)}(b)}{2}$$

then solve the initial value problem and see if $y_1^{(mid)}(b) > y_b'$ or $y_1^{(mid)}(b) < y_b'$ and either replace $y_1^{(upper)}(b)$ or $y_1^{(lower)}(b)$.

Using the Newton-Raphson method for the above problem can be quite involved since we need the derivative of the function. On the other hand, we can easily use the secant method as follows: start with solving two initial value problems, one with $y_1^{(0)}(a)$, and the other with $y_1^{(1)}(a)$. Results are $y_1^{(0)}(b)$ and $y_1^{(1)}(b)$. The function values are now the deviations of $y_1^{(0)}(b)$ and $y_1^{(1)}(b)$ from the desired value y_b' : *i.e.*,

$$F^{(0)} = y_1^{(0)} - y_b'$$

and

$$F^{(1)} = y_1^{(1)} - y_b'$$

We can the use interpolation to find the new guess for the initial value

$$y_1^{(2)}(a) = y_1^{(1)}(a) - F^{(1)} \left[\frac{y_1^{(1)}(a) - y_1^{(0)}(a)}{F^{(1)} - F^{(0)}} \right]$$

7.3 Summary

In this chapter we have developed two different approaches for solving boundary value problems, (i) finite difference methods and (ii) shooting methods.

Finite difference solutions are easy to implement for any type of boundary conditions. The boundary conditions are incorporated into the equations to be solved. The accuracy of finite difference methods is limited to second order (using centered difference approximation). When applied to non-linear problems, the finite difference solution requires the solution of a system of non-linear equations.

Shooting methods involve conversion of the boundary value problem into initial value problem and using the the marching methods of chapter 6 for solution. They have the advantage of being able to solve both linear and non-linear problems easily. They can also be devised for high order accuracy. The shooting method may, however, involve guesses and iterative solutions which may make it time consuming.

7.4   Exercise Problems

P7.1. Using a uniform grid-size with 4 subintervals, write out the system of finite difference equations for the following equations

(a) $\frac{d^2y}{dx^2} = 100y = 2000 \qquad y(0) = y(1) = 10$

(b) $\frac{d^2y}{dx^2} + x\frac{dy}{dx} = x^2 \qquad y(0) = 0, y(1) = 1$

(c) $\frac{d^2u}{dx^2} + \sin(x) = x^2 \qquad u(2) = 5, u(10) = 20$

(d) $x\frac{d^2y}{dx^2} + 8\frac{dy}{dx} = x \qquad y(1) = -1, y(2) = 1$

P7.2. Find the solution to the following system using finite differences

$$\frac{d^2y}{dx^2} - y = 1y(0) = 0, y'(1) = 1$$

P7.3. Find the solution to the following system using finite differences

$$\frac{d^2y}{dx^2} + x\frac{dy}{dx} + y = x \qquad y'(0) = 0, y(1) = 1$$

P7.4. The following equations are going to be solved using the shooting method. Determine the initial value problems that must be solved and the shooting parameters.

P7.5. $\frac{d^2y}{dx^2} = -\frac{2}{2+x}$, $y(0) = y'(1) = 0$

P7.6. $\frac{d^2y}{dx^2} = \frac{1}{x}\frac{dy}{dx} = 2$, $y(0) = y(1) = 1$

P7.7. Solve the following problem using the shooting method

$$\frac{d^2y}{dx^2} + \frac{1}{x}\frac{dy}{dx} + y = 1$$

P7.8. The amplitude of vibration of a string is given by the 1-dimensional Helmhotz equation

$$\frac{d^2A}{dx^2} + \frac{1}{\lambda^2}A = 0$$

with the boundary conditions $A(x = 0) = 0$ and $A(x = L) = 1$. Given that $L = 400mm$ and $\lambda = 50mm$, you are required to determine the amplitude of at different positions along the string.

(a) Find the amplitude along the string using shooting method with an initial guess of $\frac{dA}{dx}\big|_{x=0} = 0.01$. Perform only one pass using using **Explicit Euler** method with a step size of $\Delta x = 100$. Was your initial guess correct?

(b) Show how you would implement the shooting method with **Implicit Euler** method to find the value of the amplitude at $x = 100$. Use the same initial guessand step size $\Delta x = 100$ as part (a) above.

(c) Show how you will implement the shooting method with 4th order **Runge Kutta** (RK4) method to find the value of the amplitude at $x = 100$. Use the same initial guess and step size $\Delta x = 100$ as part (a) above.

(d) Use finite difference method to solve the problem with $\Delta x = 100$. Use centered differences. Show the coefficient matrix, the vector of unknowns and the constant vector. Solve the resulting system using any method for a system of lagebraic equations (*e.g.*, Gauss elimination).

P7.9. **Boundary value problem** - finite difference method

The dimensionless conduction heat transfer through a fin is modelled by the equation,

$$\frac{d^2\theta}{d\xi^2} - (mL)^2\theta = 0 \qquad (7.15)$$

with the boundary conditions,

$$\theta(\xi = 0) = 1 \qquad \text{and} \qquad \frac{d\theta}{d\xi}\bigg|_{\xi=1} = 0 \qquad (7.16)$$

One is interested in finding out both the temperature distribution $\theta(\xi)$ and the fin efficiency which is given by,

$$\eta = \frac{-\left[\frac{d\theta}{d\xi}\right]_{\xi=0}}{(mL)^2} \qquad (7.17)$$

$$\eta = \int_0^1 \theta \, d\xi \qquad (7.18)$$

Use the finite difference method to discretize equation (1). The region $\xi \in \{0, 1\}$ must be discretized into $N + 1$ regions with grid points numbered as follows: $\{\xi_i \mid i = 0, 1, \cdots, N+1\}$ so that you have N interior grid points and the spacing between grid points is given by $h = 1/(N+1)$.

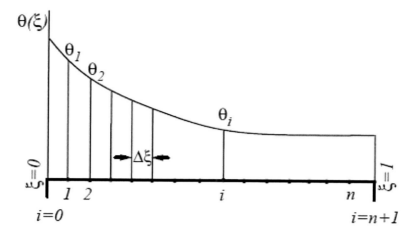

Figure 7.3: One dimensional finite difference grid of equally spaced data points

You must solve for the discrete values of temperatures at these points. Let the unknown vector be

$$\underline{x} = [\theta_1, \theta_2, \cdots \theta_{N+1}]$$

Your program must be general enough to specify the number of interior grid points N and the parameter mL as inputs.

a) Show the development of the discretized equations.

b) Show the structure of the matrix and arrange them in a form suitable for use with Thomas algorithm.

c) Solve the resulting system of linear algebraic equations for $N = 9, 19$ and 39 and $mL = 1$ and $mL = 2$.

d) Compare the temperature profiles obtained in part (c) with the three grids.

e) Evaluate the fin efficiency using both equations (4-5) for all three grid sizes.

P7.10. Boundary value problem - *shooting method*

Recall that the conduction heat transfer through a fin is modelled by the equation,

$$\frac{d^2\theta}{d\xi^2} - (mL)^2\theta = 0 \tag{7.19}$$

with the boundary conditions,

$$\theta(\xi = 0) = 1 \tag{7.20}$$

$$\left.\frac{d\theta}{d\xi}\right|_{\xi=1} = -Bi\ \theta \tag{7.21}$$

For any given mL and Bi, one is interested in finding out both the temperature distribution $\theta(\xi)$ and the fin efficiency which is given by,

$$\eta = \frac{-\left[\frac{d\theta}{d\xi}\right]_{\xi=0}}{(mL)^2} \tag{7.22}$$

$$\eta = \int_0^1 \theta\ d\xi \tag{7.23}$$

Use the *shooting method* to solve the above problem. The program must be general enough to accept any value of mL and Bi. You will need an initial value problem solver.

a) Show the reformulation of the problem suitable for solution by ODE.

b) Show the development of the interpolation scheme for the shooting method.

c) Solve the resulting system of linear equations for (i) $mL = 1$, $Bi = 0$, (ii) $mL = 2$, $Bi = 0$ and (iii) $mL = 1$, $Bi = 1$.

d) Print out the temperature profile for each case in intervals of $\Delta\xi = 0.05$.

e) Check how accurately your boundary condition (3) is satisfied in each case.

f) Evaluate the fin efficiency for each case in (c) using equation (4).

P7.11. Ordinary differential equations

Consider the following system of coupled ordinary differential equations.

$$10x^2 \frac{d^2c}{dx^2} + 2x\frac{dc}{dx} + c = ce^\theta \qquad (7.24)$$

$$\theta^2 \frac{d^2\theta}{dx^2} + 3c\frac{d\theta}{dx} + \theta = ce^\theta \qquad (7.25)$$

together with the following conditions.

$$c(x = 0) = 1 \qquad (7.26)$$

$$\left.\frac{dc}{dx}\right|_{x=1} = 1 \qquad (7.27)$$

$$\theta(x = 0) = 1 \qquad (7.28)$$

$$\left.\frac{d\theta}{dx}\right|_{x=1} = 0 \qquad (7.29)$$

• Does this model represent an *initial value problem* or a *boundary value problem?*

- Is the system *linear* or *non-linear*? If you think it is non-linear identify such non-linear terms.
- Discretize the equations with *central-difference* approximations to develop a set of algebraic equations over the interval $x \in [0, 1]$ with grid points $\{i|i = 0, \cdots, N+1\}$.
- Recommend a numerical algorithm for solving the resulting equation and outline the numerical procedure.

P7.12. The temperature distribution across a cylindrical pipe is given by the following differential equation:

$$\frac{d^2T}{dr^2} + \frac{1}{r}\frac{dT}{dr} = 0$$

Determine the temperaure distribution accross the pipe wall with inner diameter 6 inches and outer diameter of 12 inches if the inner side is maintained at a temperature of $60°C$ and the outer surface is at $20°C$.

(a) Solve the problem using the shooting method and RK4. Show the first step of RK4 by hand.

(b) Solve the problem using finite differences.

In both cases use a step size of $\Delta r = 0.2$ Plot both results in a single graph.

CHAPTER 8

PARTIAL DIFFERENTIAL EQUATIONS (PDES)

Partial differential equations are differential equations which contain more than one independent variable. Such equations may also be solved using finite difference method, as shown for ordinary differential equations. In this chapter we discuss the different forms of partial differential equations, boundary conditions and techniques for their discretization. The main difference being that the discretization is carried out in more than one dimension (variable).

8.1 Definitions

We will limit the discussion to PDEs of first and second order with mostly two independent variables (e.g. x and y or x and t). Just as with ODE's, the order of a PDE is related to the highest derivative in the equation.

PDEs can be linear and non-linear. The general form of a second-order, linear PDE in two independent variables x and y is:

$$A\frac{\partial^2 \phi}{\partial x^2} + B\frac{\partial^2 \phi}{\partial x \partial y} + C\frac{\partial^2 \phi}{\partial y^2} + D\frac{\partial \phi}{\partial x} + E\frac{\partial \phi}{\partial y} + F\phi = H \qquad (8.1)$$

In general A, B, C, D, E, F, H are functions of x and y. If H=0 Eq. 8.1 is called homogeneous. For a linear homogeneous PDEs, if $\phi^{(1)}$ and $\phi^{(2)}$ are solutions to the PDE, $c_1 \phi^{(1)} + c_2 \phi^{(2)}$ is also a solution.

If we consider A, B, C etc. to be constant, second-order, linear PDEs may be qualified according to the value of the discriminant, $B^2 - 4AC$:

- $B^2 - 4AC < 0$: Elliptic equation

- $B^2 - 4AC = 0$: Parabolic equation

- $B^2 - 4AC > 0$: Hyperbolic equation

It should be noted that this is not just a mathematical classification but it is related to the physical processes represented by PDEs. Elliptic equations usually describe steady-state (time independent), distributed systems. The equation for two dimensional steady state temperature distribution in rectangular coordinates is elliptic:

$$\frac{\partial^2 T}{\partial x^2} + \frac{\partial^2 T}{\partial y^2} = 0 \qquad (8.2)$$

Parabolic equations describe time-dependent diffusion problems like the heat equation

$$\frac{\partial T}{\partial t} = \alpha \frac{\partial^2 T}{\partial x^2} \qquad (8.3)$$

Hyperbolic equations time dependent physical processes which are not evolving towards steady state, *e.g.*, vibration and waves:

$$\frac{\partial^2 u}{\partial t^2} = c^2 \frac{\partial^2 u}{\partial y^2} = 0 \tag{8.4}$$

They are less frequently encountered in chemical engineering.

The requirements for boundary / initial conditions sufficient to solve the PDE are related to the type of PDE. A second-order parabolic equation requires one initial condition, and two boundary conditions. An elliptic equation requires boundary conditions on all its boundaries in order to get a unique solution.

Boundary conditions for PDEs come with their own naming convention:

- **Dirichlet condition:** values of the function ϕ (as introduced in Eq. (8.1) are specified at the boundary (e.g. specification of the temperature at the edges of the plate or concentration at the inlet of a reactor). *Also known as boundary condition of the first kind.*

- **Neumann condition:** specification of (the) gradient(s) of ϕ at the boundary, e.g. the gradient in the direction normal to the boundary $\frac{\partial \phi}{\partial n}$. *This is also known as boundary condition of the second kind.*

- **Mixed condition:** a combination of the above, see e.g. the boundary condition of the heated rod problem at $x = 0$ that contained the temperature and the gradient of the temperature at $x = 0$. *Also known as boundary condition of the third kind.*

Analytical solutions to PDEs are limited to relatively simple systems (simple in terms of the PDE itself, its boundary conditions, or the shape of the domain). In many cases, a numerical approach is required to solve problems involving PDEs.

8.2   Elliptic Equations

As an example covering most of the features involved in numerical solution of elliptic PDEs, lets consider the following case:

$$\nabla^2\phi = \frac{\partial^2\phi}{\partial x^2} + \frac{\partial^2\phi}{\partial y^2} = f(x,y) \qquad (8.5)$$

to be solved on a rectangular domain with extending from $0 \leq x \leq a$ and $0 \leq y \leq b$ with boundary conditions as shown in figure 8.1, i.e. at $y = 0$ and $y = b$, boundary specified as $\phi = 0$; at $x = 0$ $\phi = 1$. and at $x = a$ $\frac{\partial\phi}{\partial x} = 0$.

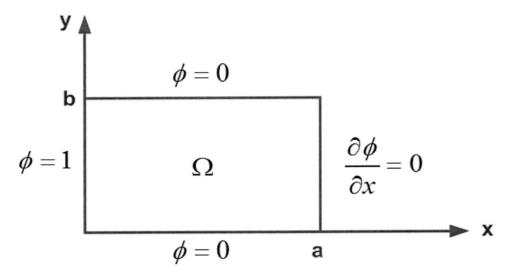

Figure 8.1: A rectangular domain with boundary conditions

The numerical solution procedure is based on discretization as shown in figure 8.2. Instead of solving a continuous function $\phi(x,y)$, we solve a discrete version of ϕ : $\phi_{i,j}$ with $\phi_{i,j}$ being the value of ϕ at the location $x = i\Delta x, y = j\Delta y$. The index i increases from 1 to m, and index j from 1 to n, thus

$$\Delta x = \frac{a}{m}$$

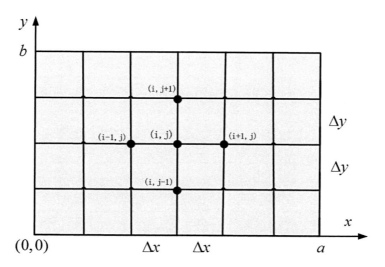

Figure 8.2: Discretized domain

$$\Delta y = \frac{b}{n}$$

We can write the discrete form of the PDE as a system of linear, algebraic equations in the unknowns :

$$\frac{\phi_{i+1,j} - 2\phi_{i,j} + \phi_{i-1,j}}{(\Delta x)^2} + \frac{\phi_{i,j+1} - 2\phi_{i,j} + \phi_{i,j-1}}{(\Delta y)^2} = f_{i,j} \qquad (8.6)$$

Here we have used central differences to approximate the second derivatives. From the analysis in Chapter 5, we know that this scheme is second order accurate, thus the error in discretizing the PDE then is of order $\mathcal{O}(h^2)$, where $h = \Delta x = \Delta y$.

The Dirichlet boundary conditions (at $x = 0$ and $y = 0$) can be incorporated into our equation system quite easily. If in Eq. (8.6) $i = 1$, we need $\phi_{i-1,j}$, which is obtained from the boundary value at $x = 0$. The same procedure applies for $j = 1$, where we use the boundary conditions at $y = 0$ to supply the value for $\phi_{i,j-1}$. For the Neumann boundary conditions at $x = a$ and $y = b$, there are a several ways to incorporate the conditions. We can apply backward differentiation to implement the boundary conditions or introduce a fictitious point outside the domain which will enable us to apply centered differences.

8.2.1   Approach 1: Backward differences

We determine the derivative $\frac{\partial \phi}{\partial x}$ at $x = a$ via backward differentiation, viz. :

$$\frac{\partial \phi}{\partial x}\bigg|_{i=m,j} \approx \frac{\phi_{m,j} - \phi_{m-1,j}}{\Delta x}$$

Since at $x = a$ the boundary is specified as $\frac{\partial \phi}{\partial x} = 0$, the backward difference implies that $\phi_{m,j} = \phi_{m-1,j}$. For all points $i = m - 1$, equation 8.6 becomes:

$$\frac{\phi_{m-2,j} - \phi_{m-1,j}}{(\Delta x)^2} + \frac{\phi_{m-1,j+1} - 2\phi_{m-1,j} + \phi_{m-1,j-1}}{(\Delta y)^2} = f_{m-1,j} \quad (8.7)$$

For the boundary at $y = b$, a similar procedure can be followed. One point of caution about this approach is that the two-point backward differentiation method is only first order accurate. The first-order accurate treatment of the boundary conditions leads to a first-order accurate overall result (although we discretized the PDE with second-order accuracy). This approach is therefore not recommended if one needs to preserve the second oder accuracy.

8.2.2   Approach 2: Centered derivative

An effective way to overcome the accuracy problem with Approach 1 is taking the central derivative at $x = a$ which is second order accurate:

$$\frac{\partial \phi}{\partial x}\bigg|_{i=m,j} \approx \frac{\phi_{m+1,j} - \phi_{m-1,j}}{2\Delta x} \quad (8.8)$$

In doing this, however, we have introduced points which lie outside the domain (fictitious points). We solve this problem by considering also these points to be part of the domain and eliminate them by applying the boundary condition. In this case, for $i = m$, combined with $\phi_{m+1,j} = \phi_{m-1,j}$ as a result of the boundary condition ($\frac{\partial \phi}{\partial x} = 0$) equation (8.4) becomes:

$$\frac{2\phi_{m-1,j} - 2\phi_{m,j}}{(\Delta x)^2} + \frac{\phi_{m,j+1} - 2\phi_{m,j} + \phi_{m,j-1}}{(\Delta y)^2} = f_{m,j} \qquad (8.9)$$

For the boundary at $y = b$ an analogous procedure can be followed. In this way, we have preserved the second order accuracy of the original equation by using a second order accurate boundary condition.

The same approach could be used if we had mixed boundary conditions at $x = a$ in the form $\frac{\partial \phi}{\partial x} + r\phi = w$, with r and w being constant. In this case, the approach with fictitious point is as follows:

Discretize the boundary condition at $x = a$ using central differences:

$$\frac{\phi_{m+1,j} - \phi_{m-1,j}}{2\Delta x} + r\phi_{m,j} = w \qquad (8.10)$$

We can then write an equation in $\phi_{m+1,j}$ as $\phi_{m+1,j} = \phi_{m-1,j} + 2\Delta x(w - r\phi_{m,j})$, and use this to substitute in equation 8.3:

$$\frac{2\phi_{m-1,j} - 2\phi_{m,j}}{(\Delta x)^2} + \frac{2(w - r\phi_{m,j})}{\Delta x} + \frac{\phi_{m,j+1} - 2\phi_{m,j} + \phi_{m,j-1}}{(\Delta y)^2} = f_{m,j}$$
$$(8.11)$$

EXAMPLE 8.1 (Elliptic PDE's) *Solve the Laplaces's equation*

$$\frac{\partial^2 \phi}{\partial x^2} + \frac{\partial^2 \phi}{\partial y^2} = 0 \quad 0 \le x \le 3, 0 \le y \le 3 \qquad (8.12)$$

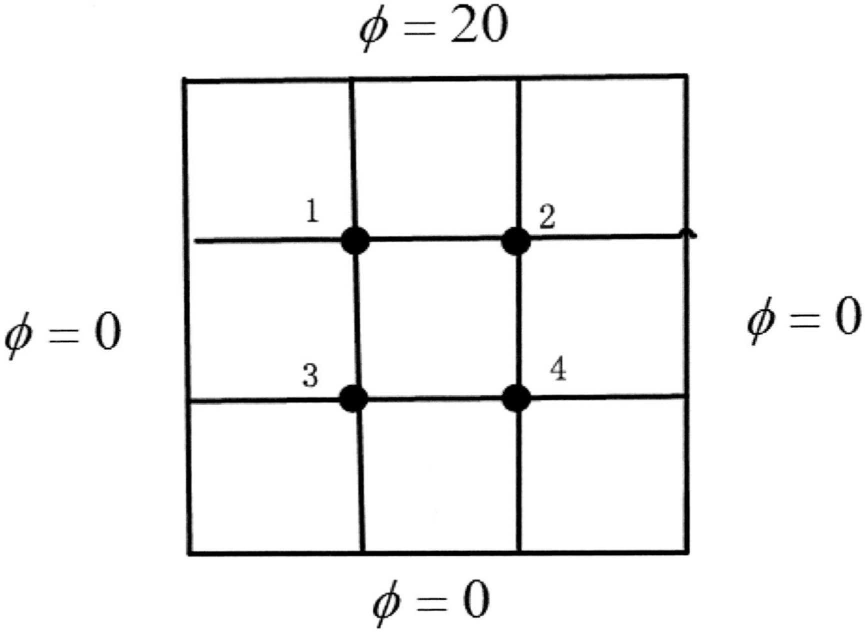

Figure 8.3: Grid for Laplace equation

With the boundary conditions:

$$\phi(0, y) = \phi(1, y) = 0, \phi(x, 0) = 0$$
$$\phi(x, 1) = 20$$

Determine the temperature (ϕ) at the points 1,2,3,4. Use centred difference approximations.

Centred difference approximation:

$$\frac{\phi_{i-1,j} - 2\phi_{i,j} + \phi_{i+1,j}}{(\Delta x)^2} + \frac{\phi_{i,j-1} - 2\phi_{i,j} + \phi_{i,j+1}}{(\Delta y)^2} = 0$$

All unknown nodes are interior with $\Delta x = \Delta y = 1$ we can write:

$$\phi_{i-1,j} - 4\phi_{i,j} + \phi_{i+1,j} + \phi_{i,j-1} + \phi_{i,j+1} = 0$$

- *node 1*

$$0 - 4\phi_1 + \phi_2 + 20 + \phi_3 = 0$$
$$-4\phi_1 + \phi_2 + \phi_3 = -20$$

- *Node 2:*

$$\phi_1 - 4\phi_2 + \phi_4 + 20 + 0 = 0$$
$$\phi_1 - 4\phi_2 + \phi_3 = -20$$

- *Node 3:*

$$0 - 4\phi_3 + \phi_4 + \phi_1 + 0 = 0$$
$$\phi_1 - 4\phi_3 + \phi_4 = 0$$

- *Node 4:*

$$\phi_3 - 4\phi_4 + 0 + \phi_2 + 0 = 0$$
$$\phi_2 + \phi_3 - 4\phi_4 = 0$$

Four equations and four unknowns

$$\begin{bmatrix} -4 & 1 & 1 & 0 \\ 1 & -4 & 1 & 0 \\ 1 & 0 & -4 & 1 \\ 0 & 1 & 1 & -4 \end{bmatrix} \begin{Bmatrix} \phi_1 \\ \phi_2 \\ \phi_3 \\ \phi_4 \end{Bmatrix} = \begin{Bmatrix} -20 \\ -20 \\ 0 \\ 0 \end{Bmatrix}$$

Solution by Gauss elimination gives:

$$\begin{Bmatrix} \phi_1 \\ \phi_2 \\ \phi_3 \\ \phi_4 \end{Bmatrix} = \begin{Bmatrix} 7.50 \\ 7.50 \\ 2.50 \\ 2.50 \end{Bmatrix}$$

We notice that $\phi_1 = \phi_2 = 7.50$ and $\phi_3 = \phi_4 = 2.50$, which implies symmetry. The problem could have been solved by considering only half of the domain (left side or right side).

EXAMPLE 8.2 (Elliptic PDE) *The electric potential (ϕ) in a medium is governed by the equation:*

$$\frac{\partial^2 \phi}{\partial x^2} + \frac{\partial^2 \phi}{\partial y^2} = 0 \quad 0 \le x \le 1.5, 0 \le y \le 1.5$$

With the boundary conditions:

$$\phi(1.5, y) = 0, \phi(x, 1.5) = 0$$
$$\phi(0, 0.5) = \phi(0.5, 0.5) = \phi(0.5, 0) = 100$$
$$\frac{\partial \phi}{\partial x}(0, y) = 0, \frac{\partial \phi}{\partial y}(x, 0) = 0$$

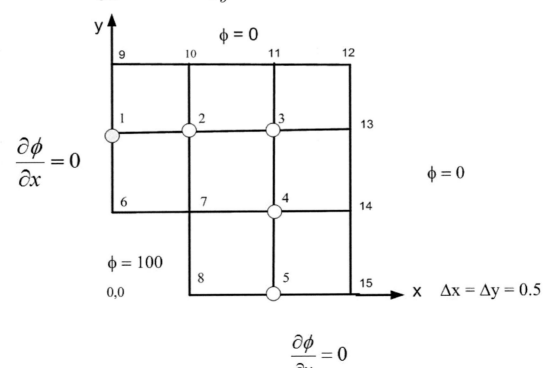

Determine the potential (ϕ) at the points 1,2,3,4 and 5 for the medium. Use centred difference approximations only.

Central difference approximation:

$$\frac{\phi_{i-1,j} - 2\phi_{i,j} + \phi_{i+1,j}}{(\Delta x)^2} + \frac{\phi_{i,j-1} - 2\phi_{i,j} + \phi_{i,j+1}}{(\Delta y)^2} = 0$$

- *Write the finite difference equation for the left boundary point (1).*

  Node 1 is on the left boundary where Neumann conditions are specified. In order to use centered difference for node 1, we introduce a fictitious point on the left of node 1, say ϕ_1^-

$$\frac{\phi_1^- - 2\phi_1 + \phi_2}{(0.5)^2} + \frac{\phi_6 - 2\phi_1 + \phi_9}{(0.5)^2} = 0$$

  Applying central difference for boundary conditions, we obtain equation for ϕ_1^-

$$\frac{\phi_2 - \phi_1^-}{2\Delta x} = 0 \Rightarrow \phi_1^- = \phi_2$$

  Substituting for ϕ_1^-, the equation becomes:

$$\phi_2 - 2\phi_1 + \phi_2 + \phi_6 - 2\phi_1 + \phi_9 = 0$$
$$-4\phi_1 + 2\phi_2 + 100 + 0 = 0$$
$$-4\phi_1 + 2\phi_2 = -100$$

- *Equation for Node 2:*

  Applying the boundary conditions and combining

$$\phi_1 - 2\phi_2 + \phi_3 + \phi_7 - 2\phi_2 + \phi_1 0 = 0$$

  after applying the boundary conditions and combining we obtain

$$\phi_1 - 4\phi_2 + \phi_3 + 100 + 0 = 0$$

  or

$$\phi_1 - 4\phi_2 + \phi_3 = -100$$

Node 3

$$\phi_2 - 2\phi_3 + \phi_{13} - 2\phi_3 + \phi_{11} = 0$$

Applying bcs and combining terms we obtain

$$\phi_2 - 4\phi_3 + \phi_4 = 0$$

Node 4

$$\phi_7 - 2\phi_4 + \phi_5 - 2\phi_4 + \phi_3 = 0$$

Applying bcs and combining terms

$$\phi_3 - 4\phi_4 + \phi_5 = -100$$

- *Write the finite difference equation for points on the bottom boundary (5). Again in order to apply central differences to the bottom point we introduce a fictitious point below point 5, $\phi_{\bar{5}}$*

$$\phi_8 - 2\phi_5 + \phi_{15} + \phi_{\bar{5}} - 2\phi_5 + \phi_4 = 0$$

Applying centered difference approximation for the boundary point

$$\frac{\phi_4 - \phi_{\bar{5}}}{2\Delta y} = 0 \Rightarrow \phi_{\bar{5}} = \phi_4$$

Substituting for the fictitious point

$$\phi_8 - 4\phi_5 + \phi_{15} + \phi_4 + \phi_4 = 0$$

applying the bc's and rearranging

$$100 - 4\phi_5 + 0 + 2\phi_4 = 0$$

$$2\phi_4 - 4\phi_5 = -100$$

We therefore have five equations and five unknowns

$$-4\phi_1 + 2\phi_2 = -100$$
$$\phi_1 - 4\phi_2 + \phi_3 = -100$$
$$\phi_2 - 4\phi_3 + \phi_4 = 0$$
$$\phi_3 - 4\phi_4 + \phi_5 = -100$$
$$2\phi_4 - 4\phi_5 = -100$$

- *We can now solve the resulting system of equations. Writing the equations in matrix form:*

$$
\begin{bmatrix}
-4 & 2 & 0 & 0 & 0 \\
1 & -4 & 1 & 0 & 0 \\
0 & 1 & -4 & 1 & 0 \\
0 & 0 & 1 & -4 & 1 \\
0 & 0 & 0 & 1 & -4
\end{bmatrix}
\begin{Bmatrix}
\phi_1 \\
\phi_2 \\
\phi_3 \\
\phi_4 \\
\phi_5
\end{Bmatrix}
=
\begin{Bmatrix}
-100 \\
-100 \\
0 \\
-100 \\
-100
\end{Bmatrix}
$$

Solution by Gauss elimination gives:

$$
\begin{Bmatrix}
\phi_1 \\
\phi_2 \\
\phi_3 \\
\phi_4 \\
\phi_5
\end{Bmatrix}
=
\begin{Bmatrix}
45.83 \\
41.67 \\
20.83 \\
41.67 \\
45.83
\end{Bmatrix}
$$

8.3 Parabolic equations

Parabolic equations describe time dependent physical processes which are evolving towards steady state, *e.g.*, diffusion. An archetypical parabolic equation is

$$\frac{\partial \phi}{\partial t} = \alpha^2 \frac{\partial^2 \phi}{\partial x^2} \tag{8.13}$$

with ϕ being a function of (location) x, and (time) t. Suppose we want to evaluate Eq. (8.13) in the x-interval $[0, 1]$, starting at $t = 0$ for $t > 0$. The conditions needed to solve the equation are an initial condition, *i.e.*, the full function at $t = 0$, and boundary conditions at $x = 0$, and $x = 1$ for all times t:

$$\phi(x, t = 0) = h(x), \tag{8.14a}$$
$$\phi(x = 0, t) = f(t), \tag{8.14b}$$
$$\phi(x = 1, t) = g(t) \tag{8.14c}$$

The functions h, f and g are usually constant.

We have two broad options for solving such problems, namely fully discrete and semi discrete. In *fully discrete* methods where discretize both the space and time dimensions, whereas in semi discretize methods we only the space dimensions.

8.3.1   Fully discrete methods

In these methods, discretization in space and time is the key to numerically solving Eq. (8.13) with the boundary conditions(8.10). Define a time step Δt, and a spatial step Δx such that $x_i = i\Delta x$ (with i running from 0 to m with $m\Delta x = 1$), and $t_j = j\Delta t$ (with j running from 0 to whatever end time you wish to compute). The discrete version of $\phi(x, t)$ then can be written as $\phi(x_i, t_i) = \phi_{ij}$. Now let's go back to the PDE (Eq (8.13)). The second derivative at position i in space, and j in time can be discretized with central differences (second order accurate):

$$\frac{\partial^2 \phi}{\partial x^2}\Big|_{i,j} = \frac{\phi_{i+1,j} - 2\phi_{i,j} + \phi_{i-1,j}}{(\Delta x)^2} + O(\Delta x^2) \tag{8.15}$$

Forward time centred space - FTCS method

The choice on how we discretize the first order term, $\frac{\partial \phi}{\partial t}$, has some far-reaching consequences as discussed below: The simplest algorithm is the forward difference approximation

$$\frac{\partial \phi}{\partial t}|_{i,j} = \frac{\phi_{i,j+1} - \phi_{i,j}}{\Delta t} \tag{8.16}$$

We now have a simple rule to update $\phi_{i,j+1}$ from the (known) solution at the previous time step $\phi_{i,j}$:

$$\phi_{i,j+1} = \phi_{i,j} + \alpha^2 \Delta t \frac{\phi_{i+1,j} - 2\phi_{i,j} + \phi_{i-1,j}}{(\Delta x)^2} \tag{8.17}$$

This is the called **explicit** method. There are two problems with this method:

- It is not very accurate; forward differences are first-order accurate. The error is proportional to .

- The method can get unstable (just as the Euler forward method for ODEs). If we write Eq. (8.17) as

$$\phi_{i,j+1} = p\phi_{i+1,j} + q\phi_{i,j} + r\phi_{i-1,j}$$

it can be shown that the conditions for this equation to remain stable are (i) the constants p, q, and r should all be positive; and $p + q + r \leq 1$. Since $p = \frac{\alpha^2 \Delta t}{\Delta x^2}, q = 1 - 2\frac{\alpha^2 \Delta t}{\Delta x^2}$ and $r = \frac{\alpha^2 \Delta t}{\Delta x^2}$, the second condition is always met. The first condition implies that $2\frac{\alpha^2 \Delta t}{\Delta x^2} \leq 1$, which at any given Δx is a time step limitation: $\Delta t \leq \frac{1}{2}\frac{\Delta^2}{\alpha^2}$. If (for instance) we want high spatial resolution (i.e. small Δx), Δt can become impractically small.

Backward time centred space - BTCS method

A simple cure for the instability is to make the method **implicit**, which implies making the time derivative in Eq. (8.9) a backward difference:

$$\frac{\partial \phi}{\partial t}\Big|_{i,j} = \frac{\phi_{i,j} - \phi_{i,j-1}}{\Delta t} \tag{8.18}$$

Then the update equation becomes:

$$\phi_{i,j-1} = -\frac{\alpha^2 \Delta t}{\Delta x^2}\phi_{i+1,j} + \left(1 + \frac{\alpha^2 \Delta t}{\Delta x^2}\right)\phi_{i,j} - \frac{\alpha^2 \Delta t}{\Delta x^2}\phi_{i-1,j} \tag{8.19}$$

Or (shifting one step in j and defining $\lambda = \frac{\alpha^2 \Delta t}{\Delta x^2}$):

$$\phi_{i,j} = -\lambda\phi_{i+1,j+1} + (1 + 2\lambda)\phi_{i,j+1} - \lambda\phi_{i-1,j+1} \tag{8.20}$$

This is an unconditionally stable method (no time step limitation with regard to stability). The method, however, has multiple unknowns (ϕ at the new time level $j + 1$) on the left-hand side making Eq. (8.20) a (tridiagonal) system of linear equations. Furthermore, it is still first-order accurate in time.

Crank Nicholson scheme

We could also consider an intermediate time level $j + \frac{1}{2}$. At this level, $\frac{\phi_{i,j+1} - \phi_{i,j}}{\Delta t}$ is a second order accurate estimate of $\frac{\partial \phi}{\partial t}$. In doing so, we also need to evaluate the right-hand side of Eq. (8.9) at time $j + \frac{1}{2}$. Thus:

$$\frac{\partial^2 \phi}{\partial x^2}\Big|_{i,j+1/2} = \frac{\phi_{i+1,j} - 2\phi_{i,j} + \phi_{i-1,j}}{2(\Delta x)^2} + \frac{\phi_{i+1,j+1} - 2\phi_{i,j+1} + \phi_{i-1,j+1}}{2(\Delta x)^2} \tag{8.21}$$

Here we have taken the average at time level j and $j + 1$. This expression is second order accurate in Δx . The overall updating rule (with the unknowns on the left-hand side, and the known (from the old time step) on the right-hand side becomes:

$$-\frac{1}{2}\lambda\phi_{i+1,j+1} + (1 + 2\lambda)\phi_{i,j+1} - \frac{1}{2}\lambda\phi_{i-1,j+1} = \frac{1}{2}\lambda\phi_{i+1,j} + (1 - 2\lambda)\phi_{i,j} + \frac{1}{2}\lambda\phi_{i-1,j} \tag{8.22}$$

This is known as the **Crank-Nicholson scheme**. It is second order accurate in space and time, it can be shown to be stable for any time step size, and it requires solving a (tridiagonal) linear system.

Extension to more spatial dimensions is straightforward. Lets consider a second spatial dimension y. The equivalent of Eq. (8.9) becomes

$$\frac{\partial \phi}{\partial t} = \alpha^2 \left(\frac{\partial^2 \phi}{\partial x^2} + \frac{\partial^2 \phi}{\partial y^2} \right) \qquad (8.23)$$

The simplest way to tacke this problem is the explicit method (again). If we discretize in y-direction with step size Δy and index k (*i.e.*, $y_k = k\Delta y$) then an explicit update scheme looks as follows:

$$\phi_{i,k,j+1} = \phi_{i,k,j} + \alpha^2 \Delta t \frac{\phi_{i+1,k,j} - 2\phi_{i,k,j} + \phi_{i-1,k,j}}{(\Delta x)^2}$$
$$+ \alpha^2 \Delta t \frac{\phi_{i,k+1,j} - 2\phi_{i,k,j} + \phi_{i-1,k-1,j}}{(\Delta y)^2} \qquad (8.24)$$

Incorporation of initial and boundary conditions in parabolic equations is quite straightforward. The initial conditions are used to start-off the solution process. Boundary conditions (in terms of the spatial coordinate x and y as in Eq.(8.17)) come in the same flavours as with elliptic PDEs: Dirichlet, Neumann, mixed. They are implemented in schemes for parabolic PDEs in the same way as for elliptic equations.

8.3.2   Semi-discrete methods

In semi discrete methods, a time dependent PDE is discretized in space, but the time variable is left to be continuous. As a result, a system of ODE's result which may be solved by the techniques discussed in chapter 6, for example Euler's method or Runge Kutta methods. One such method is the method of lines described here.

Method of lines (MOL)

In the method of lines (MOL) the spatial derivatives in the PDE are replaced with their finite difference approximations. This method is therefore sometimes called *the differential difference method*. Once the derivatives have been discretized, only the initial value variable, typically time in a physical problem, remains. In other words, with only one remaining independent variable, we have a system of ODEs that approximate the original PDE. The challenge, then, is to formulate the approximating system of ODEs. Once this is done, we can apply any integration algorithm for initial value ODEs to compute an approximate numerical solution to the PDE. Thus, one important features of the MOL method is the use of existing, and generally well established, numerical methods for ODEs.

Lets recall equation 8.13

$$\frac{\partial \phi}{\partial x} = \alpha^2 \frac{\partial^2 \phi}{\partial x^2} \tag{8.25}$$

To illustrate this procedure, we consider the MOL solution for the above equation. First we need to replace the spatial derivative $\frac{\partial^2 \phi}{\partial x^2}$ with an algebraic approximation. In this case we will use centered difference

$$\frac{\partial^2 \phi}{\partial x^2} = \frac{\phi_{i+1} - 2\phi_i + \phi_{i-1}}{\Delta x} + \mathcal{O}(\Delta x^2) \tag{8.26}$$

where i is an index designating a position along a grid in x and Δx is the spacing in x along the grid, assumed constant. Thus, for the left end value of $x, i = 1$, and for the right end value of x, $i = m$, i.e., the grid in x has m nodes.

Substituting equation 8.26 into equation 8.25 we obtain the MOL approximation:

$$\frac{d\phi}{dt} = \alpha^2 \left(\frac{\phi_{i+1} - 2\phi_i + \phi_{i-1}}{\Delta x} \right) \qquad i = 1, 2, \cdots m \qquad (8.27)$$

Note that equation 8.27 is written as an ODE since there is now only one independent variable, t . Note also that equation 8.27 represents a system of m ODE's. Since equation 8.27 is first order in t and first order in x , it requires one initial condition (IC) and one boundary condition (BC).

The integration in t can be carried out using any of the methods seen in chapter 6, viz. explicit Euler, implicit Euler or any other method for initial value problem.

Since equation 8.27 constitute m initial value ODEs, m initial conditions are required.

8.4 Hyperbolic equations:

Consider a first order hyperbolic equation

$$\frac{\partial \phi}{\partial t} + c \frac{\partial \phi}{\partial x} = 0 \qquad (8.28)$$

which represents *linear advection equation,* where c is the linear velocity. The general solution to this equation has the form

$$\phi(x, t) = f(x - ct) \qquad (8.29)$$

We can interpret this graphically as saying that as t increases, the initial function $\phi(x, 0)$ will move to the right with speed c.

Typically, therefore, we may say that hyperbolic equations describe wave-like phenomena. The archetypical hyperbolic equation is:

$$\frac{\partial^2 \phi}{\partial t^2} - c^2 \frac{\partial^2 \phi}{\partial x^2} = 0 \tag{8.30}$$

This we can be factored and written as a product:

$$\left(\frac{\partial}{\partial t} + c \frac{\partial}{\partial x} \right) \left(\frac{\partial}{\partial t} - c \frac{\partial}{\partial x} \right) = 0 \tag{8.31}$$

which basically means that:

$$\left(\frac{\partial}{\partial t} + c \frac{\partial}{\partial x} \right) = 0 \text{ or } \left(\frac{\partial}{\partial t} - c \frac{\partial}{\partial x} \right) = 0 \tag{8.32}$$

Now suppose as an initial condition we have $\phi(x, t = 0) = h(x)$. If we disregard boundary conditions with respect to x, solutions to the PDE look like $h(x + ct)$ and $h(x - ct)$. This can be shown though substitution: For $h(x - ct)$, lets define $x - ct = \eta$, thus:

$$\left(\frac{\partial}{\partial t} + c \frac{\partial}{\partial x} \right) h(\eta) = \frac{dh}{d\eta} \frac{\partial \eta}{\partial dt} + c \frac{dh}{d\eta} \frac{\partial \eta}{\partial x} = \frac{dh}{d\eta}(-c) + c \frac{dh}{d\eta}(1) = 0 \tag{8.33}$$

For $h(x + ct)$, lets define $x + ct = \eta$, thus:

$$\left(\frac{\partial}{\partial t} - c \frac{\partial}{\partial x} \right) h(\eta) = \frac{dh}{d\eta} \frac{\partial \eta}{\partial dt} - c \frac{dh}{d\eta} \frac{\partial \eta}{\partial x} = \frac{dh}{d\eta}(-c) - c \frac{dh}{d\eta}(1) = 0 \tag{8.34}$$

The functions $h(x+ct)$ and $h(x-ct)$ are travelling waves. $h(x-ct)$ travels in positive x-direction with speed c, and $h(x + ct)$ travels in negative x-direction with speed c.

Such problems can be solved by a combination of time and space differencing, *e.g.*, FTCS (forward time, centered space), BTCS (Backward time centred space) and the Crank Nicholson method. These methods and applications will be explored through problem sets at the end of this chapter.

8.5   Summary

In this chapter, we have explored the solution of differential equations with more than one independent variable, *i.e.*, partial differential equations. In general, the most widely used technique involves the finite different approximation of the derivatives in the respective space and time domains. The condition for the stability and accuracy of various the time schemes has also been explored.

Elliptic problems are quite stable because they do not involve time derivatives. Parabolic and hyperbolic schemes involve time derivatives and the time marching schemes for their solution require stability and accuracy considerations.

Explicit methods like the FTCS are conditionally stable and require small time steps to satisfy stability conditions. Implicit methods like the BTCS methods and Crank Nicholson scheme are unconditionally stable, and are therefore useful for a large range of problems.

8.6   Exercise Problems

P8.1. Elliptic PDE by finite difference scheme Consider the following elliptic partial differential equation.

$$\frac{\partial^2 \theta}{\partial x^2} + \frac{\partial^2 \theta}{\partial y^2} = 1 \qquad (8.35)$$

The domain of interest is $x \in [0,1]$ and $y \in [0,1]$ and we have homogeneous boundary conditions on the boundary. Using central difference approximations, discretize the equations into a form,

$$\boldsymbol{A}\,\boldsymbol{\theta} = \boldsymbol{b} \tag{8.36}$$

where $\{\boldsymbol{\theta} = \theta(x_i, y_j) = \theta_{i,j} \mid i = 1, 2 \cdots N, j = 1, 2, \cdots M\}$ are the interior nodal values of the temperatures.

Solve the resulting linear algebraic equations for $\boldsymbol{\theta}$ by (a) SOR iterative method and (b) direct method using $(N, M) = (19, 19)$ and $(29, 29)$ grid points.

P8.2. The governing equation for the temperature distribution in a metal wall is given by

$$\frac{\partial^2 \theta}{\partial x^2} + \frac{\partial^2 \theta}{\partial y^2} = 0 \qquad 0 \leq x \leq 0.5, 0 \leq y \leq 1$$

with the boundary conditions

$$T(0, y) = 500, \quad T(x, 1) = 500$$

$$\frac{\partial T}{\partial x}\Big|_{(0.5, y)} = 0 \quad \frac{\partial T}{\partial x}\Big|_{(x, 0)} = 450$$

Derive the finite difference approximation for the temperature for all nodes and solve the system using gauss elimination.

P8.3. Consider a metal bar with cross section $0.2m \times 0.3m$. The top and bottom of the bar are maintained at $150°C$. The left side is insulated and the right side is subjected to convective heat transfer with $T_\infty = 20°C$.

The governing equation is the poisson equation

$$\frac{\partial^2 \theta}{\partial x^2} + \frac{\partial^2 \theta}{\partial y^2} = 0 \qquad 0 \leq x \leq 0.2, 0 \leq y \leq 0.3$$

Boundary conditions

$$T(x,0) = T(x,0.3) = 150°C$$

$$\left.\frac{\partial T}{\partial x}\right|_{(x=0)} = 0, \quad k\left.\frac{\partial T}{\partial x}\right|_{(x=0.2)} = h(T_\infty - T)$$

If the thermal conductivity of the metal is $2W/mK$ and the heat transfer coefficient is $h = 50W/m^2K$, determine the temperature distribution in the plate. Use a discretization size of $0.05m$ for both x and y dimensions.

P8.4. Parabolic partial differential equations - Method of lines

Consider the unsteady state conduction heat transfer through a fin. The equations developed in Chapter 1 of this text are:

$$\frac{\partial \theta}{\partial \tau} = \frac{\partial^2 \theta}{\partial \xi^2} - (mL)^2\theta \tag{8.37}$$

together with the following conditions.

$$\theta(\xi, \tau = 0) = 0 \tag{8.38}$$

$$\theta(\xi = 0, \tau) = 1 \tag{8.39}$$

$$\left.\frac{d\theta}{d\xi}\right|_{(\xi=1,\tau)} = 0 \tag{8.40}$$

a) Does this model represent an *dynamic* or a *steady-state* situation?

b) Is the system *linear* or *non-linear*?

c) Convert the equations into a system of *first order or-dinary differential* equations using the following procedure.

- Construct a set of uniformly spaced grid points $\{\xi_i \mid i = 0, \cdots N + 1\}$ with $\xi_i = i\,h$ where the grid spacing $h = 1/(N + 1)$. Note that τ is still treated as a continuous variable at this stage.
- Let the unknown vector be $\underline{y}(\tau) = [\theta_1(\tau), \theta_2(\tau), \cdots, \theta_{N+1}(\tau)]$. Note that each element in the unknown vector $\underline{y}$ represents temperature at a fixed spatial position and is now a function of τ only.
- At each grid point i, discretize the *spatial derivatives* by central difference approximations.
- Hence rearrange equation (8.37) into a system of first order ordinary differential equations of the form,

$$\frac{d\underline{y}}{d\tau} = \underline{f}(\underline{y}) \tag{8.41}$$

- Obtain the necessary initial conditions for the set of equations (8.41)

d) Is the resulting system *autonomous* or *non-autonomous?*

f) Solve the equations using ode45 integrator available in MATLAB for (i) mL $= 1$ and (ii) mL $= 2$. Estimate the dimensionless time required to reach the steady state.

P8.5. Advection equation

Solve advection equation

$$\frac{\partial \phi}{\partial t} + c\frac{\partial \phi}{\partial x} = 0 \tag{8.42}$$

for the particular case where the initial condition is the cosine modulated Gaussian pulse,

$$\phi(x,0) = \cos(kx)exp\left(\frac{x^2}{2\sigma^2}\right)$$

with the periodic boundary conditions:

$$\phi\left(-\frac{L}{2}, t\right) = \phi\left(\frac{L}{2}, t\right)$$

and

$$\left.\frac{d\phi}{dx}\right|_{x=-L/2} = \left.\frac{d\phi}{dx}\right|_{x=L/2}$$

Solve the problem for the case where $c = 1, L = 1$ and $\Delta x = 0.02$. Investigate the stability of the chosen method by changing the value of Δx. Use the forward time centered space (FTCS) scheme.

P8.6. Repeat problem **P8.5.** using the backward time centered space method (BTCS).

APPENDIX A

MATLAB

A.1 Introduction

MATLAB is a powerful, *interactive* software tool for numerical computations normally encountered in engineering and science. It is available on several platforms including personal computers using DOS, workstations, mainframes and supercomputers using UNIX. It brings together a large collection of powerful numerical algorithms (from LINPACK, EISPACK etc) for solving a variety of linear algebra problems and makes them available to the user through an *interactive* and easy-to-use interface. Very little programming effort is required to use many of its standard functions. Yet, an experienced programmer can write advanced functions and even develop entire tool boxes for specific applications like control system design and signal processing. In fact several such tool boxes already exist.

Since MATLAB is interactive, you are encouraged to try out the examples as you read this manual. After each step, observe the outcome carefully. Since computers are programmed to respond in predictable manner, the key to mastering them is to be very observant.

Familiarity with the basic concepts of the operating system and the networked environment are assumed. In this notes you will be introduced to some of the basic numerical and graphical capabilities of the MATLAB. In particular the following will be explored.

- Starting a MATLAB session

- Using built in HELP, DEMO features

- data entry, line editing features of MATLAB.

- Summary of some of the built in functions in MATLAB for solving problems in

    linear algebra

    root finding

    curve fitting

    numerical integration

    integration of initial value problems

    nonlinear equations and optimization

    basic plotting capabilities

    Writing MATLAB functions and scripts - the m-file

For the adventurous, here are some of its advanced features. Explore them on your own! The package provides features (or tool boxes) for signal processing, control system design, identification and optimization through what are called m-files. The graphic features support include 3D and contour plotting as well as device drivers for a variety of output devices including Postscript and meta file capabilities for producing high quality plots (not just screen dumps!). It also provides facilities for developing ones own tool boxes as well as facilities for interfacing with other high level languages such as FORTRAN or C and invoke such routines from within MATLAB.

A.2   MATLAB basics

Once you start MATLAB successfully, you will be confronted with several windows on the screen. The main command window allows you to type a command,

>>

This provides you with an interactive workspace in which you can define any number of variables and invoke any function. To exit MATLAB at any time enter

>> **quit**

The commands that you enter within MATLAB are acted upon immediately. As soon as you enter a line like,

>> *fname*

MATLAB checks if "fname" is a valid MATLAB command or a built in function. If so it will be executed immediately. If not MATLAB searches the path to look for a external function or a file by the name "fname.m". Such a file is called a m-file, as its file extension is "m". If such a file is found it will execute the contents of that file. If not, MATLAB will generate an appropriate error message. m-files can be either scripts (i.e. a series of valid MATLAB commands that are executed often and hence stored in a file) or they can be used to define entirely new MATLAB functions of your own. More on m-files later.

A.2.1   Using built in HELP, DEMO features

MATLAB provides extensive online help using commands like
help, demo, type, lookfor, whatsnew. They are not only
useful for checking the syntax of a particular function, but also
for exploring and learning about new topics. Since the **help** command often generates lots of text that tend to scroll by very
quickly, it is useful to enable a feature called "more" with the
command,

   >> more on

When this is enabled, you will be shown one screen full of information at a time. Note that this is also UNIX feature that you
can use with any program that generates lots of scrolling text.
To get started with the online help, first get a list of help topics
using

   >> help

Table A.1 provides a list of help topics which should give you
some idea about the broad scope of MATLAB. You can obtain a
list of functions under each topic (or directory) by entering **help**
topic. For example to get a listing of general purpose commands
(the first item in the above table) enter,

   >> help *general*

The list so produced is given in Table A.2 to serve as a reference
material.   Many of the functions that will be useful in a numerical methods course are listed in subsequent sections of this
chapter. One way to become proficient in MATLAB is to use this
HELP feature liberally - *i.e.*, when ever you are in doubt call on
the HELP!

directory/topic	Brief description
matlab/general	General purpose commands
matlab/ops	Operators and special characters
matlab/lang	Language constructs and debugging
matlab/elmat	Elementary matrices and matrix manipulation
matlab/specmat	Specialized matrices
matlab/elfun	Elementary math functions
matlab/specfun	Specialized math functions
matlab/matfun	Matrix functions & numerical linear algebra
matlab/datafun	Data analysis and Fourier transform functions
matlab/polyfun	Polynomial and interpolation functions
matlab/funfun	Function functions & nonlinear numerical methods
matlab/sparfun	Sparse matrix functions
matlab/plotxy	Two dimensional graphics
matlab/plotxyz	Three dimensional graphics
matlab/graphics	General purpose graphics functions
matlab/color	Color control and lighting model functions
matlab/sounds	Sound processing functions
matlab/strfun	Character string functions
matlab/iofun	Low-level file I/O functions
matlab/demos	Demonstrations and samples
toolbox/control	Control System Toolbox
toolbox/ident	System Identification Toolbox
toolbox/local	Local function library
toolbox/optim	Optimization Toolbox
toolbox/signal	Signal Processing Toolbox
simulink/simulink	SIMULINK model analysis and construction functions
simulink/blocks	SIMULINK block library
simulink/simdemos	SIMULINK demonstrations and samples

Table A.1: List of MATLAB help topics

Function	Brief description
Managing commands and functions	
help	On-line documentation
what	Directory listing of M-, MAT- and MEX-files
type	List M-file
lookfor	Keyword search through the HELP entries
which	Locate functions and files
demo	Run demos
path	Control MATLAB's search path
Managing variables and the workspace	
who	List current variables
whos	List current variables, long form
load	Retrieve variables from disk
save	Save workspace variables to disk
clear	Clear variables and functions from memory
pack	Consolidate workspace memory
size	Size of matrix
length	Length of vector
disp	Display matrix or text
Working with files and the operating system	
cd	Change current working directory
dir	Directory listing
delete	Delete file
getenv	Get environment value
!	Execute operating system command
unix	Execute operating system command & return result
diary	Save text of MATLAB session
Controlling the command window	
cedit	Set command line edit/recall facility parameters
clc	Clear command window
home	Send cursor home
format	Set output format
echo	Echo commands inside script files
more	Control paged output in command window
Starting and quitting from MATLAB	
quit	Terminate MATLAB
startup	M-file executed when MATLAB is invoked
matlabrc	Master startup M-file

Table A.2: General purpose MATLAB commands

There is also a built in DEMO feature. To invoke this feature simply enter

>> **demo**

It will provide you with a menu of items. Select the ones that interest you most. You can also search by keywords using the command **lookfor**. Try,

>> **lookfor** *inverse*

which will scan for and print out the names of functions which have the keyword "inverse" in their help information. The result is reproduced below.

```
INVHILB Inverse Hilbert matrix.
ACOS    Inverse cosine.
ACOSH   Inverse hyperbolic cosine.
ASIN    Inverse sine.
ASINH   Inverse hyperbolic sine.
ATAN    Inverse tangent.
ATAN2   Four quadrant inverse tangent.
ATANH   Inverse hyperbolic tangent.
ERFINV  Inverse of the error function.
INVERF  Inverse Error function.
INV     Matrix inverse.
PINV    Pseudoinverse.
IFFT    Inverse discrete Fourier transform.
IFFT2   Two-dimensional inverse discrete Fourier transform.
UPDHESS Performs the Inverse Hessian Update.
```

A.2.2   Data entry, line editing features of MATLAB

The basic variables in MATLAB are treated as matrices. Vectors and scalar are special cases of a general matrix data structure. Similarly MATLAB handles complex variables and numbers in a natural way. Real variables, then are, special cases. Note that MATLAB is *case* sensitive.

- MATLAB remembers the previous command lines that you have entered. You can recall them by simply using the up and down arrow keys (or **ctrl-p** and **ctrl-n** key combinations) and then edit them and reenter the edited command as a new command.

- To *assign* a value to a variable use the assignment operator "=". For example,

  >> $A = [1\ 2\ 3; 4\ 5\ 6; 7\ 8\ 9]$

  will result in a 3x3 matrix. Note that there is no need to explicitly declare the dimension of an array. Since MATLAB is case sensitive you have defined only "A" and "a" remains undefined. Similarly

  >> x=[2+4*i, 3+5*i]

  will generate a complex vector with two elements. If you want to add another element enter *

  >> x(4)=5+6*i

  Note that the dimension of the vector x is now automatically increased to 4. Observe that the square brackets are used in forming vectors and matrices. Semicolon is used to

---

*what would the value of x(3) be?

separate rows in a matrix. Comma is used to separate individual elements of a vector (or matrix). Parentheses are used to identify individual array elements. (Try **help punct** and **help paren**)

- After you have defined the variables A and x as above, go through the following exercise and make sure you understand the result.

> > **A(2:3,1:2)**

Observe the use of () and : to select a sub block of A. Next, try *

> > **B(4:5,2:3)=A(2:3,1:2)**

This demonstrates how to extract a sub-block matrix of A and assign it to another sub-block of B. Next, try, [†]

> > **x(4:-1:1)**

which reverses the order of elements of x. Next, try the command,

> > **p=[1 3]; x(p)**

Observe that there are two commands, separated by semicolon. This example also demonstrates a powerful way of selecting specific elements of a vector. This is easily extended to matrices also. Well, try,

> > **q=[2 3]; A(p,q)**

---

*What might happen if the size of sub-blocks are different?
[†]What would be the value of x after you execute this command? Why?

- To *examine* the value of a variable simply enter the name of the variable. All the variables that you define during a MATLAB session are stored in the workspace (*i.e.*, in computer memory) and they remain available for all subsequent calculations during the entire MATLAB session *i.e.*, until you "quit" MATLAB.

- You can declare any variable to be *global* in nature using,

  >> **global** A

  If the same variable is also declared as *global* in several functions, then all those functions share the same value. To check if a variable is *global* use,

  >> **isglobal(A)**

  A value of 1 is returned if it is global.

- To examine the list of variables currently defined in your workspace and the attributes of those variables, use one of the two commands "`who`" and "`whos`".

  >> **whos**

- To generate a set of equally spaced values in a simple manner follow the example below:

  >> $x = 0 : 0.05 : 1.0$

  will generate $x = [0\ 0.05\ 0.1\ 0.15\ 0.2\ \cdots\ 1.0]$. (Try `help colon`).

- To suppress the automatic echoing of any line that you enter

from keyboard, terminate such a line with a semi-colon ";".
For example

$$>> x = 0 : 0.05 : 1.0;$$

will define x as before, but will not echo its value. (Try help
punct).

- To continue the entry of a long statement onto the next line
  use an ellipsis consisting of three or more dots at the end of
  a line to be continued. For example

$$>> s = 1 - 1/2 + 1/3 - 1/4 + 1/5 - 1/6 + 1/7 \cdots$$
$$>> -1/8 + 1/9 - 1/10 + 1/11$$

- Anything that follows a % sign is treated as a comment. For
  example the following is a valid command line.

$$>> I = 1 : 1 : 20 \qquad \text{\%generating a set of integers from}$$
1 to 20

- The numeric display format is controlled by the "format"
  command. Use

  >> format long

for 14 digits display. (Try help format)

- You can save the contents of a workspace with the "save"
  command. Try,   **>> save jnk**

In the next few statements examine the currently defined
variables, clear the workspace and load a previously saved
workspace.

>> **whos**
>> **clear**
>> **whos**
>> **load jnk**
>> **whos**

- The following matrix operations are available in MATLAB. You can use help on each of them to find out more precise information on them.

  $+$ addition, *e.g.*, $C = A + B \Rightarrow C_{ij} = A_{ij} + B_{ij}$

  $-$ subtraction, *e.g.*, *e.g.*, $C = A - B \Rightarrow C_{ij} = A_{ij} - B_{ij}$

  $*$ matrix multiplication, *e.g.*, $C = A*B \Rightarrow C_{ij} = \sum_k A_{ik}B_{kj}$

  $\hat{}$ Matrix power. $Z = X\hat{}y$ is X to the y power if y is a scalar and X is square. If y is an integer greater than one, the power is computed by repeated multiplication. For other values of y the calculation involves eigenvalues and eigenvectors. (try **help arith**).

  $'$ Matrix transpose. X' is the complex conjugate transpose of X. $X.'$ is the non-conjugate transpose. (try **help punct**).

  $\backslash$ left division. $A \backslash B$ is the matrix division of A into B, which is roughly the same as **inv(A)*B** , except it is computed in a different way. If A is an N-by-N matrix and B is a column vector with N components, or a matrix with several such columns, then $X = A \backslash B$ is the solution to the equation $A * X = B$ computed by Gaussian elimination. (try **help slash**)

  $/$ right division. B/A is the matrix division of A into B, which is roughly the same as **B*inv(A)**.

Note that the dimensions of the matrices must be compatible for the above operations to be valid; if you attempt matrix operations between incompatible matrices an appropriate error message is generated.

- The following relational operators are available in MATLAB. Try **help relop** for additional details.

$<$ Less than relational operator

$>$ Greater than relational operator

$<=$ Less than or equal

$>=$ Greater than or equal

$==$ equal

$\tilde{}=$ not equal

They are applied element-by-element between matrices of the same size, producing a resultant matrix consisting of 0's and 1's.

- Element-by-element multiplicative operations are obtained as follows:

operator	example	index notation
.*	C = A.*B	$C_{ij} = A_{ij}B_{ij}$
.^	C = A.^B	$C_{ij} = A_{ij}^{B_{ij}}$
./	C = A./B	$C_{ij} = A_{ij}/B_{ij}$
.\	C = A.\B	$C_{ij} = B_{ij}/A_{ij}$

A.2.3 Linear algebra related functions in MATLAB

A list of all advanced matrix related functions in MATLAB is given in Table A.3 Use the help command on each of these functions to find out more about the function and its exact syntax.

Function name	Action
Matrix analysis	
cond	Matrix condition number
norm	Matrix or vector norm
rcond	LINPACK reciprocal condition estimator
rank	Number of linearly independent rows or columns
det	Determinant
trace	Sum of diagonal elements
null	Null space
orth	Orthogonalization
rref	Reduced row echelon form
Linear equations	
\ and /	Linear equation solution; use "help slash"
chol	Cholesky factorization
lu	Factors from Gaussian elimination
inv	Matrix inverse
qr	Orthogonal-triangular decomposition
qrdelete	Delete a column from the QR factorization
qrinsert	Insert a column in the QR factorization
nnls	Non-negative least-squares
pinv	Pseudoinverse
lscov	Least squares in the presence of known covariance
Eigenvalues and singular values	
eig	Eigenvalues and eigenvectors
poly	Characteristic polynomial
hess	Hessenberg form
qz	Generalized eigenvalues
rsf2csf	Real block diagonal form to complex diagonal form
cdf2rdf	Complex diagonal form to real block diagonal form
schur	Schur decomposition
balance	Diagonal scaling to improve eigenvalue accuracy
svd	Singular value decomposition
Matrix functions	
expm	Matrix exponential
expm1	M-file implementation of expm
expm2	Matrix exponential via Taylor series
expm3	Matrix exponential via eigenvalues and eigenvectors
logm	Matrix logarithm
sqrtm	Matrix square root
funm	Evaluate general matrix function

Table A.3: Linear algebra related functions in MATLAB

Work through the following exercise to become familiar with the usage of some of the linear algebra functions and refresh some of the results from a first year linear algebra course.

Exercise - *review of linear algebra*

- Define the matrix, A and a vector, b as

  *   >> A = [1 0 0.307; 0 1 0.702; -2 1 0]
          >> b = [0.369*275;0.821*275;0];

  Observe the two different ways semicolon has been used here. What are they?

- Solve the equation $Ax = b$ using,

  >> $x = A\backslash b$

- Verify that x satisfies the equation by calculating,

  >> A*x - b

- Next calculate the norm of the residual,

  >> norm(A*x - b)

- Determine the rank of A using

  >> rank(A)

- Carry out the LU decomposition using

  †   >> [L,U]=lu(A)

---

*Why was "A" echoed on the screen, while "b" was not? Is "b" a row or a column vector?
†Why does "L" not appear to be lower triangular?

- Calculate the determinant of A using

    >> det(A)
    >> det(L)*det(U)

- Calculate the eigenvalues and eigenvectors of A.

      >> [v,d]=eig(A)
    *   >> prod(diag(d))

- Find out the characteristic polynomial of A and its roots.

    >> c1=poly(A)
    >> roots(c1)
    >> prod(ans)

A.2.4   Root finding

x=fsolve('fun',x0) solution to a system of nonlinear equations (or zeros of a multivariable function).
fun(x) is a function that you should write to evaluate f(x) - *i.e.*, you define your problem in an m-file.
x0 is the initial guess for the root. [There is obviously more to it than I can describe here! Read the manual or try `help fsolve`].

fzero('fun',x0,tol) finds the root of a single nonlinear algebraic equation.
fun(x) is the external function describing

---

*Can you explain this result?

your problem that you should write in a m-file.

x0 is the initial guess.

poly(V) if V is a vector then it returns the coefficients of the polynomial with roots determined by V. *i.e.*, roots and poly are inverse functions of each other.

roots(c) computes all the roots of a polynomial whose coefficients are in **c**. *i.e.*, $P_n(x) = (c_1 x^n + c_2 x^{n-1} + \cdots + c_{n+1})$.

A.2.5 Curve fitting

c=polyfit(x,y,n) least-squares curve fitting of degree n. The coefficients in descending powers of x are returned in c.

polyval(c,s) evaluates the polynomial whose coefficients are in **c** at locations determined by **s**.

yi=spline(x,y,xi) Generates a cubic spline through the data vectors (x, y) and then computes a vector of interpolated values of yi at xi.

diff(x,n) computes the **n** forward differences from the vector **x**.

The other functions of possible interest are **fmin, fmins, residue, conv , table1**.

A.2.6 Numerical integration, ordinary differential equations

quad('fun',a,b,tol,trace) computes the definite integral over the limit (a,b) using adaptive recursive Simpson's rule.

fun(x) is an external function that you must provide in a m-file.

tol is the acceptable global error. **trace** is an optional flag to monitor the integration process.

[t,y]=ode45('fun',t0,tf,y0,tol,trace) integrates a system of non-stiff differential equations of the form $dy/dt = f(y)$ using 4 and 5 order Runge-Kutta methods.

fun(y) is the external function which defines your problem. You must provide this via a m-file.

(t0,y0) is the initial condition.

tf is the final point at which you want to stop the integration.

tol is the acceptable global error in the solution. **trace** trace is the optional flag to print intermediate results.

The other functions of possible interest are **ode23, quad8**

A.2.7   Basic graphics capabilities

MATLAB maintains separate graphics windows and a text window. Your interactive dialogue takes place on the text window. When you enter any graphics command, MATLAB plots that graph immediately on the graphics window. It can open several graphics windows. So, clearly commands are needed to select a specific window to be the current one. The list of graphics related commands are given in Table A.4. Work through the following exercise interactively and observe the computer response in order to understand the basic graphic capabilities of MATLAB. Text

Function name	Action
Figure window creation and control	
figure	Create Figure (graph window)
gcf	Get handle to current figure
clf	Clear current figure
close	Close figure
Axis creation and control	
subplot	Create axes in tiled positions
axes	Create axes in arbitrary positions
gca	Get handle to current axes
cla	Clear current axes
axis	Control axis scaling and appearance
caxis	Control pseudocolor axis scaling
hold	Hold current graph
Handle Graphics objects	
figure	Create figure window
axes	Create axes
line	Create line
text	Create text
patch	Create patch
surface	Create surface
image	Create image
uicontrol	Create user interface control
uimenu	Create user interface menu
Handle Graphics operations	
set	Set object properties
get	Get object properties
reset	Reset object properties
delete	Delete object
drawnow	Flush pending graphics events
newplot	M-file preamble for NextPlot property
Hardcopy and storage	
print	Print graph or save graph to file
printopt	Configure local printer defaults
orient	Set paper orientation
capture	Screen capture of current figure
Movies and animation	
moviein	Initialize movie frame memory
getframe	Get movie frame
movie	Play recorded movie frames
Miscellaneous	
ginput	Graphical input from mouse
ishold	Return hold state
whitebg	Set graphics window defaults for white background
graymon	Set graphics window defaults for gray-scale monitors

Table A.4: Graphics related function in MATLAB

following the percent sign (%) are explanatory comments. You
need not enter them.

Exercise - *producing a simple graph*

```
>>x=0:0.1:2*pi;          % create a vector x in the range (0,2 Pi)
>>figure(1)              % open a graphics window labeled Figure 1
>>figure(2)              % open a graphics window labeled Figure 2
>>plot(x,sin(x))        % plot sin(x)
>>hold                  % keep the graph of sin(x)
>>plot(x,cos(x),'go')   % add graph of cos(x) with line type 'go'
>>title('My first plot') % put some title
>>xlabel('x-axis')      % label the x-axis
>>ylabel('y-axis')      % label the x-axis
>>gcf                   % get current figure (should be 2)
>>figure(1)             % make figure 1 the current figure
>>close(1)              % close window 1
>>gcf                   % get current figure (should be 2)
>>close(2)              % close window 1
```

In this exercise you produced the data from within MATLAB.
If you have columns of data in a file, you can read them into
MATLAB and plot them as above. The postscript file produced
in the above example can be merged with other documents or
printed on a postscript printer. Use **help print** to find out about
support for other type of printers and plotters.

A.2.8   Control System Toolbox

The Control system toolbox, which uses MATLAB matrix functions, was built to provide specialized functions in control engineering. The Control system toolbox is a collection of algorithms,

expressed in m-files, that implement common control system design, analysis, and modeling techniques.

Dynamic systems can be modeled as transfer functions or in state-space form. Both continuous-time and discrete-time system are handled. Conversions between various model representations are possible. Time responses, frequency responses, and root-locus measures can be computed and plotted. Other functions allow pole-placement, optimal control, and estimation.

The following example shows the use of some of the control system design and analysis tools available in MATLAB.

Example

The process transfer function, G is defined as:

$$G = \frac{1}{(s+1)(s+2)(s+3)}$$

The transfer function is entered into Matlab by entering the numerator and the denominator coefficients separately as follows:

```
>> num = 1;
>> den1 = [1 1];
>> den2 = [1 2];
>> den3 = [1 3];
```

The denominator polynomial is the product of the three terms. Convolution, **conv**, is used to obtain the polynomial product:

```
>> den = conv(den1,conv(den2,den3));
```

To get an open-loop process response to a unit step change, the function **step** can be used:

```
*     >> t = 0:0.5:5;
```

---

*Define time in the range 0-5. Generate step response and plot.

```
>> y = step(num,den,t);
>> plot(t,y,'*');
```

The **Bode plot** can be obtained by first defining a vector of frequencies, and then using the function **bode**:

```
*       >> w = logspace(-1,1);
     >> [mag,phase] = bode(num,den,w);
```

The bode plots for amplitude ratio and phase can be obtained by typing:

```
>> loglog(w,mag)
>> semilogx(w,phase)
```

The root-locus can be obtained by defining a vector of desired gains, and then using the function **rlocus**:

```
†       >> k = 20:5:70;
     >> y = rlocus(num,den,k);
     >> plot(y,'*')
```

The closed-loop transfer function can be represented by:

$$\frac{Y}{Y_{sp}} = \frac{G_c G_p}{1 + G_c G_p}$$

The closed-loop transfer function is calculated and entered into Matlab for analysis using the same functions used in the open-loop system.

Discretization can only be done through the state-space model representation. Therefore, it is necessary to transform transfer function models to state-space models. The transfer function

---

*Generate equally spaced data in the range 10^{-1} and 10^1

†Define gains in the range 20-70. Generate and plot the root-locus.

model can easily be transformed into the state-space model by using the function **tf2ss**:

> **[A,B,C,D] = tf2ss(num,den);**

where A, B, C, D are matrices in the differential equations $\frac{dx}{dt} := Ax + Bu$ and $y = Cx + Du$. To obtain a discretized model, the function **c2d** is used:

> **[ad,bd] = c2d(A,B,Ts); % Ts is the sample time**

This function converts state-space models from continuous time to discrete-time assuming a zero-order hold on the input. To obtain a step response on the discretized model, the function **dstep** can be used:

> **y = dstep(ad,bd,C,D,1,100);**
> **plot(y),title('step response');**

Several additional control functions that are available in Matlab are listed in Table A.5 The online help screen should be referred to for information on how to use these tools. The function **what** can be used to find out what other functions are available.

A.2.9 Producing printed output of a MATLAB session

If you want to produce a hard copy of your interactive MATLAB session, you can log a record of the entire session in a file with the **diary** command. The command

> **diary** *file*

will start recording every keyboard entry and most of the computers textual response (not graphics) in *file*. To suspend the

Function name	Purpose
Functions for model conversion	
$[num, den] = ss2tf(a, b, c, d, iu)$	State-space to transfer function
$[z, p, k] = sstzp(a, b, c, d, iu)$	State-space to zero-pole
$[a, b, c, d] = tf2ss(num, den)$	Transfer function to state-space
$[z, p, k] = tf2zp(num, den)$	Transfer function to zero-pole
$[a, b, c, d] = zp2ss(z, p, k)$	Zero-pole to state-space
$[num, den] = zp2tf(z, p, k)$	Zero-pole to transfer function
$[ad, bd] = c2d(a, b, Ts)$	Continuous to discrete
$[a, b] = d2c(ad, bd, Ts)$	Discrete to continuous
Functions for modeling	
append	Append system dynamics
connect	System interconnection
parallel	Parallel system connection
series	Series system connection
ord2	Generate A,B,C,D for a second order system
Continuous time and frequency domain analysis	
impulse	impulse response
step	Step response
lsim	Simulation with arbitrary inputs
bode	Bode and Nichols plots
nyquist	Nyquist plots
Discrete time and frequency domain analysis	
dimpulse	Unit sample response
dstep	Step response
dlsim	Simulation with arbitrary inputs
dbode	Discrete Bode plots

Table A.5: List of functions from control system tool box

recording, use

>> **diary off**

and to resume recording you can use,

>> **diary on**

The *file* contains simple text (ASCII) and can be printed on the network printer.

A.2.10 What are m-files?

MATLAB derives its strength and wide popularity from being extensible through the m-file facility. Extensibility means that using a core set of built-in functions, users can extend the capabilities of MATLAB by writing their own functions. The functions are stored in files with the extension ".m". Any file with the extension ".m" in the search path of MATLAB is treated as a MATLAB m-file. To find out the current path of MATLAB enter,

>> **path**

You can list the contents of a m-file with the **type** command. While the **help** command produces only documentation on the function, the **type** command produces a complete listing of the function. Try,

>> **type sin**
>> **help sin**
>> **type erf**
>> **help erf**

Note the "sin" is a built-in function and hence no code is listed. On the other hand "erf" is the error function implemented as a m-file and hence a complete listing is produced.

The m-files can take two forms - viz. (i) a script file and (ii) files that define entirely new functions. Such files should be in the MATLAB search path.

Example of a script file

In a script file, you can put any MATLAB commands that you would normally enter in an interactive session. Simply entering the name of the file would then execute the contents of that file. For example to enter a large matrix, create a file called "A.m" in your home directory using your favorite editor. This file should contain the following text.

```
B = [ 1 2 3 4 5 6 7 8 9;
       2 3 4 5 6 7 8 9 0;
       3 4 5 6 7 8 9 0 1;
       4 5 6 7 8 9 0 1 2;
       5 6 7 8 9 0 1 2 3]
b=sin(B)
```

To execute the contents of this file from within MATLAB enter,

>> **A**

Note that a matrix variable "B" of size (5×9) has been defined in your workspace and the variable "b" contains the values of sin(B).

In a script file you can include any such sequence of valid MATLAB commands, including program flow control commands like for, if, while loops *etc.* However a script file is *not* a function file and hence you cannot pass any arguments to the script. Also, when you execute a script file from the workspace, all of the variables defined in a script file become *global* variables. In contrast any variable defined within a function file is *local* to that function and only the results returned by the function become global in nature.

Example of a function file

Let us take the example of an isothermal, multicomponent flash equation, given by,

$$f(\psi) := \sum_{i=1}^{N} \frac{z_i(1-K_i)}{1+\psi(K_i-1)} = 0$$

In this equation, (z_i, K_i) are known vectors of length N and ψ is the unknown scalar variable. So we should like to write a function, say, flash(psi) that would return the value of $f(\psi)$. This function should be saved in a file named "flash.m" in your home directory. Such a function might look as follows:

    function f=flash(psi)
    global K z f=((1-K).*z) ./ (1+(K-1)*psi); f=sum(f);
    oooooo

Let us understand the anatomy of this function. The first line should always contain the keyword "function" in order to identify it as a function definition and not a script file. Then a list of values computed and returned by the function should appear - in the present case only "f" is being returned. If you have more variables being returned you would list them as " [f1, f2, f3] *etc.* Next, the equal sign is followed by the name of the *function.* * Then the list of input variables are given in parenthesis. The next several lines begin with the percent sign (%) and hence are treated as comments. Here is the place to put the documentation

---

*Note that the file name is constructed by appending ".m" to the function name. In the above example the file name will be flash.m

on what the function does and how to use it. This is also the part that is printed out when a user asks for help on this function. A blank line signifies the end of the help message. The actual code follows the blank line. Notice the use of element-by-element multiplication of two vectors which avoids the use of do loops. How elegant!

Assuming that you have created a file called "`flash.m`" containing the above lines, work through the following steps.

>> **help flash**
>> **type flash**
>> **global K z**
>> **z=[.25 .25 .25 .25]**
>> **K=[1 .5 .4 .1]**
>> **whos**
>> **flash(0.1)**

As a challenge, take up the task of modifying the function `flash` such that it will take in a vector of ψ values and return the corresponding function values!

A.2.11   Programming features

If you know any one high level programming language such a FORTRAN, C or even BASIC, you should have no difficulty in understanding the elementary program flow control features of MATLAB. A list of help topics is given in Table A.6. Let us take the example of "flash.m" and illustrate the use of "if" and "for" constructs. First we check if the length of vectors K, z are the same; if not we generate an error message. Note the `length` and `error` are built-in MATLAB functions. In the next section we determine the length of input vector "x" and build a loop to calculate the function for each element of "x" and store it in the corresponding element of "f". Use "**help relop**" and "**help lang**" to find out more about relational operators and programming language features.

Example

```
function f=flash(x)
% K is a vector of any length of equil ratios.
% z is the feed composition (same length as K)
% K, z are defined as global in main
% x is the vapor fraction
% The following is the isothermal flash eqn.

global K z

if ( length(K) ~= length(z) )
 error('Number of K values & compositions do not match')
end

n=length(x);     %Find the length of the input vector
for i = 1:n      %setup a loop for each element of x
 t=((K-1).*z) ./ (1+(K-1)*x(i));
 t=sum(t);
 f(i) = t;
end
```

Function name	Action
MATLAB as a programming language	
script	About MATLAB scripts and M-files
function	Add new function
eval	Execute string with MATLAB expression
feval	Execute function specified by string
global	Define global variable
nargchk	Validate number of input arguments
Control flow	
if	Conditionally execute statements
else	Used with IF
elseif	Used with IF
end	Terminate the scope of FOR, WHILE and IF statements
for	Repeat statements a specific number of times
while	Repeat statements an indefinite number of times
break	Terminate execution of loop
return	Return to invoking function
error	Display message and abort function
Interactive input	
input	Prompt for user input
keyboard	Invoke keyboard as if it were a Script-file
menu	Generate menu of choices for user input
pause	Wait for user response
uimenu	Create user interface menu
uicontrol	Create user interface control
Debugging commands	
dbstop	Set breakpoint
dbclear	Remove breakpoint
dbcont	Resume execution
dbdown	Change local workspace context
dbstack	List who called whom
dbstatus	List all breakpoints
dbstep	Execute one or more lines
dbtype	List M-file with line numbers
dbup	Change local workspace context
dbquit	Quit debug mode

Table A.6: Program control related help topics

BIBLIOGRAPHY

[1] AMES, W. F. *Numerical methods for partial differential equations* 1977: New York: Academic Press. Random House, N.Y.

[2] AMUNDSON, N. R. *Mathematical methods in chemical engineering: Matrices and their application.* 1966: Englewood Cliffs: Prentice-Hall.

[3] ANDERSON, D. A., TANNEHILL, J. C., & PLETCHER, R. H. *Computational fluid mechanics and heat transfer.* 1984: Hemishpere.

[4] ATKINSON, K. E. *An Introduction to Numerical Analysis.* 1978: New York: John Wiley & Sons.

[5] BAKER, C. T. H., & PHILLIPS, C. *The numerical solution of nonlinear problems.* 1981: Clarendon Press.

[6] BARNETT, S. *Matrices: Methods and Applications.* 1990: Oxford: Clarendon Press.

[7] BIRD, R. B., STEWART, W. E., & LIGHTFOOT, E. N. *Transport phenomena.* 1960: New York: John Wiley & Sons.

[8] BIRKHOFF, G., & LYNCH, R. *Numerical solution of elliptic problems.* 1984: Philadelphia: SIAM.

[9] BYRNE, G. D., & HALL, C. A. *Numerical solutions of systems of nonlinear algebraic equations.* 1973: New York: Academic Press.

[10] CHAPRA, S. *Numerical methods for enginneers and scientists* . 2005: New York: McGraw-Hill.

[11] CONSTANTINIDES, A. *Applied numerical methods with personal computers.* 1987: New York: McGraw-Hill.

[12] CULLUM, J., & WILLOUGHBY, R. A. *Large Scale Eigenvalue Problems.* 1985: Noth-Holland.

[13] DAHLQUIST, G., & BJÖRCK, A. *Numerical Methods.* 1974: Englewood Cliffs: Prentice-Hall.

[14] DAVIS, M. E. *Numerical Methods and Modelling for Chemical Engineers.* 1984: New York: John Wiley.

[15] DRAZIN, P. G. *Nonlinear Systems.* 1992: Cambridge: Cambridge University Press.

[16] *et al.* , C. CANUTO. *Spectral methods in fluid dynamics.* 1988: New York: Springer-Verlag.

[17] FEYNMAN, R. *The Character of Physical Law.* 1967: Cambridge, Ma.: M.I.T. Press.

[18] FINLAYSON, B. A. *The method of weighted residuals and variational principles.* 1972: New York: AP.

[19] FINLAYSON, B. A. *Nonlinear analysis in chemical engineering.* 1980: New York: McGraw Hill.

[20] GEORGE, A., & LIU, J. W.-H. *Computer solution of large sparse symmetric positive definite systems of linear equations.* 1981: Englewood Cliffs, NJ: Prentice-Hall.

[21] GIANONE, CHRISTINE. *Using MS-DOS Kermit.* 1991: Bedford, MA, USA: Digital Press.

[22] GOTTLIEB, D., & ORSZAG, S. A. *Numerical Analysis of Spectral Methods: Theory and Applications.* 1977: Philadelphia: Society for Industrial and Applied Mathematics.

[23] HAGER, W. W. *Applied numerical linear algebra.* 1985: Englewood Cliffs, NJ: Prentice-Hall.

[24] HOFFMAN, J. D. *Numerical methods for engineers and scientists.* 1992: New York: McGraw-Hill.

[25] JEEVES, T. A. Secant Modification of Newton's method. 1958 *Communication of the Association of Computing Machinery,* **1**, 9–10.

[26] JENSON, V. G., & JEFFREYS, G. V. *Mathematical methods in chemical engineering.* 1963: New York: Academic Press.

[27] KNUTH, D. E. *The TEX book.* 1984: Reading, MA, USA: Addison Wesley.

[28] KUBECEK, M., & MAREK, M. *Computational methods in bifurcation theory and dissipative structures.* 1983: Springer-Verlag.

[29] KUBICEK, M., & HLAVACEK, V. *Numerical solutions of nonlinear boundary value problems with applications.* 1983: Englewood Cliffs: Prentice Hall.

[30] LAMBERT, J.D. *Computational methods for ordinary differential equations.* 1973: New York: John Wiley & Sons.

[31] LAMPORT, L. *A Document Preparation System - LATEX. User's guide & reference manual.* 1986: Reading, MA, USA: Addison Wesley.

[32] LAPIDUS, L. *Digital computation for chemical engineers.* 1962: New York: McGraw-Hill.

[33] LAPIDUS, L., & PINDER, G. F. *Numerical solution of partial differential equations in science and engineering.* 1982: New York: John Wiley & Sons.

[34] LAPIDUS, L., & SEINFELD, J. H. *Numerical solution of ordinary differential equations.* 1971: New York: Academic Press.

[35] MITCHELL, A. R. *Computational methods in partial differential equations.* 1969: John Wiley & Sons.

[36] ORTEGA, J., & RHEINBOLDT, W. *Iterative solution of nonlinear equations in several variables.* 1970: Academic Press.

[37] PARKER, T. S., & CHUA, L. O. *Practical Numerical Algorithms for Chaotic Systems*. 1989: Springer-Verlag.

[38] PATANKAR, S. V. *Numerical heat transfer and fluid flow*. 1980: Hemisphere.

[39] PEYRET, R., & TAYLOR, T. D. *Computational methods for fluid flow*. 1983: New York: Springer-Verlag.

[40] RABINOWITZ, P. *Numerical methods for nonlinear algebraic equations*. 1970: Gordon & Breach.

[41] RAMAKRISHNA, D., & AMUNDSON, N. R. *Linear operator methods in Chemical Engineering*. 1985: Englewood Cliffs, NJ: Prentice Hall.

[42] RAO, S. *Numerical methods for engineers and scientists*. 2002: Englewood Cliffs, NJ: Prentice Hall.

[43] RICE, J. R., & BOISVERT, R. F. *Solving Elliptic Problems using **ELLPACK***. 1984: Springer-Verlag.

[44] ROACHE, P. J. *Computational fluid mehcanics*. 1972: Hermosa publishers.

[45] ROSENBROCK, H. H. Some general implicit processes for the numerical solution of differential equations. 1963: *Comput. J.*, **5**, 329.

[46] ROSENBROCK, H. H. *Computational techniques for chemical engineers*. revised english edition edn. 1966: Oxford: Pergamon.

[47] SCALES, L. E. *Introduction to non-linear optimization*. 1985: Springer-Verlag.

[48] SCARBOROUGH, I. B. *Numerical mathematical analysis*. 1966: Baltimore : John Hopkins Press.

[49] SCHECHTER, R. S. *The Variational Method in Engineering*. 1967: New York: McGraw-Hill.

[50] SEYDEL, R. *From equilibrium to chaos: practical bifurcation and stability analysis*. 1988: New York: Elsevier.

[51] Sod, G. A. *Numerical Methods in Fluid Dynamics.* 1985: Cambridge: Cambridge University Press.

[52] Southwell, R. V. *Relaxation methods in engineering science.* 1940: London: Oxford University Press.

[53] Stewart, I., & Golubitsky, M. *Fearful Symmetry: Is God a geometer?* 1993: New York: Penguib Books.

[54] Usmani, R. A. *Applied Linear Algebra.* 1987: Marcel Dekker.

[55] Villadsen, J., & Michelsen, M. L. *Solution of Differential Equation Models by Polynomial Approximation.* 1978: Englewood Cliffs: Prentice-Hall.

[56] Wilkinson, J. H. *The algebraic eigenvalue problem.* 1965: Clarendon Press.

[57] Wolfram, S. *Mathematica.* 1988: Redwood City, Ca: Addison Wesley.

[58] Young, D. *Iterative Solution of Large Linear Systems.* 1971: New York: Academic Press.

[59] Zangwill, W. I., & Garcia, C. B. *Pathways to solutions, fixed points and equilibria.* 1981: Englewood Cliffs: Prentice-Hall.

To order more copies of this book, find books by other
Canadian authors, or make inquiries about publishing
your own book, contact PageMaster at:

PageMaster Publication Services Inc.
11340-120 Street, Edmonton, AB T5G 0W5
books@pagemaster.ca
780-425-9303

catalogue and e-commerce store
www.ShopPageMaster.ca